The Open University

MST124

Essential mathematics 1

Book A

This publication forms part of an Open University module. Details of this and other
Open University modules can be obtained from the Student Registration and Enquiry Service, The
Open University, PO Box 197, Milton Keynes MK7 6BJ, United Kingdom (tel. +44 (0)845 300 6090;
email general-enquiries@open.ac.uk).

Alternatively, you may visit the Open University website at www.open.ac.uk where you can learn
more about the wide range of modules and packs offered at all levels by The Open University.

To purchase a selection of Open University materials visit www.ouw.co.uk, or contact Open
University Worldwide, Walton Hall, Milton Keynes MK7 6AA, United Kingdom for a brochure
(tel. +44 (0)1908 858779; fax +44 (0)1908 858787; email ouw-customer-services@open.ac.uk).

The Open University, Walton Hall, Milton Keynes, MK7 6AA.

First published 2014.

Edited, designed and typeset by The Open University, using the Open University TeX System.

Printed in the United Kingdom by Latimer Trend & Company Ltd, Plymouth

ISBN 978 1 7800 7209 8

1.1

Contents

Contents

Unit 1

Algebra

Welcome to MST124

In this module you'll learn the essential ideas and techniques that underpin university-level study in mathematics and mathematical subjects such as physics, engineering and economics. You'll also develop your skills in communicating mathematics.

Here are some of the topics that you'll meet.

Vectors are quantities that have both a size and a direction. For example, a ship on the ocean moves not only with a particular speed, but also in a particular direction. Speed in a particular direction is a vector quantity known as *velocity*.

The motion of a ship consists of speed and direction

Calculus is a fundamental topic in mathematics that's concerned with quantities that change continuously. If you know that an object is moving at a constant speed, then it's straightforward to work out how much distance it covers in any given period of time. It's not so easy to do this if the object's speed is *changing* – for example, if it's accelerating, as a falling object does. Calculus can be used to deal with situations like this.

Matrices are rectangular arrays of numbers – for example, any rectangular table of numbers forms a matrix. Matrices have many applications, which involve performing operations on them that are similar to the operations that you perform on individual numbers. For example, you can add, subtract and multiply matrices.

Sequences are lists of numbers. Sequences whose numbers have a connecting mathematical relationship arise in many different contexts. For example, if you invest £100 at a 5% rate of interest paid annually, then the value in pounds of your investment at the beginning of each year forms the sequence $100, 105, 110.25, 115.76, 121.55, \ldots$.

The **complex numbers** include all the real numbers that you know about already, and also many 'imaginary' numbers, such as the square root of -1. Amazingly, they provide a simple way to deal with some types of complicated mathematics that arise in practical problems.

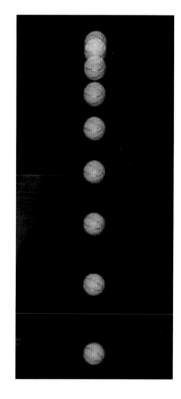

The speed of a falling ball increases as it falls

You'll see that not only do the topics above have important practical applications, but they're also intriguing areas of study in their own right.

One of the main aims of the first few units of MST124 is to make sure that you're confident with the basic skills in algebra, graphs, trigonometry, indices and logarithms that you'll need. The mathematics in the later units of the module depends heavily on these basic skills, and you'll find it much easier and much quicker to study and understand if you can work with all the basic skills fluently and correctly.

To help you attain confidence with these skills, the first few units of the module include many revision topics, as well as some new ones. Which parts, and how much, of the revision material you'll need to study will depend on your mathematical background – different students start MST124 with widely differing previous mathematical experiences. When you're deciding which revision topics you need to study, remember that even though you'll have met most of them before, you won't necessarily have acquired the 'at your fingertips' fluency in working with them that you'll need. Where that's the case, you'll benefit significantly from working carefully through the revision material.

Information for joint MST124 and MST125 students

If you are studying *Essential mathematics 2* (MST125) with the same start date as MST124, then you should *not* study the MST124 units on the dates shown on the main MST124 study planner. Instead, you should follow the MST124 and MST125 joint study planner, which is available from the MST124 and MST125 websites. This is important because you will not be prepared to study many of the topics in MST125 if you have not already studied the related topics in MST124. The MST124 and MST125 joint study planner ensures that you study the units of the two modules interleaved in the correct order.

The MST124 assignment cut-off dates shown in the MST124 and MST125 joint study planner are the same as those shown on the MST124 study planner.

Introduction

The main topic of this first unit is basic algebra, the most important of the essential mathematical skills that you'll need. You'll find it difficult to work through many of the units in the module, particularly the calculus units, if you're not able to manipulate algebraic expressions and equations fluently and accurately. So it's worth spending some time now practising your algebra skills. This unit gives you the opportunity to do that.

The unit covers a lot of topics quite rapidly, in the expectation that you'll be fairly familiar with much of the material. You should use it as a resource to help you make sure that your algebra skills are as good as they can be. You may not need to study all the topics – you should concentrate on those in which you need practice. For many students these will be the topics in Sections 3 to 6. A good strategy might be to read through the whole unit, doing the activities on the topics in which you know you need practice. For the topics in which you think you *don't* need practice, try one or two of the later parts of each activity to make sure – there may be gaps and rustiness in your algebra skills of which you're unaware. Remember to check all your answers against the correct answers provided (these are at the end of the unit in the print book, and can be obtained by pressing the 'show solution' buttons in some screen versions).

As with all the units in this module, further practice questions are available in both the online practice quiz and the exercise booklet for the unit.

Working through the revision material in this unit should also help you to clarify your thinking about algebra. For example, you might know *what to do* with a particular type of algebraic expression or equation, but you might not know, or might have forgotten, *why* this is a valid thing to do. If you can clearly understand the 'why', then you'll be in a much better position to decide whether you can apply the same sort of technique to a slightly different situation, which is the sort of thing that you'll need to do as you study more mathematics.

Some of the topics in the unit may seem very easy – basic algebra is revised starting from the simplest ideas. Others may seem quite challenging – some of the algebraic expressions and equations that you're asked to manipulate may be more complicated than those that you've dealt with before, particularly the ones involving algebraic fractions and indices.

The final section of the unit, Section 6, describes some basic principles of communicating mathematics in writing. This will be important throughout your study of this module and in any further mathematical modules that you study.

If you find that much of the content of this unit (and/or Unit 2) is unfamiliar to you, then contact your tutor and/or Learner Support Team as soon as possible, to discuss what to do.

The word 'algebra' is derived from the title of the treatise *al-Kitāb al-mukhtaṣar fī ḥisāb al-jabr wa'l-muqābala* (Compendium on calculation by completion and reduction), written by the Islamic mathematician Muḥammad ibn Mūsā al-Khwārizmī in around 825. This treatise deals with solving linear and quadratic equations, but it doesn't use algebra in the modern sense, as no letters or other symbols are used to represent numbers. Modern, symbolic algebra emerged in the 1500s and 1600s.

1 Numbers

In this section you'll revise different types of numbers, and some basic skills associated with working with numbers.

1.1 Types of numbers

We'll make a start by briefly reviewing some different types of numbers.

Remember that all the definitions given here, and all the other definitions and important facts and techniques given in the module, are also set out in the *Handbook*, so you can refer to them easily.

The **natural numbers**, also known as the **positive integers**, are the counting numbers,

$$1, \ 2, \ 3, \ \ldots.$$

(The symbol '…' here is called an *ellipsis* and is used when something has been left out. You can read it as 'dot, dot, dot'. In some texts the natural numbers are defined to be $0, 1, 2, 3, \ldots.$)

The natural numbers, together with their negatives and zero, form the **integers**:

$$\ldots, \ -3, \ -2, \ -1, \ 0, \ 1, \ 2, \ 3, \ \ldots.$$

> The Latin word *integer* consists of the prefix *in*, meaning 'not', attached to the root of *tangere*, meaning 'to touch'. So it literally means 'untouched', in the sense of 'whole'.

The **rational numbers** are the numbers that can be written in the form

$$\frac{\text{integer}}{\text{integer}};$$

that is, as an integer divided by an integer.

For example, all the following numbers are rational numbers:

$$\tfrac{3}{4}, \quad 2\tfrac{1}{3}, \quad 4, \quad -4, \quad -\tfrac{8}{7}, \quad 0.16, \quad 7.374.$$

You can check this by writing them in the form above, as follows:

$$\frac{3}{4}, \quad \frac{7}{3}, \quad \frac{4}{1}, \quad \frac{-4}{1}, \quad \frac{-8}{7}, \quad \frac{16}{100}, \quad \frac{7374}{1000}.$$

The **real numbers** include all the rational numbers, and many other numbers as well. A useful way to think of the real numbers is to envisage them as lying along a straight line that extends infinitely far in each direction, called the **number line** or the **real line**. Every point on the number line corresponds to a real number, and every real number corresponds to a point on the line. Some points on the line correspond to rational numbers, while others correspond to numbers that are not rational, which are known as **irrational** numbers. Figure 1 shows some numbers on the number line.

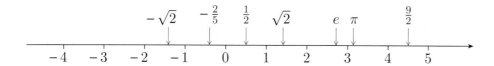

Figure 1   Some numbers on the number line

Four of the numbers marked in Figure 1 are irrational, namely $-\sqrt{2}$, $\sqrt{2}$, e and π. The number $\sqrt{2}$ is the positive square root of 2, that is, the positive number that when multiplied by itself gives the answer 2. Its value is approximately 1.41. The number $-\sqrt{2}$ is the negative of this number. The numbers e and π are two important constants that occur frequently in mathematics. You probably know that π is the number obtained by dividing the circumference of any circle by its diameter (see Figure 2). Its value is approximately 3.14. (The symbol π is a lower-case Greek letter, pronounced 'pie'.) The constant e has value approximately 2.72, and you'll learn more about it in this module, starting in Unit 3.

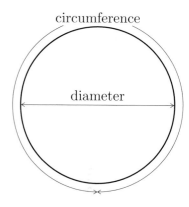

Figure 2   The circumference and diameter of a circle

To check that the numbers $-\sqrt{2}$, $\sqrt{2}$, e and π are irrational, you have to prove that they can't be written as an integer divided by an integer. If you'd like to see how this can be done for $\sqrt{2}$, then look at the document *A proof that $\sqrt{2}$ is irrational* on the module website. Proving that e and π can't be written as an integer divided by an integer is more difficult, and outside the scope of this module.

Every *rational* number can be written as a decimal number. To do this, you divide the top number of the fraction of the form $\dfrac{\text{integer}}{\text{integer}}$ by the bottom number. For example,

$\frac{1}{8} = 0.125,$

$\frac{2}{3} = 0.666\,666\,666\ldots,$

$\frac{83}{74} = 1.1\,216\,216\,216\,216\ldots.$

As you can see, the decimal form of $\frac{1}{8}$ is **terminating**: it has only a finite number of digits after the decimal point. The decimal forms of both $\frac{2}{3}$ and $\frac{83}{74}$ are **recurring**: each of them has a block of one or more digits after the decimal point that repeats indefinitely. There are two alternative notations for indicating a recurring decimal: you can either put a dot above the first and last digit of the repeating block, or you can put a line above the whole repeating block. For example,

$\frac{2}{3} = 0.666\,666\,666\ldots = 0.\dot{6} = 0.\overline{6},$ and

$\frac{83}{74} = 1.1\,216\,216\,216\,216\ldots = 1.1\dot{2}1\dot{6} = 1.1\overline{216}.$

In fact, the decimal form of *every* rational number is either terminating or recurring. Also, every terminating or recurring decimal can be written as an integer divided by an integer and is therefore a rational number. If you'd like to know why these facts hold, then look at the document *Decimal forms of rational numbers* on the module website.

The decimal numbers that are neither terminating nor recurring – that is, those that are infinitely long but have no block of digits that repeats indefinitely – are the irrational numbers. This gives you another way to distinguish between the rational and irrational numbers, summarised below.

Decimal forms of rational and irrational numbers

The rational numbers are the decimal numbers that terminate or recur.

The irrational numbers are the decimal numbers with an infinite number of digits after the decimal point but with no block of digits that repeats indefinitely.

So, for example, the irrational number π has a decimal expansion that is infinitely long and has no block of digits that repeats indefinitely. Here are its first 40 digits:

$$\pi = 3.141\,592\,653\,589\,793\,238\,462\,643\,383\,279\,502\,884\,197\ldots.$$

You might like to watch the one-minute video clip entitled *The decimal expansion of* π, available on the module website.

In 2006, a Japanese retired engineer and mental health counsellor, Akira Haraguchi, recited the first 100 000 digits of π from memory. It took him 16 hours.

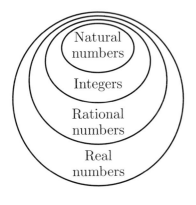

Figure 3   Types of numbers

Figure 3 is a summary of the types of numbers mentioned in this subsection. It illustrates that all the natural numbers are also integers, all the integers are also rational numbers, and all the rational numbers are also real numbers.

In Unit 12 you'll learn about yet another type of number. The *complex numbers* include all the numbers in Figure 3, and also many 'imaginary' numbers, such as the square root of -1. The idea of imaginary numbers might seem strange, but these numbers are the foundation of a great deal of interesting and useful mathematics. They provide a natural, elegant way to work with seemingly complicated mathematics, and have many practical applications.

1.2 Working with numbers

In this subsection, you'll revise some basic skills associated with working with numbers. It's easy to make mistakes with these particular skills, and people often do! So you should find it helpful to review and practise them.

Before doing so, notice the label '(1)' on the right of the next paragraph. It's used later in the text to refer back to the contents of the line in which it appears. Labels like this are used throughout the module.

The BIDMAS rules

When you *evaluate* (find the value of) an expression such as

$$200 - 3 \times (1 + 5 \times 2^3) + 7, \tag{1}$$

it's important to remember the following convention for the order of the operations, so that you get the right answer.

Order of operations: BIDMAS

Carry out mathematical operations in the following order.

B brackets
I indices (powers and roots)
D divisions $\left.\right\}$ same precedence
M multiplications
A additions $\left.\right\}$ same precedence
S subtractions

Where operations have the same precedence, work from left to right.

As you can see, the I in the BIDMAS rules refers to 'indices (powers and roots)'. Remember that raising a number to a **power** means multiplying it by itself a specified number of times. For example, 2^3 (2 to the power 3) means three 2s multiplied together:

$$2^3 = 2 \times 2 \times 2.$$

In particular, **squaring** and **cubing** a number mean raising it to the powers 2 and 3, respectively. When you write an expression such as 2^3, you're using **index notation**. Taking a *root* of a number means taking its square root, for example, or another type of root. Roots are revised in Subsection 4.1.

If you type an expression like expression (1) into a calculator of the type recommended in the *MST124 guide*, then it will be evaluated according to the BIDMAS rules. However, it's essential that you understand and remember the rules yourself. For example, you'll need to use them when you work with algebra.

Example 1 reminds you how to use the BIDMAS rules. It also illustrates another feature that you'll see throughout the module. Some of the worked examples include lines of blue text, marked with the following icons 🗨 🗨.

This text tells you what someone doing the mathematics might be thinking, but wouldn't write down. It should help you understand how you might do a similar calculation yourself.

Example 1   *Using the BIDMAS rules*

Evaluate the expression

$$200 - 3 \times (1 + 5 \times 2^3) + 7$$

without using your calculator.

Solution

The brackets have the highest precedence, so start by evaluating what's inside them. Within the brackets, first deal with the power, then do the multiplication, then the addition.

$$
\begin{aligned}
200 - 3 \times (1 + 5 \times 2^3) + 7 &= 200 - 3 \times (1 + 5 \times 8) + 7 \\
&= 200 - 3 \times (1 + 40) + 7 \\
&= 200 - 3 \times 41 + 7
\end{aligned}
$$

Now do the multiplication, then the addition and subtraction from left to right.

$$
\begin{aligned}
&= 200 - 123 + 7 \\
&= 77 + 7 \\
&= 84
\end{aligned}
$$

You can practise using the BIDMAS rules in the next activity. Remember that where division is indicated using fraction notation, the horizontal line not only indicates division but also acts as brackets for the expressions above and below the line. For example,

$$\frac{1+2}{1+3^2} \quad \text{means} \quad \frac{(1+2)}{(1+3^2)}, \quad \text{that is,} \quad (1+2) \div (1+3^2).$$

In a line of text, this expression would normally be written as $(1+2)/(1+3^2)$, with a slash replacing the horizontal line. The brackets are needed here because $1 + 2/1 + 3^2$ would be interpreted as $1 + (2/1) + 3^2$.

Part (b) of the activity involves algebraic expressions. Remember that multiplication signs are usually omitted when doing algebra – quantities that are multiplied are usually just written next to each other instead (though, for example, 3×4 can't be written as 34).

Activity 1 *Using the BIDMAS rules*

(a) Evaluate the following expressions without using your calculator.

   (i) $23 - 2 \times 3 + (4 - 2)$ (ii) $2 - \frac{1}{2} \times 4$ (iii) 4×3^2

   (iv) $2 + 2^2$ (v) $\dfrac{1 + 2}{1 + 3^2}$ (vi) $1 - 2/3^2$

(b) Evaluate the following expressions when $a = 3$ and $b = 5$, without using your calculator.

   (i) $3(b - a)^2$ (ii) $a + b(2a + b)$ (iii) $a + 9\left(\dfrac{b}{a}\right)$ (iv) $30/(ab)$

Rounding

When you use your calculator to carry out a calculation, you often need to round the result. There are various ways to round a number. Sometimes it's appropriate to round to a particular number of **decimal places** (often abbreviated to 'd.p.'). The decimal places of a number are the positions of the digits to the right of the decimal point. You can also round to the nearest whole number, or to the nearest 10, or to the nearest 100, for example. More often, it's appropriate to round to a particular number of **significant figures** (often abbreviated to 's.f.' or 'sig. figs.'). The first significant figure of a number is the first non-zero digit (from the left), the next significant figure is the next digit along (whether zero or not), and so on.

Once you've decided where to round a number, you need to look at the digit immediately after where you want to round. You round up if this digit is 5 or more, and round down otherwise. When you round a number, you should state how it's been rounded, in brackets after the rounded number, as illustrated in the next example.

Notice the 'play button' icon next to the following example. It indicates that the example has an associated *tutorial clip* – a short video in which a tutor works through the example and explains it. You can watch the clip, which is available on the module website, instead of reading through the worked example. Many other examples in the module have tutorial clips, indicated by the same icon.

Example 2 *Rounding numbers*

Round the following numbers as indicated.

(a) 0.0238 to three decimal places

(b) 50 629 to three significant figures

(c) 0.002 958 2 to two significant figures

Solution

(a) 🔍 Look at the digit after the first three decimal places: 0. 023 8.
It's 8, which is 5 or more, so round up. 💬

   0.0238 = 0.024 (to 3 d.p.)

(b) 🔍 Look at the digit after the first three significant figures:
506 29. It's 2, which is less than 5, so round down. 💬

   50 629 = 50 600 (to 3 s.f.)

(c) 🔍 Look at the digit after the first two significant figures:
0.00 29 582. It's 5, which is 5 or more, so round up. 💬

   0.002 958 2 = 0.0030 (to 2 s.f.)

Notice that in Example 2(c), a 0 is included after the 3 to make it clear
that the number is rounded to *two* significant figures. You should do
likewise when you round numbers yourself.

Activity 2 *Rounding numbers*

Round the following numbers as indicated.

(a) 41.394 to one decimal place

(b) 22.325 to three significant figures

(c) 80 014 to three significant figures

(d) 0.056 97 to two significant figures

(e) 0.006 996 to three significant figures

(f) 56 311 to the nearest hundred

(g) 72 991 to the nearest hundred

The use of the digit 0 to indicate an empty place in the representation of a number seems essential nowadays. For example, the digit 0 in 3802 distinguishes it from 382. However, many civilisations managed to use place-value representations of numbers for hundreds of years with no symbol for the digit zero. Instead, they distinguished numbers by their context. Evidence from surviving clay tablets shows that the Babylonians used place-value representations of numbers from at least 2100 BC, and used a place-holder for zero from around 600 BC.

A Babylonian clay tablet from around 1700 BC

When you need to round a negative number, you should round the part after the minus sign in the same way that you would round a positive number. For example,

$$-0.25 = -0.3 \text{ (to 1 d.p.)}.$$

When you're rounding an answer obtained from your calculator, it's often useful to write down a more precise version of the answer before you round it. You can do this by using the '...' symbol, like this:

$$9.869\,604\,40\ldots = 9.87 \text{ (to 2 d.p.)}.$$

Also, as an alternative to writing in brackets how you rounded a number, you can replace the equals sign by the symbol $\approx$, which means, and is read as, 'is approximately equal to'. For example, you can write

$$9.869\,604\,40\ldots \approx 9.87.$$

The activities and TMA questions in this module will sometimes tell you what rounding to use in your answers. In other situations where you need to round answers, a useful rule of thumb is to round to the number of significant figures in the *least* precise number used in your calculation. For example, suppose that you're asked to calculate how long it would take to travel 11 400 metres at a speed of 8.9 metres per second. The first and second numbers here seem to be given to three and two significant figures, respectively, so you would round your answer to two significant figures. Note, however, that there are situations where this rule of thumb is not appropriate. Note also that if an activity or TMA question includes a number with no units, such as '120', then you should usually assume that this number is exact, whereas if it includes a number with units, such as '120 cm', then you should usually assume that this is a measurement and has been rounded.

Now try the following activity. Don't skip it: it might look easy, but it illustrates an important point about rounding – one that's a common source of errors. To do the activity, you need to use the facts that the radius r, circumference c and area A of any circle (see Figure 4) are linked by the formulas

$$c = 2\pi r \quad \text{and} \quad A = \pi r^2.$$

Remember to use the π button on your calculator to obtain a good approximation for π.

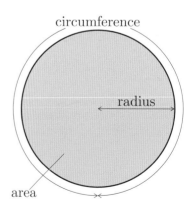

Figure 4 The radius, circumference and area of a circle

> **Activity 3** *Rounding in a multi-stage calculation*
>
> The circumference of a circle is 77.2 cm.
>
> (a) Find the radius of the circle, in cm to three significant figures.
>
> (b) Find the area of the circle, in cm² to two significant figures.

The correct answer to part (b) of Activity 3 is 470 cm². If you obtained the answer 480 cm², then this was probably because you carried out your calculation in part (b) using the rounded answer for the radius that you found in part (a). To obtain the correct answer in part (b), you need to use a more precise value for the radius, such as the value that you obtained on your calculator before you rounded it. (Alternatively, you could combine the two formulas $c = 2\pi r$ and $A = \pi r^2$ to obtain the formula $A = c^2/(4\pi)$ for A in terms of c, and use that to obtain the answer to part (b).)

Errors of this sort are known as **rounding errors**. To avoid them, whenever you carry out a calculation using an answer that you found earlier, you should use the full-calculator-precision version of the earlier answer. One way to do this is to write down the full value and re-enter it in your calculator, but a more convenient way is to store it in your calculator's memory. Another convenient way to avoid rounding errors is to carry out your calculations using a computer algebra system. You'll start to learn how to do this in Unit 2.

> Sometimes people who work with numbers, such as statisticians, use slightly different rounding conventions to those described above. These alternative conventions usually differ only in how they deal with cases in which the digit immediately after where you want to round is the last non-zero digit of the unrounded number, and it's a 5. For example, with some conventions, $3.65 = 3.6$ (to 1 d.p.), and there are conventions for which $-0.25 = -0.2$ (to 1 d.p.).

Negative numbers

Negative numbers occur frequently in mathematics, so it's important that you're confident about working with them.

When you're carrying out calculations that involve negative numbers, it's sometimes helpful to mention the **sign** of a number. This is either $+$ or $-$, that is, plus or minus, according to whether the number is positive or negative, respectively. The number zero doesn't have a sign.

Here's a reminder of how to deal with addition and subtraction when negative numbers are involved.

When you have a number (positive, negative or zero), and you want to add or subtract a *positive* number, you simply increase or decrease the number that you started with by the appropriate amount. For example, as shown in Figure 5, to add 3 to -5 you increase -5 by 3, and to subtract 3 from -5 you decrease -5 by 3. This gives:

$$-5 + 3 = -2 \quad \text{and} \quad -5 - 3 = -8.$$

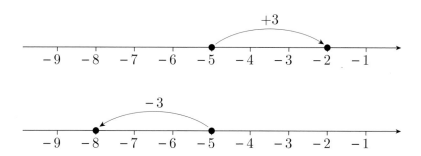

Figure 5 Increasing -5 by 3 and decreasing -5 by 3

When you have a number (positive, negative or zero), and you want to add or subtract a *negative* number, you use the rules below.

Adding and subtracting negative numbers

Adding a negative number is the same as subtracting the corresponding positive number.

Subtracting a negative number is the same as adding the corresponding positive number.

For example,

$$7 + (-3) = 7 - 3 = 4 \quad \text{and} \quad -9 - (-3) = -9 + 3 = -6.$$

Now here's a reminder of how to deal with multiplication and division when you're working with negative numbers.

To multiply or divide two negative or positive numbers, you multiply or divide them without their signs in the usual way, and use the rules below to find the sign of the answer.

> **Multiplying and dividing negative numbers**
>
> When two numbers are multiplied or divided:
>
> - if the signs are *different*, then the answer is *negative*
> - if the signs are *the same*, then the answer is *positive*.

For example,

$$2 \times (-3) = -6,$$
$$\frac{-8}{-2} = 4,$$
$$2 \times (-3) \times (-5) = (-6) \times (-5) = 30.$$

Notice that some of the negative numbers in the calculations above are enclosed in brackets. This is because no two of the mathematical symbols $+$, $-$, $\times$ and $\div$ should be written next to each other, as that would look confusing (and is often meaningless). So if you want to show that you're adding -2 to 4, for example, then you shouldn't write $4 + -2$, but instead you should put brackets around the -2 and write $4 + (-2)$.

If you'd like to know more about *why* negative numbers are added, subtracted, multiplied and divided in the way that they are, then have a look at the document *Arithmetic of negative numbers* on the module website.

You can practise working with negative numbers in the next activity. Remember that the BIDMAS rules apply in the usual way.

Activity 4   *Working with negative numbers*

Evaluate the following expressions without using a calculator.

(a) $-3 + (-4)$ (b) $2 + (-3)$ (c) $2 - (-3)$ (d) $-1 - (-5)$

(e) $5 \times (-4)$ (f) $\dfrac{-15}{-3}$ (g) $(-2) \times (-3) \times (-4)$

(h) $6(-3 - (-1))$ (i) $20 - (-5) \times (-2)$

(j) $-5 + (-3) \times (-1) - 2 \times (-2)$ (k) $\dfrac{-2 - (-1) \times (-2)}{-8}$

When you're working with negative numbers, there's an extra operation that you have to deal with, as well as the usual operations of addition, subtraction, multiplication and division. When you put a minus sign in front of a number, the new number that you get is called the **negative** of the original number. For example, the negative of 4 is -4. The operation of putting a minus sign in front of a number is called **taking the negative** of the number.

You can take the negative of a number that's already negative. This changes its sign to plus. For example,

$$-(-7) = +7 = 7.$$

To see why this is, notice that taking the negative of a *positive* number is the same as subtracting it from zero: for example, $-3 = 0 - 3$. It's just the same for negative numbers: $-(-7) = 0 - (-7) = 0 + 7 = 7$.

You can also take the negative of zero. This leaves it unchanged: $-0 = 0 - 0 = 0$.

In general, taking the negative of a positive or negative number changes its sign to the opposite sign. Taking the negative of zero leaves it unchanged. Another helpful way to think about negatives is that a number and its negative always add up to zero.

The operation of taking a negative has the same precedence in the BIDMAS rules as subtraction. For example, in the expression -3^2, the operation of taking the power is done *before* the operation of taking the negative, by the BIDMAS rules. So -3^2 is equal to -9, not 9, as you might have expected. However, $(-3)^2$ is equal to 9.

Activity 5   *Practice with taking negatives*

Evaluate the following expressions without using a calculator. Then check that your calculator gives the same answers.

(a) -5^2 (b) $(-5)^2$ (c) $-(-8)$ (d) $-(-8)^2$ (e) $-2^2 + 7$

(f) $-(-5) - (-1)$ (g) $-4^2 - (-4)^2$ (h) $-3 \times (-2^2)$

When you substitute a negative number into an algebraic expression, you usually have to enclose it in brackets, to make sure that you evaluate the expression correctly. For example, to evaluate the expression $x^2 - 2x$ when $x = -3$, you proceed as follows:

$$\begin{aligned} x^2 - 2x &= (-3)^2 - 2 \times (-3) \\ &= 9 - (-6) \\ &= 9 + 6 = 15. \end{aligned}$$

Activity 6   *Substituting negative numbers into algebraic expressions*

Evaluate the following expressions when $a = -2$ and $b = -3$, without using a calculator.

(a) $-b$ (b) $-a - b$ (c) $-b^2$ (d) $a^2 + ab$ (e) $\dfrac{3 - a^2}{b}$

(f) $a^2 - 2a + 5$ (g) $(6 - a)(2 + b)$ (h) a^3 (i) $-b^3$

Units of measurement

Most of the units of measurement used in this module come from the standard metric system known as the Système International d'Unités (SI units). This system is used by the scientific community generally and is the main system of measurement in nearly every country in the world.

There are seven SI **base units**, from which all the other units are derived. The base units (and their abbreviations) used in this module are the metre (m), the kilogram (kg) and the second (s). Prefixes are used to indicate smaller or larger units. Some common prefixes are shown in Table 1.

Table 1 Some prefixes for SI units

Prefix	Abbreviation	Meaning	Example
nano	n	a billionth $\left(\frac{1}{10^9}\right)$	1 nanometre (nm) $= \frac{1}{10^9}$ metre
micro	μ	a millionth $\left(\frac{1}{10^6}\right)$	1 micrometre (μm) $= \frac{1}{10^6}$ metre
milli	m	a thousandth $\left(\frac{1}{1000}\right)$	1 millimetre (mm) $= \frac{1}{1000}$ metre
centi	c	a hundredth $\left(\frac{1}{100}\right)$	1 centimetre (cm) $= \frac{1}{100}$ metre
kilo	k	a thousand (1000)	1 kilometre (km) $= 1000$ metres
mega	M	a million (10^6)	1 megametre (Mm) $= 10^6$ metres

The metric system was founded in France after the French Revolution. Its modern form, the SI, was founded in 1960 and continues to evolve, keeping pace with the increasing precision of measurement. At the time of writing, only three countries have chosen not to adopt SI units as their sole/primary system of measurement.

Four mathematical words

Finally in this subsection, here's a reminder of four standard mathematical words that are used frequently throughout the module.

- The **sum** of two or more numbers is the result of adding them.
- The **product** of two or more numbers is the result of multiplying them.
- A **difference** of two numbers is the result of subtracting one from the other.
- A **quotient** of two numbers is the result of dividing one by the other.

Each pair of numbers has *two* differences and (provided neither of the numbers in the pair is zero) *two* quotients. For example, the numbers 2 and 8 have the two differences $8 - 2 = 6$ and $2 - 8 = -6$, and the two quotients $\frac{8}{2} = 4$ and $\frac{2}{8} = \frac{1}{4}$. When we say *the* difference of a pair of positive numbers, we mean their positive difference. For example, the difference of 2 and 8 is 6.

1.3 Integers

In this subsection, you'll revise some properties of the integers

$$\dots, -3, -2, -1, 0, 1, 2, 3, \dots.$$

If an integer a divides exactly into another integer b, then we say that

- b is a **multiple** of a, or
- b is **divisible** by a, or
- a is a **factor** or **divisor** of b.

For example, 15 is a multiple of 5; also 15 is divisible by 5; and 5 is a factor of 15. Similarly, -15 is a multiple of 5, and so on.

Notice that every integer is both a multiple and a factor of itself: for example, 5 is a multiple of 5, and 5 is a factor of 5.

A **factor pair** of an integer is a pair of its factors that multiply together to give the integer. For example, the factor pairs of 12 are

$$1, 12; \quad 2, 6; \quad 3, 4; \quad -1, -12; \quad -2, -6; \quad -3, -4;$$

and the factor pairs of -4 are

$$1, -4; \quad 2, -2; \quad -1, 4; \quad -2, 2.$$

(The order of the two numbers within a factor pair doesn't matter – for example, the factor pair 1, 12 is the same as the factor pair 12, 1.)

A **positive factor pair** of a positive integer is a factor pair in which both factors are positive. For example, the positive factor pairs of 12 are

$$1, 12; \quad 2, 6; \quad 3, 4.$$

An integer that has a factor pair in which the same factor is repeated – in other words, an integer that can be written in the form a^2 for some integer a – is called a **square number** or a **perfect square**. For example, 9 is a square number, since $9 = 3^2$. Here are the first few square numbers.

The square numbers up to 15^2

1, 4, 9, 16, 25, 36, 49, 64, 81, 100, 121, 144, 169, 196, 225

You can use the following strategy to help you find all the positive factor pairs (and hence all the positive factors) of a positive integer.

> **Strategy:**
> **To find the positive factor pairs of a positive integer**
>
> - Try dividing the integer by each of the numbers $1, 2, 3, 4, \ldots$ in turn. Whenever you find a factor, write it down along with the other factor in the factor pair.
>
> - Stop when you get a factor pair that you have already.

Activity 7   *Finding factor pairs of integers*

(a) For each of the following positive integers, find all its positive factor pairs and then list all its positive factors in increasing order.

    (i) 28   (ii) 25   (iii) 36

(b) Use your answer to part (a)(i) to find *all* the factor pairs of the following integers.

    (i) 28   (ii) -28

An integer greater than 1 whose only factors are 1 and itself is called a prime number, or just a **prime**. For example, 3 is a prime number because its only factors are 1 and 3, but 4 is not a prime number because its factors are 1, 2 and 4. Note that 1 is not a prime number.

Here are the first 25 prime numbers.

> **The prime numbers under 100**
>
> 2, 3, 5, 7, 11, 13, 17, 19, 23, 29, 31, 37, 41, 43, 47, 53, 59, 61, 67, 71, 73, 79, 83, 89, 97

An integer greater than 1 that isn't a prime number is called a **composite number**. The first ten composite numbers are

    4, 6, 8, 9, 10, 12, 14, 15, 16, 18.

You can break down any composite number into a product of prime factors. For example, here's how you can break down the composite number 504:

$$504 = 2 \times 252$$
$$= 2 \times 2 \times 126$$
$$= 2 \times 2 \times 2 \times 63$$
$$= 2 \times 2 \times 2 \times 3 \times 21$$
$$= 2 \times 2 \times 2 \times 3 \times 3 \times 7.$$

The product of prime numbers in the last line of this working is the *only* product of prime numbers that's equal to 504 (except that you can change the order of the primes in the product, of course: for example, $504 = 2 \times 7 \times 2 \times 2 \times 3 \times 3$). In general, the following important fact holds.

> ## The fundamental theorem of arithmetic
>
> Every integer greater than 1 can be written as a product of prime factors in just one way (except that you can change the order of the factors).

The **prime factorisation** of an integer greater than 1 is any expression that shows it written as a product of prime factors. For example, the working above shows that the prime factorisation of 504 is

$$504 = 2^3 \times 3^2 \times 7.$$

Here the prime factors are written using index notation, with the prime factors in increasing order. This is the usual way that prime factorisations are written.

Notice that the fundamental theorem of arithmetic applies to all integers greater than 1, not just composite numbers. The prime factorisation of a prime number is just the prime number itself (a 'product of one prime'!).

The strategy that was used above to find the prime factorisation of 504 is summarised below. You can use it to find the prime factorisation of any integer greater than 1 (though for a large integer it can take a long time).

Strategy:
To find the prime factorisation of an integer greater than 1

- Repeatedly 'factor out' the prime 2 until you obtain a number that isn't divisible by 2.
- Repeatedly factor out the prime 3 until you obtain a number that isn't divisible by 3.
- Repeatedly factor out the prime 5 until you obtain a number that isn't divisible by 5.

Continue this process with each of the successive primes, 2, 3, 5, 7, 11, 13, 17, ..., in turn. Stop when you have a product of primes.

Write out the prime factorisation with the prime factors in increasing order, using index notation for any repeated factors.

Your calculator may be able to find prime factorisations of integers, but it's useful to know how to do this yourself, to improve your understanding of numbers and algebra.

Activity 8   *Finding prime factorisations*

Find the prime factorisations of the following integers, without using your calculator.

(a) 594   (b) 525   (c) 221   (d) 223

We finish this section with a reminder about *common multiples* and *common factors*.

A **common multiple** of two or more integers is a number that is a multiple of all of them. For example, the common multiples of 4 and 6 are $\ldots, -36, -24, -12, 0, 12, 24, 36, \ldots$.

The **lowest** (or **least**) **common multiple** (**LCM**) of two or more integers is the *smallest positive* integer that is a multiple of all of them. For example, the lowest common multiple of 4 and 6 is 12.

Similarly, a **common factor** of two or more integers is a number that is a factor of all of them. For example, the common factors of 24 and 30 are $-6, -3, -2, -1, 1, 2, 3$ and 6.

The **highest common factor** (**HCF**)(or **greatest common divisor** (**GCD**)) of two or more integers is the *largest positive* number that is a factor of all of them. For example, the highest common factor of 24 and 30 is 6.

Notice that the lowest common multiple and highest common factor of two or more integers are the same as the lowest common multiple and highest common factor of the corresponding *positive* integers. For example, the lowest common multiple of -4 and 6 is the same as the lowest common multiple of 4 and 6, which is 12. So you only ever need to find the lowest common multiple and the highest common factor of two or more *positive* integers.

You can often find the lowest common multiple or highest common factor of two or more fairly small positive integers simply by thinking about their common multiples or common factors. For larger integers, or more tricky cases, you can use their prime factorisations, as illustrated in the next example.

Example 3   *Using prime factorisations to find LCMs and HCFs*

Find the lowest common multiple and highest common factor of 594 and 693.

Solution

 Find and write out the prime factorisations, lining up each prime with the same prime in the other factorisation(s), where possible.

$$594 = 2 \times 3^3 \quad\ \times 11$$
$$693 = \quad\ 3^2 \times 7 \times 11$$

To find the lowest common multiple, identify the *highest* power of the prime in each column, and multiply all these numbers together.

The LCM of 594 and 693 is

$$2 \times 3^3 \times 7 \times 11 = 4158.$$

To find the highest common factor, identify the *lowest* power of the prime in each column, and multiply all these numbers together. (Omit any primes, such as 2 and 7 here, that are missing from one or more rows.)

The HCF of 594 and 693 is

$$3^2 \times 11 = 99.$$

$2\!\!\times\!\! 3^3 \quad\ \times 11$
$3^2 \times 7 \times 11$

Figure 6 Highest powers of primes in columns

$2 \times 3^3 \quad\ \times 11$
$3^2 \times 7 \times 11$

Figure 7 Lowest powers of primes in columns

The methods used in Example 3 can be summarised as follows.

> **Strategy:**
> **To find the lowest common multiple or highest common factor of two or more integers greater than 1**
>
> - Find the prime factorisations of the numbers.
> - To find the LCM, multiply together the highest power of each prime factor occurring in any of the numbers.
> - To find the HCF, multiply together the lowest power of each prime factor common to all the numbers.

Activity 9 *Using prime factorisations to find LCMs and HCFs*

Find the prime factorisations of 9, 18 and 24, and use them to find the lowest common multiple and highest common factor of each of the following sets of numbers.

(a) 18 and 24   (b) 9, 18 and 24   (c) -18 and -24

There's an efficient method, known as *Euclid's algorithm*, for finding lowest common multiples and highest common factors, without having to find prime factorisations first. You can learn about it in the module *Essential Mathematics 2* (MST125).

2 Algebraic expressions

In this section you'll revise some basic skills that you need when working with algebraic expressions.

2.1 Algebraic terminology

In mathematics, an **expression** is an arrangement of letters, numbers and/or mathematical symbols (such as $+$, $-$, $\times$, $\div$, brackets, and so on), which is such that if numbers are substituted for any letters present, then you can work out the value of the arrangement. So, for example, $3x + 4$ is an expression, but $3x + \div 4$ isn't, because '$+ \div$' doesn't make sense.

An expression that contains letters (usually as well as numbers and mathematical symbols) is an **algebraic expression**. An expression, such as $10 - 2 \times 4$, that contains only numbers and mathematical symbols is a **numerical expression**. An expression that's part of a larger expression, and can be enclosed in brackets without affecting the meaning of the larger expression, is called a **subexpression** of the larger expression. For example, the expression $3x$ is a subexpression of the expression $3x + 4$, but $x + 4$ is not, because $3(x + 4)$ has a different meaning.

Letters representing numbers in algebraic expressions can be any of three different types. A letter may be a **variable**: this means that it represents any number, or any number of a particular kind, such as any positive number, or any integer. Alternatively, it may be an **unknown**: this means that it represents a particular number that you don't know, but usually you want to discover, perhaps by solving an equation. Or it may represent a **constant**, a particular number whose value is specified, or regarded as unchanging for a particular calculation.

For example, as you saw earlier, there's a mathematical constant, whose value is approximately 2.72, that's denoted by the letter e. The word 'variable' is sometimes used as a catch-all for both variables and unknowns. When you're working with algebraic expressions, you don't usually need to think about which types of letter they contain – you treat all letters that represent numbers in a similar way.

As you know, multiplication signs are usually omitted in algebraic expressions (unless they are between two numbers) – things that are multiplied are just written next to each other instead. For example, $3 \times x$ is written as $3x$. Similarly, division signs are not normally used – fraction notation is used instead. For example, $3 \div x$ is usually written as

$$\frac{3}{x},$$

or as $3/x$, within a line of text. However, sometimes it's helpful to include multiplication signs or division signs in algebraic expressions.

You use equals signs when you're working with expressions, but expressions don't *contain* equals signs. For example, the statement

$$x + 2x = 3x$$

isn't an expression – it's an equation. An **equation** is made up of *two* expressions, with an equals sign between them.

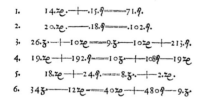

1.   14.ℨℯ.—+—.15.9——71.9.
2.   20.ℨℯ.———.18.9——.102.9.
3.   26.ℨ.—+—10ℨℯ——9.ℨ—10ℨℯ—+—213.9.
4.   19.ℨℯ—+—192.9——10ℨ—+—1089—19ℨℯ
5.   18.ℨℯ—+—24.9.——8.ℨ.—+—2.ℨℯ.
6.   34ℨ.——12ℨℯ—40ℨℯ—+—4809——9.ℨ.

Figure 8   The first equations written using equals signs, from Robert Recorde's *The Whetstone of Witte* (1577)

The equals sign was introduced by the Tudor mathematician Robert Recorde. It first appeared in his algebra book *The Whetstone of Witte* of 1577, where he described his invention as a useful abbreviation: 'And to auoide the tedioufe repetition of thefe woordes: is equalle to: I will fette as I doe often in woorke vfe, a paire of paralleles, or Gemowe [twin] lines of one lenghte, thus: =, bicaufe noe .2. thynges can be moare equalle.' This statement is immediately followed by the first equations to be written using his new notation, which are reproduced in Figure 8.

If an expression is a list of quantities that are all added or subtracted, then it's often helpful to think of it as a list of quantities that are all *added*. For example, the expression

$$5ab - 2a^2 + 3b + 6\sqrt{a} - 4 \qquad (2)$$

means the same as

$$5ab + (-2a^2) + 3b + 6\sqrt{a} + (-4).$$

The quantities that are added are called the **terms** of the expression. For example, the terms of expression (2) are

$$5ab, \quad -2a^2, \quad 3b, \quad 6\sqrt{a} \quad \text{and} \quad -4.$$

A term like -4, that doesn't contain any variables, is known as a **constant term** (because its value doesn't change when the values of the variables in the expression are changed). On the other hand, if a term has the form

a fixed value × a combination of variables,

then the fixed value is called the **coefficient** of the term, and we say that the term is a term *in* whatever the combination of variables is. For example, in expression (2),

$5ab$ has coefficient 5 and is a term in ab;

$-2a^2$ has coefficient -2 and is a term in a^2;

$3b$ has coefficient 3 and is a term in b;

$6\sqrt{a}$ has coefficient 6 and is a term in $\sqrt{a}$;

-4 is a constant term.

It's possible for a term to have coefficient 1 or -1. For example, in the expression $x^2 - x$, the two terms x^2 and $-x$ have coefficients 1 and -1, respectively. This is because these terms can also be written as $1x^2$ and $-1x$, though normally we wouldn't write them like that, as the forms x^2 and $-x$ are simpler. It's also possible for a coefficient to include constants. For example, in the expression $8r^3 - \frac{4}{3}\pi r^3$ the term $-\frac{4}{3}\pi r^3$ is a term in r^3 and its coefficient is $-\frac{4}{3}\pi$.

Sometimes two different expressions 'mean the same thing'. For example, $x + x$ and $2x$ are two ways of saying that there are 'two lots of x'. Expressions like these, that mean the same, are said to be *equivalent*.

More precisely, we say that two expressions are **equivalent**, or different **forms** of the same expression, if they have the same value as each other whatever values are chosen for their variables. We usually indicate this by writing an equals sign between them. (In some texts, the symbol $\equiv$ is used instead.) We also say that either expression can be **rearranged**, **manipulated** or **rewritten** to give the other. **Simplifying** an expression means rewriting it as a simpler expression.

One way to change an expression into an equivalent expression is to change the order of the terms. This doesn't change the meaning of the expression, because the order in which you add quantities doesn't affect the overall result. For example, the expressions

$$5ab - 2a^2 + 3b + 6\sqrt{a} - 4 \quad \text{and} \quad -2a^2 - 4 + 5ab + 6\sqrt{a} + 3b$$

are equivalent, because they are each the sum of the same five terms

$$5ab, \quad -2a^2, \quad 3b, \quad 6\sqrt{a} \quad \text{and} \quad -4.$$

2.2 Simplifying algebraic expressions

When you're working with an algebraic expression, you should usually try to write it in as simple a form as you can. One way in which some expressions can be simplified is by **collecting like terms**. If two or more terms of an expression differ only in the value of their coefficients, then you can combine them into a single term by adding the coefficients. For example:

$$3h + 9h - h \qquad \text{can be simplified to} \quad 11h;$$
$$a^2 - 3ab - 5a^2 + ab \quad \text{can be simplified to} \quad -4a^2 - 2ab.$$

You can also often simplify the individual terms in an expression. For example, the term

$$ab(-a) \quad \text{can be simplified to} \quad -a^2b.$$

Usually a term in an expression consists of a product of numbers and letters (and possibly other items like square roots). If such a term isn't in its simplest form, then you can simplify it by using the following strategy.

Strategy:
To simplify a term

1. Find the overall sign and write it at the front.
2. Simplify the rest of the coefficient and write it next.
3. Write any remaining parts of the term in an appropriate order; for example, letters are usually ordered alphabetically. Use index notation to avoid writing letters (or other items) more than once.

In Step 1 of the strategy, you find the overall sign of the term by using the following rules, which you saw for numbers on page 16.

When multiplying or dividing:

two signs the same give a plus sign;

two different signs give a minus sign.

Remember that a plus sign or a minus sign at the start of a term has the same effect as multiplying the term by 1 or -1, respectively, so you can apply the rule in the box above to such signs.

Example 4   *Simplifying single terms*

Simplify the following single-term expressions.

(a) $+(-2x)$ (b) $-(-7y)$ (c) $-3a^3b \times (-2a^2b)$

(d) $-c \times (-c) \times d \times (-d)$ (e) $(2x)^3$

Solution

(a) 🔍 A positive times a negative gives a negative, so the overall sign is minus. 💬

   $+(-2x) = -2x$

(b) 🔍 A negative times a negative gives a positive, so the overall sign is plus. 💬

   $-(-7y) = +7y = 7y$

(c) 🔍 First find the overall sign. A negative times a negative gives a positive, so the overall sign is plus. The rest of the coefficient is $3 \times 2 = 6$. The last part of the term is $a^3b \times a^2b = a^5b^2$. 💬

   $-3a^3b \times (-2a^2b) = +6a^5b^2 = 6a^5b^2$

(d) 🔍 First find the overall sign. A negative times a negative gives a positive, then this positive times a positive gives a positive, then this positive times a negative gives a negative. So the overall sign is minus. The rest of the term is $c \times c \times d \times d = c^2d^2$. 💬

   $-c \times (-c) \times d \times (-d) = -c^2d^2$

(e) 🔍 Use the fact that the cube of a number is three copies of the number multiplied together. Then proceed in the same way as in the earlier parts. 💬

   $(2x)^3 = (2x) \times (2x) \times (2x) = 8x^3$

Parts (a) and (b) of Example 4 illustrate the following rules, which you saw for numbers on page 15.

- Adding the negative of something is the same as subtracting the something.
- Subtracting the negative of something is the same as adding the something.

Notice also that in Example 4(c) the final power of a was found by calculating $a^3 \times a^2 = a^5$. That's because

$$a^3 \times a^2 = (a \times a \times a) \times (a \times a) = a^5.$$

You can see that, in general, for any natural numbers m and n, we have $a^m \times a^n = a^{m+n}$. This is an example of an *index law*. There's much more about index laws in Subsection 4.3.

Activity 10 *Simplifying single terms*

Simplify the following single-term expressions.

(a) $-(-uv)$ (b) $+(-9p)$ (c) $-(-4r^2)$ (d) $-(8z)$

(e) $2x^2y^2 \times 5xy^4$ (f) $-P(-PQ)$ (g) $5m \times (-\frac{2}{5}n)$

(h) $(-a^3)(-2b^3)(-2a^3)$ (i) $(cd)^2$ (j) $(-3x)^2$ (k) $-(3x)^2$

(l) $-(-3x)^2$ (m) $(-2x)^3$ (n) $-(-2x)^3$

You can simplify an expression that has more than one term by using the strategy below. In the first step you have to identify where each term begins and ends. You can do that by scanning through the expression from left to right – each time you come across a plus or minus sign that isn't inside brackets, that's the start of the next term.

Strategy:
To simplify an expression with more than one term

1. Identify the terms. Each term after the first starts with a plus or minus sign that isn't inside brackets.

2. Simplify each term, using the strategy on page 27. Include the sign (plus or minus) at the start of each term (except the first term, of course, if it has a plus sign).

3. Collect any like terms.

Example 5   *Simplifying an expression with more than one term*

Simplify the expression $3x \times 2x - 4y(-3x) - 10x^2$.

Solution

🔍 First identify the terms: you might find it helpful to mark them in the way shown below. Then simplify each term individually. Finally, collect any like terms. 💬

$$\underbrace{3x \times 2x}\ \underbrace{-\,4y(-3x)}\ \underbrace{-\,10x^2} = 6x^2 + 12xy - 10x^2$$
$$= 12xy - 4x^2$$

🔍 The answer could also be written as $-4x^2 + 12xy$, but $12xy - 4x^2$ is slightly shorter and tidier. 💬

Activity 11   *Simplifying expressions with more than one term*

Simplify the following expressions.

(a) $3a \times 3b - 2b \times 3b$ (b) $5x \times 8x - 3x(-3x)$

(c) $3x^2 - (-3y^2) + (-x^2) + (2y^2)$ (d) $-3cd + (-5c \times 2d^2) - (-cd^2)$

(e) $-6p(-\tfrac{1}{3}p) + (-5p \times p) - 2(-\tfrac{1}{2}p^2)$

(f) $A(-B) + (-AB) - (-AB) + (-A)(-B)$

2.3 Multiplying out brackets

In this subsection you'll revise how to rewrite an expression that contains a pair of brackets, such as

$$3b(1 + 2a),$$

as an expression that doesn't contain brackets. This process is called **multiplying out the brackets**, **expanding the brackets**, or simply **removing the brackets**. The new form of the expression, with no brackets, is called the **expansion** of the original expression.

In an expression like the one above, the subexpression that multiplies the brackets is called the **multiplier**. For example, the multiplier in the expression above is $3b$. The basic rule for multiplying out brackets is as follows.

Strategy:
To multiply out brackets

Multiply each term inside the brackets by the multiplier.

For example,

$$3b(1 + 2a) = 3b \times 1 + 3b \times 2a$$
$$= 3b + 6ab.$$

Remember that you have to multiply *each* term inside the brackets by the multiplier. Multiplying only the first term is a common mistake!

When you multiply out brackets, it's usually best *not* to write down an expression that contains multiplication signs, and then simplify it, as was done above. Instead, you should simplify the terms in your head as you multiply out. This leads to tidier expressions and fewer errors, and it's particularly helpful when minus signs are involved. Here's an example.

Example 6   *Multiplying out brackets*

Multiply out the brackets in the expression

$$-x(2x - y + 5).$$

Solution

The first term in the expanded form of the expression is $-x \times 2x$. Simplify this in your head (using the strategy of first finding the overall sign, then the rest of the coefficient, then the letters) and write it down. Do likewise for the other terms, which are $-x \times (-y)$ and $-x \times 5$.

$$-x(2x - y + 5) = -2x^2 + xy - 5x$$

When you multiply out brackets, it doesn't matter whether the multiplier is before or after the brackets. Here's an example of multiplying out where the multiplier is after the brackets:

$$(5g - 1)h = 5gh - h.$$

Activity 12   *Multiplying out brackets*

Multiply out the brackets in the following expressions.

(a) $a(a^4 + b)$ (b) $-x(6x - x^2)$ (c) $3pq(2p + 3q - 1)$

(d) $(C^3 - C^2 - C)C^2$ (e) $-\frac{1}{2}x\left(\frac{1}{3}x^2 + \frac{2}{3}x\right)$

Sometimes you have to remove brackets that have just a minus or plus sign in front, such as

$$-(p + 5q - s) \quad \text{or} \quad +(a - b).$$

You do this by using the following strategy.

Strategy:
To remove brackets with a plus or minus sign in front

- If the sign is plus, keep the sign of each term inside the brackets the same.

- If the sign is minus, change the sign of each term inside the brackets.

For example,

$$-(p + 5q - s) = -p - 5q + s \quad \text{and} \quad +(a - b) = a - b.$$

The strategy comes from the fact that a minus sign in front of brackets is just the same as multiplying by -1, and a plus sign in front is just the same as multiplying by 1.

Activity 13   *Plus and minus signs in front of brackets*

Remove the brackets in the following expressions.

(a) $-(-2x^2 + x - 1)$ (b) $+(2x - 3y + z)$ (c) $-(p - 2q)$

Notice that, for any expressions A and B,

$$-(A - B) = -A + B = B - A.$$

So we have the following useful fact.

For any expressions A and B,
the negative of $A - B$ is $B - A$.

It's helpful to remember this fact. For example, it tells you immediately that

$$-(x - y) = y - x \quad \text{and} \quad -(n - 3n^2) = 3n^2 - n,$$

and so on.

The strategy for multiplying out brackets leads to two further useful facts. You've seen how to use the strategy to write, for example,

$$(a - b + 2)c = ac - bc + 2c.$$

In effect this says that when you want to multiply the expression $a - b + 2$ by c, you simply multiply each of its terms by c to obtain $ac - bc + 2c$.

Similarly, since dividing by c is the same as multiplying by $1/c$,

$$\frac{a - b + 2}{c} = \frac{1}{c}(a - b + 2) = \frac{1}{c} \times a - \frac{1}{c} \times b + \frac{1}{c} \times 2 = \frac{a}{c} - \frac{b}{c} + \frac{2}{c}.$$

So when you want to divide the expression $a - b + 2$ by c, you simply divide each of its terms by c to obtain the result $(a/c) - (b/c) + (2/c)$.

In general, you can use the following facts.

Multiplying an expression that contains several terms by a second expression is the same as multiplying *each term* of the first expression by the second expression.

Similarly, dividing an expression that contains several terms by a second expression is the same as dividing *each term* of the first expression by the second expression.

Brackets in expressions with more than one term

Sometimes you have to multiply out brackets in an expression that contains more than one term. For example, the expression

$$2c(c + d) + 5c^2 - d(c - d)$$

has three terms, two of which contain brackets, as follows:

$$\underline{2c(c + d)} \; \underline{+ 5c^2} \; \underline{- d(c - d)}.$$

If you multiply out the brackets in both the first and last terms, then you obtain a new expression with five terms. You can then collect any like terms. The approach is summarised in the following strategy.

> **Strategy:**
> **To multiply out brackets in an expression with more than one term**
>
> 1. Identify the terms. Each term after the first starts with a plus or minus sign that isn't inside brackets.
> 2. Multiply out the brackets in each term. Include the sign (plus or minus) at the start of each resulting term.
> 3. Collect any like terms.

Example 7   *Multiplying out brackets when there's more than one term*

Multiply out the brackets in the expression
$$2c(c + d) + 5c^2 - d(c - d),$$
and simplify your answer.

Solution

 Identify the terms; you might find it helpful to mark them. Multiply out the brackets in each term individually to obtain a new expression with five terms. Finally, collect any like terms.

$$\underline{2c(c + d)} \ \underline{+ 5c^2} \ \underline{- d(c - d)} = 2c^2 + 2cd + 5c^2 - cd + d^2$$
$$= 7c^2 + cd + d^2$$

> **Activity 14**   *Multiplying out brackets when there's more than one term*
>
> Multiply out the brackets in the following expressions, simplifying where possible.
>
> (a) $x + x^2(1 + 3x)$ (b) $7ab - b(a + 2b)$ (c) $-6(c + d) + 3(c - d)$
>
> (d) $2X - 5Y(-4X + 2Y)$ (e) $(1 - p^4)p + p^2 - p$

Multiplying out two pairs of brackets

Some expressions, such as the one in Example 8 below, contain two pairs of brackets multiplied together. You can multiply out brackets like these by choosing one of the two bracketed expressions to be the multiplier, and multiplying out the other pair of brackets in the usual way. This gives you an expression with several terms each containing a pair of brackets, which again you can multiply out in the usual way.

It doesn't matter which of the two bracketed expressions you choose to be the multiplier to start with, but it's probably slightly easier to go for the second one, as illustrated in the next example.

Example 8   *Multiplying out two pairs of brackets*

Multiply out the brackets in the expression

$$(x - xy + 3y)(x - 2y),$$

and simplify your answer.

Solution

💬 Take the second bracketed expression to be the multiplier. Multiply each term in the first pair of brackets by this multiplier. 💬

$$(x - xy + 3y)(x - 2y) = x(x - 2y) - xy(x - 2y) + 3y(x - 2y)$$

💬 Multiply out the brackets in each term, then collect any like terms. 💬

$$= x^2 - 2xy - x^2y + 2xy^2 + 3xy - 6y^2$$
$$= x^2 + xy - x^2y + 2xy^2 - 6y^2$$

Activity 15   *Multiplying out two pairs of brackets*

Use the method described above to multiply out the brackets in the following expressions. Simplify your answers where possible.

(a) $(a + b)(c + d + e)$ (b) $(x + 3)(x + 5)$

(c) $(x^2 - 2x + 3)(3x^2 - x - 1)$

You can see from Example 8 and Activity 15 that the effect of multiplying out two pairs of brackets is that *each* term in the first pair of brackets is multiplied by *each* term in the second pair of brackets, and the resulting terms are added. So, for example, if there are three terms in the first pair of brackets and two terms in the second pair (as there are in Example 8, for instance), then altogether there will be $3 \times 2 = 6$ multiplications, which gives six terms in the multiplied-out expression before any like terms are collected.

You can use this fact to give you an alternative method for multiplying out two pairs of brackets, though you have to be careful not to miss out any of the multiplications! It's a good way to multiply out two pairs of brackets that each contain only two terms. In this case there are only four multiplications to be done, and you can use the acronym FOIL (first terms, outer terms, inner terms, last terms) to help you remember them. Here's an example.

Example 9   *Using FOIL to multiply out brackets*

Multiply out the brackets in the expression

$$(x + 2)(3x - 5),$$

and simplify your answer.

Solution

$(x + 2)\ (3x - 5)$

First: $x \times 3x = 3x^2$.
Outer: $x \times (-5) = -5x$.
Inner: $(+2) \times 3x = +6x$.
Last: $(+2) \times (-5) = -10$.

$$(x + 2)(3x - 5) = 3x^2 - 5x + 6x - 10 = 3x^2 + x - 10$$

You can practise using FOIL in the next activity.

Activity 16   *Multiplying out brackets containing two terms each*

Multiply out the brackets in the following expressions, and simplify your answers.

(a) $(x + 5)(x - 7)$ (b) $(x - 3)(x - 1)$ (c) $(2x - 1)(8x + 3)$

(d) $(2 - 5x)(x - 9)$ (e) $(c - 2d)(1 + c)$ (f) $(A - B)(2A - 3B^2)$

(g) $(a - 1)(a + 1)$ (h) $(2 + 3x)(2 - 3x)$

(i) $x(1 + x) + (x - 1)(2 - x)$

Make sure that you've done parts (g) and (h) of Activity 16, in particular, as they illustrate a useful fact that's discussed next.

Differences of two squares

In each of parts (g) and (h) of Activity 16, you'll have noticed that the product of the inner terms and the product of the outer terms added to zero. This happens whenever you multiply out an expression of the form

$$(A + B)(A - B),$$

where A and B are subexpressions. In fact, as you can check by multiplying out the brackets, the following holds.

> **Difference of two squares**
>
> For any expressions A and B,
> $$(A + B)(A - B) = A^2 - B^2.$$

Any expression that has the form of the right-hand side of the equation in the box above is known as a **difference of two squares**. The fact in the box will be useful in Subsection 4.2, and also in Unit 2.

Squared brackets

Sometimes you have to multiply out squared brackets, such as $(x - 5)^2$. You can do this by first writing the squared brackets as two pairs of brackets multiplied together, and then multiplying them out in the usual way. For example,

$$\begin{aligned}
(x - 5)^2 &= (x - 5)(x - 5) \\
&= x^2 - 5x - 5x + 25 \\
&= x^2 - 10x + 25.
\end{aligned}$$

Notice that $(x - 5)^2$ is *not* equal to $x^2 - 5^2$.

> **Activity 17**   *Multiplying out squared brackets*
>
> Multiply out the brackets in the following expressions, and simplify your answers.
>
> (a) $(x + 1)^2$ (b) $(3x - 2)^2$ (c) $(2p + 3q)^2$

A quick way to multiply out squared brackets that contain two terms, like those in Activity 17, is to use the fact that they all follow a similar pattern.

To see this pattern, notice what happens when you multiply out the expressions $(A + B)^2$ and $(A - B)^2$:

$$(A + B)^2 = (A + B)(A + B)$$
$$= A^2 + AB + AB + B^2$$
$$= A^2 + 2AB + B^2;$$

$$(A - B)^2 = (A - B)(A - B)$$
$$= A^2 - AB - AB + B^2$$
$$= A^2 - 2AB + B^2.$$

So the following useful facts hold.

Squaring brackets

For any expressions A and B,
$$(A + B)^2 = A^2 + 2AB + B^2, \quad \text{and}$$
$$(A - B)^2 = A^2 - 2AB + B^2.$$

Here's an example of how you can use these facts to quickly multiply out squared brackets.

Example 10 *Multiplying out squared brackets efficiently*

Multiply out the brackets in the following expressions, and simplify your answers.

(a) $(x + 3y)^2$ (b) $(4h - 1)^2$

Solution

(a) 🔍 The answer is the square of x, plus twice the product of x and $3y$, plus the square of $3y$. 💬
$$(x + 3y)^2 = x^2 + 2 \times x \times (3y) + (3y)^2 = x^2 + 6xy + 9y^2$$

(b) 🔍 The answer is the square of $4h$, minus twice the product of $4h$ and 1, plus the square of 1. 💬
$$(4h - 1)^2 = (4h)^2 - 2 \times (4h) \times 1 + 1^2 = 16h^2 - 8h + 1$$

Activity 18 *Multiplying out squared brackets, again*

Use the facts in the box above to multiply out the brackets in the following expressions, and simplify your answers.

(a) $(x+6)^2$ (b) $(x-2)^2$ (c) $(1+m)^2$ (d) $(1-2u)^2$

(e) $(2x-3)^2$ (f) $(3c+d)^2$

Simplest forms of expressions

As you know, you should usually write expressions in the simplest way you can. For example, you should write

$$x + 2x + 3x \quad \text{as} \quad 6x.$$

The second form of this expression is clearly simpler than the first:

- it's shorter and easier to understand, and
- it's easier to evaluate for any particular value of x.

These are the attributes to aim for when you try to write an expression in a simpler way.

However, sometimes it's not so clear that one way of writing an expression is better than another. For example,

$$x(x+1) \quad \text{is equivalent to} \quad x^2 + x.$$

Both of these forms are reasonably short, and both are reasonably easy to evaluate. So this expression doesn't have a simplest form.

They tell me it's important to simplify expressions!

The same is true of many other expressions. You should try to write each expression that you work with in a reasonably simple way, but often there's no 'right answer' for the simplest form. One form might be better for some purposes, and a different form might be better for other purposes.

In particular, multiplying out the brackets in an expression doesn't always simplify it. You should multiply out brackets only if you think that this is likely to make the expression simpler, or if you think that it will help you with the problem that you're working on.

3 Algebraic factors, multiples and fractions

In this section you'll revise what are meant by factors and multiples of algebraic expressions, how to take out common factors and how to work with algebraic fractions.

3.1 Factors and multiples of algebraic expressions

Algebraic expressions have *factors* and *multiples* in a similar way to integers, though these words are often used a little more loosely for algebraic expressions than they are for integers. Roughly speaking, if an algebraic expression can be written in the form

something $\times$ something,

then both 'somethings' are **factors** of the expression, and the expression is a **multiple** of both 'somethings'. For example, the equation

$$a^2b = a \times ab$$

shows that both a and ab are factors of a^2b, and it also shows that a^2b is a multiple of both a and ab.

Every algebraic expression is both a factor and a multiple of itself. For example, the equation

$$a^2b = 1 \times a^2b$$

shows that a^2b is both a factor and a multiple of itself.

Two or more algebraic expressions also have *common factors* and *common multiples*, in a similar way to two or more integers.

As you'd expect, a **common factor** of two or more algebraic expressions is an expression that's a factor of all of them. For example, the expression a is a common factor of the two expressions

a^2b and abc,

because

$$a^2b = a \times ab \quad \text{and} \quad abc = a \times bc.$$

Similarly, a **common multiple** of two or more algebraic expressions is an expression that's a multiple of all of them. For example, the expression $abcd$ is a common multiple of the two expressions

ab and bc,

because

$$abcd = ab \times cd \quad \text{and} \quad abcd = bc \times ad.$$

Activity 19 *Checking common factors and common multiples*

Show that:

(a) (i) $2a$ is a common factor of $4a^2$ and $2ab$;

(ii) x^2 is a common factor of x^3 and x^5;

(iii) $6z$ is a common factor of $18z^2$, $6z^2$ and $6z$;

(b) (i) $10cd^2$ is a common multiple of $5c$ and $2cd$;

(ii) p^7 is a common multiple of p^2 and p^3;

(iii) $9y^2$ is a common multiple of 3, $9y^2$ and $3y$.

Two or more algebraic expressions with integer coefficients have a *highest common factor* and a *lowest common multiple*, just as two or more integers do, though again these words are often used more loosely for algebraic expressions than they are for integers. In the context of algebraic expressions, **highest common factor** means a common factor that is a multiple of all other common factors. Similarly, **lowest common multiple** means a common multiple that is a factor of all other common multiples.

The next example shows you how to find highest common factors and lowest common multiples of algebraic expressions.

Example 11 *Finding HCFs and LCMs of algebraic expressions*

Consider the expressions

$$10a^6 \quad \text{and} \quad 15a^8b^3.$$

(a) Find the highest common factor of the expressions, and write each expression in the form

highest common factor $\times$ something.

(b) Find the lowest common multiple of the expressions, and, for each expression, write the lowest common multiple in the form

the expression $\times$ something.

Solution

(a)

🔍 First consider the coefficients. The largest integer that is a factor of both 10 and 15 (that is, their HCF) is 5.

Then consider the powers of a. The largest power of a that is a factor of both a^6 and a^8 is a^6. (Note that a^6 is a factor of both a^6 and a^8 because $a^6 = a^6 \times 1$ and $a^8 = a^6 \times a^2$.)

Finally, consider the powers of b. There is no power of b in $10a^6$, so there is no power of b in the highest common factor. 💭

The highest common factor of the two terms is

$$5a^6.$$

The expressions can be written as

$$10a^6 = 5a^6 \times 2 \quad \text{and} \quad 15a^8b^3 = 5a^6 \times 3a^2b^3.$$

(b)

🔍 First consider the coefficients. The smallest positive integer that is a multiple of both 10 and 15 (that is, their LCM) is 30.

Then consider the powers of a. The smallest power of a that is a multiple of both a^6 and a^8 is a^8.

Finally, consider the powers of b. The smallest power of b that is a multiple of both 'no power of b' and b^3 is b^3. 💭

The lowest common multiple of the two terms is

$$30a^8b^3.$$

It can be written as

$$30a^8b^3 = 10a^6 \times 3a^2b^3 \quad \text{and} \quad 30a^8b^3 = 15a^8b^3 \times 2.$$

Activity 20 *Finding HCFs and LCMs of algebraic expressions*

(a) Consider the expressions

$$3x^2 \quad \text{and} \quad 9xy.$$

   (i)   Find the highest common factor of the expressions, and write each expression in the form

          highest common factor $\times$ something.

(ii) Find the lowest common multiple of the expressions, and, for each expression, write the lowest common multiple in the form

the expression × something.

(b) Repeat part (a) for the expressions

$6p^2q^3$, $4pq^2$ and $2pq$.

3.2 Taking out common factors

Factorising an expression means writing it as the *product* of two or more expressions, neither of which is 1 (and, usually, neither of which is -1).

If all of the terms of an expression have a common factor other than 1, then the expression can be factorised. For example, consider the expression

$x^3y + xy$.

The terms of this expression, x^3y and xy, have xy as a common factor. So the expression can be written as

$xy \times x^2 + xy \times 1$.

From your work on multiplying out brackets, you know that this is the same as

$xy(x^2 + 1)$.

The original expression has now been factorised. We say that we have **taken out the common factor** xy. This example illustrates the thinking behind the following general strategy for taking out common factors.

> **Strategy:**
> **To take out a common factor from an expression**
>
> 1. Find a common factor of the terms (usually the highest common factor).
>
> 2. Write the common factor in front of a pair of brackets.
>
> 3. Write what's left of each term inside the brackets.

Example 12   *Taking out a common factor*

Factorise the expression $-8g^5 + 4g^2h^2 - 2g^2$.

Solution

The highest common factor of the three terms is $2g^2$.

$$-8g^5 + 4g^2h^2 - 2g^2 = 2g^2(-4g^3 + 2h^2 - 1)$$

Notice that if you're taking out a common factor, and it's the same as, or the negative of, one of the terms, then 'what's left' of the term is 1 or -1. This is illustrated in Example 12 above, and also in the example in the text at the beginning of this subsection.

Remember that you can check whether a factorisation that you've carried out is correct by just multiplying out the brackets again. It's often a good idea to carry out some sort of check on an answer that you've found to a mathematical problem, where this is possible, especially when you're learning a new technique, or when you're answering an assignment question.

If you're trying to take out the *highest* common factor from an expression, then it's worth checking the expression inside the brackets when you've finished, to make sure that you haven't missed any common factors.

Activity 21   *Taking out common factors*

Factorise the following expressions. Take out the highest common factor in each case.

(a) $pq + 12qr$ (b) $14cd - 7cd^2$ (c) $m^3 - m^7 - 8m^2$

(d) $-6AB + 3A^2B - 12A^3B^2$ (e) $\sqrt{T} - s\sqrt{T}$

(f) $5x^2 - 10x$ (g) $18y^2 + 6$

Sometimes it's convenient to take out a common factor with a minus sign. When you do this, 'what's left' of each term will have the opposite sign to the original sign. For example, an alternative way to factorise the expression in Example 12 is

$$-8g^5 + 4g^2h^2 - 2g^2 = -2g^2(4g^3 - 2h^2 + 1).$$

You can also take out *just* a minus sign from an expression. For example,

$$-a - b + c = -(a + b - c).$$

It can be helpful to do these things when all or most of the terms in an expression have minus signs.

Activity 22   *Taking out common factors with minus signs*

Factorise each of the following expressions by taking out the negative of the highest common factor of the terms. (If the highest common factor of the terms is 1, then take out just a minus sign.)

(a) $-2x^3 + 3x^2 - x - 5$ (b) $-ab - a - b$ (c) $5cd^2 - 10c^2d - 5cd$

If the coefficients of the terms of an expression aren't integers, then you can often still factorise the expression in a helpful way. For example, sometimes you can simplify an expression by taking out a fraction as a 'common factor', leaving terms with integer coefficients inside the brackets. To achieve this, usually the fraction that you take out must have a denominator that is a common multiple of the denominators of the coefficients. Here's an example:

$$\tfrac{1}{2}n^2 - \tfrac{2}{3}n + 1 = \tfrac{1}{6}(3n^2 - 4n + 6).$$

Sometimes the expression in the brackets has further common factors that can also be taken out, as in Activity 23(a) and (d) below.

Activity 23   *Working with non-integer coefficients*

Simplify each of the following expressions by factorising them.

(a) $\tfrac{1}{2}a^2 + \tfrac{3}{2}a$ (b) $\tfrac{1}{3}x - \tfrac{1}{6}$ (c) $2x^2 - \tfrac{1}{2}x + \tfrac{1}{4}$ (d) $\tfrac{2}{3}u^2v^2 + \tfrac{1}{2}u^3v$

3.3   Algebraic fractions

As you know, in algebraic expressions, division is normally indicated by fraction notation rather than by division signs. For example, the expression $2x \div (x + 1)$ is written as

$$\frac{2x}{x + 1}.$$

An algebraic expression written in the form of a fraction, such as the expression above, is called an **algebraic fraction**. As with a numerical fraction, the top and bottom of the algebraic fraction are called the **numerator** and the **denominator**, respectively.

When you want to write an algebraic fraction as part of a line of text, you can replace the horizontal line by a slash symbol, but remember that you may need to enclose the numerator and/or denominator in brackets to make it clear what's divided by what. For example, you can write the algebraic fraction above as $(2x)/(x + 1)$ or as $2x/(x + 1)$, but not as $2x/x + 1$, which means $(2x/x) + 1$.

There are other special situations where you may find the slash notation helpful. For example, it's convenient when you're dealing with a fraction whose numerator and denominator are themselves fractions, or when a fraction appears in a power, such as $2^{x/5}$. However, in most situations, and especially when you're manipulating fractions, you should use the horizontal line notation, as it's simpler to work with and helps you avoid mistakes.

You can manipulate algebraic fractions using the same rules that you use for numerical fractions. However, there's an extra issue that you need to take into account: an algebraic fraction is valid only for the values of the variables that make the denominator non-zero. This is because division by zero isn't possible. For example, the algebraic fraction $2x/(x+1)$ is valid for every value of x except -1.

> On 21 September 1997, the computer system of the US Navy cruiser USS Yorktown failed because of a division by zero error, and the ship was incapacitated.

In the rest of this subsection you'll revise and practise manipulating algebraic fractions.

Equivalence of algebraic fractions

Two numerical fractions are equal or *equivalent* if one can be obtained from the other by multiplying or dividing both the numerator and the denominator by the same (non-zero) number. For example,

$$\frac{2}{10} \quad \text{and} \quad \frac{1}{5} \quad \text{are equivalent, because} \quad \frac{2}{10} = \frac{1 \times 2}{5 \times 2}.$$

Similarly, two algebraic fractions are equal or *equivalent* if one can be obtained from the other by multiplying or dividing both the numerator and the denominator by the same expression. For example,

$$\frac{a(b-2)}{b(b-2)} \quad \text{and} \quad \frac{a}{b} \quad \text{are equivalent.}$$

Notice that the first of these two algebraic fractions is valid for all values of its variables except $b = 0$ and $b = 2$, whereas the second is valid for all values of its variables except just $b = 0$. So the two fractions aren't *exactly* the same. This sort of thing doesn't usually matter, but sometimes it does. For example, it can occasionally cause problems when you're solving equations. There's more about this in Subsections 5.3 and 5.4.

Simplifying algebraic fractions

A numerical fraction whose numerator and denominator have a common factor can be simplified by dividing both the numerator and the denominator by this factor. For example, 2 is a common factor of 2 and 10, so

$$\frac{2}{10} = \frac{1 \times 2}{5 \times 2} = \frac{1}{5}.$$

You can indicate this sort of working by crossing out the numbers on the numerator and denominator of the fraction, and replacing them with the results of the divisions, like this:

$$\frac{2}{10} = \frac{\overset{1}{\cancel{2}}}{\underset{5}{\cancel{10}}} = \frac{1}{5}.$$

In the same way, an algebraic fraction whose numerator and denominator have a common factor can be simplified by dividing both the numerator and the denominator by the factor. For example, x is a common factor of xy and x^3, so

$$\frac{xy}{x^3} = \frac{y \times x}{x^2 \times x} = \frac{y}{x^2},$$

which you can write as

$$\frac{xy}{x^3} = \frac{\overset{1}{\cancel{x}}y}{\underset{x^2}{\cancel{x^3}}} = \frac{y}{x^2}.$$

Notice that this calculation uses the fact that $x^3 \div x = x^2$. This is because $x^3 = x \times x \times x$, so dividing x^3 by x gives x^2. You can see that for any natural numbers m and n with m larger than n, we have $a^m \div a^n = a^{m-n}$. This is another *index law*. It's discussed more thoroughly in Subsection 4.3.

The process of dividing the numerator and denominator of a fraction, whether numerical or algebraic, by a common factor is known as **cancelling** the factor, or **cancelling down** the fraction.

Usually it's best to simplify a numerical or algebraic fraction as much as possible. To do this, you need to cancel the *highest* common factor of the numerator and denominator. It's often easiest to do this by cancelling in stages: first you cancel one common factor, then another, and so on, until eventually the overall effect is that you've cancelled the highest common factor. This is illustrated in the next example.

Example 13 *Simplifying algebraic fractions*

Simplify the following algebraic fractions.

(a) $\dfrac{12a^2b^4}{9a^3b}$ (b) $\dfrac{x^3(x+1)}{x(x+1)^2}$

Solution

(a) 🔍 Divide top and bottom by 3 (the highest common factor of the coefficients), then by a^2 (the highest common factor of the powers of a), and finally by b (the highest common factor of the powers of b). 💭

$$\frac{12a^2b^4}{9a^3b} = \frac{\overset{4}{\cancel{12}}a^2b^4}{\underset{3}{\cancel{9}}a^3b} = \frac{\overset{4}{\cancel{12}}\overset{1}{\cancel{a^2}}b^4}{\underset{3}{\cancel{9}}\underset{a}{\cancel{a^3}}b} = \frac{\overset{4}{\cancel{12}}\overset{1}{\cancel{a^2}}\overset{b^3}{\cancel{b^4}}}{\underset{3}{\cancel{9}}\underset{a}{\cancel{a^3}}\underset{1}{\cancel{b}}} = \frac{4b^3}{3a} \quad (b \neq 0)$$

(b) 🔍 Divide top and bottom by x (the highest common factor of the powers of x), then by $x+1$ (the highest common factor of the powers of $x+1$). 💭

$$\frac{x^3(x+1)}{x(x+1)^2} = \frac{\overset{x^2}{\cancel{x^3}}(x+1)}{\underset{1}{\cancel{x}}(x+1)^2} = \frac{\overset{x^2}{\cancel{x^3}}\overset{1}{\cancel{(x+1)}}}{\underset{1}{\cancel{x}}\underset{x+1}{\cancel{(x+1)^2}}} = \frac{x^2}{x+1} \quad (x \neq 0)$$

In order to show the cancelling-down process clearly, Example 13 displays each cancellation on a fresh copy of the original fraction. Normally, however, you should be able to show all stages of the cancellation on a single copy of the fraction.

Another feature of Example 13 is that restrictions, $b \neq 0$ and $x \neq 0$, are used to indicate that the original and the final fraction in each part are equivalent only if the restriction holds. (The symbol '$\neq$' means, and is read as, 'is not equal to'.) Often we won't note such restrictions explicitly, but you should keep in mind that they apply.

Activity 24 *Simplifying algebraic fractions*

Simplify the following algebraic fractions.

(a) $\dfrac{8xy^3}{6x^2y^2}$ (b) $\dfrac{2(3x-1)}{10(3x-1)^3}$ (c) $\dfrac{(x-1)^2(x-2)}{(x-1)(x-2)^2}$

As you become familiar with cancelling down algebraic fractions, you can make your working tidier by not actually crossing out factors. Instead, you can just write down the original form of the fraction, followed by an equals sign and then the simplified form, as you would with other types of algebraic simplification. If you do want to cross out factors in a fraction, perhaps because it's a complicated one, then you should make sure that your working also includes a copy of the unsimplified fraction with nothing crossed out.

The next example illustrates that even if there aren't any obvious common factors of the numerator and the denominator of an algebraic fraction, you may still be able to find some by factorising the numerator and/or the denominator.

Example 14 *Simplifying more algebraic fractions*

Simplify the following algebraic fractions.

(a) $\dfrac{x^2+2x}{5x^3-3x}$ (b) $\dfrac{u^2-2u}{3u-6}$

Solution

Factorise the numerator and denominator to check for common factors. Cancel any common factors.

(a) $\dfrac{x^2+2x}{5x^3-3x}=\dfrac{x(x+2)}{x(5x^2-3)}=\dfrac{x+2}{5x^2-3}$ $(x\neq 0)$

(b) $\dfrac{u^2-2u}{3u-6}=\dfrac{u(u-2)}{3(u-2)}=\dfrac{u}{3}$ $(u\neq 2)$

In part (a) of Example 14, you can avoid having to write down the middle expression in the working if you notice that *each term in both the numerator and denominator* of the original fraction has x as a common factor. In general, if all the terms in both the numerator and the denominator of a fraction have a common factor, then you can simplify the fraction by dividing each of these terms individually by this common factor. That's because, as stated in a box on page 33, if an expression is a sum of several terms, then dividing it by a second expression is the same as dividing *each term* of the expression by the second expression.

For example, each term in both the numerator and denominator of the fraction below has c^2 as a common factor, so you can simplify it by dividing each term individually by c^2:

$$\frac{c^4 + c^3 + c^2}{2c^3 + c^2} = \frac{c^2 + c + 1}{2c + 1}.$$

Activity 25   *Simplifying more algebraic fractions*

Simplify the following algebraic fractions.

(a) $\dfrac{ab + a}{a^2 + a}$ (b) $\dfrac{3}{9 + 6y^2}$ (c) $\dfrac{u^2 - u^3}{u^5}$

(d) $\dfrac{2x^2 - 4x^3}{6x^4 - 2x^2}$ (e) $\dfrac{x^3 + x^2}{2x + 2}$ (f) $\dfrac{1 - n}{n^2 - n}$

Adding and subtracting algebraic fractions

As you know, if the denominators of two or more numerical fractions are the same, then to add or subtract them you just add or subtract the numerators. For example,

$$\frac{5}{7} - \frac{2}{7} = \frac{3}{7}.$$

If the denominators are different, then before you can add or subtract the fractions, you need to write them with the same denominator. This denominator has to be a common multiple of the denominators of all the fractions to be added or subtracted. Here's an example:

$$\frac{5}{4} + \frac{2}{3} - \frac{1}{6} = \frac{15}{12} + \frac{8}{12} - \frac{2}{12} = \frac{21}{12} = \frac{7}{4}.$$

In this calculation, a common multiple of the original denominators 4, 3 and 6 is 12. So each fraction was written with denominator 12, by multiplying top and bottom by an appropriate number (namely 3, 4 and 2, respectively). Then the numerators were added and subtracted in the usual way, and the resulting answer was simplified by cancelling.

You can use the same method to add or subtract algebraic fractions, as follows.

Strategy:
To add or subtract algebraic fractions

1. Make sure that the fractions have the same denominator – if necessary, rewrite each fraction as an equivalent fraction to achieve this.

2. Add or subtract the numerators.

3. Simplify the answer if possible.

Example 15 *Adding and subtracting algebraic fractions*

Write each of the following expressions as a single algebraic fraction.

(a) $\dfrac{x+2}{x^2} - \dfrac{2}{x^2}$ (b) $\dfrac{1}{ab} + \dfrac{2}{a} - \dfrac{3}{b}$ (c) $\dfrac{x}{1-x} - \dfrac{1}{x}$ (d) $\dfrac{5}{d} + c$

Solution

(a) The denominators are the same, so subtract the second numerator from the first. Simplify the answer.

$$\dfrac{x+2}{x^2} - \dfrac{2}{x^2} = \dfrac{x+2-2}{x^2} = \dfrac{x}{x^2} = \dfrac{1}{x}$$

(b) First write the fractions with the same denominator, by multiplying the top and bottom of each fraction by an appropriate expression. Then add and subtract the numerators.

$$\dfrac{1}{ab} + \dfrac{2}{a} - \dfrac{3}{b} = \dfrac{1}{ab} + \dfrac{2b}{ab} - \dfrac{3a}{ab} = \dfrac{1+2b-3a}{ab}$$

(c) Proceed in a similar way to part (b). Simplify the answer.

$$\dfrac{x}{1-x} - \dfrac{1}{x} = \dfrac{x^2}{x(1-x)} - \dfrac{1-x}{x(1-x)} = \dfrac{x^2-(1-x)}{x(1-x)} = \dfrac{x^2+x-1}{x(1-x)}$$

(d) First write c as a fraction, then proceed as before.

$$\dfrac{5}{d} + c = \dfrac{5}{d} + \dfrac{c}{1} = \dfrac{5}{d} + \dfrac{cd}{d} = \dfrac{5+cd}{d}$$

Write each of the following expressions as a single algebraic fraction, simplifying your answer if possible.

(a) $\dfrac{1}{x} + \dfrac{y}{x}$ (b) $\dfrac{c+2}{c^2+c} - \dfrac{1}{c^2+c}$ (c) $\dfrac{1}{ab} - \dfrac{1}{bc}$ (d) $\dfrac{2}{3a} + \dfrac{1}{2a}$

(e) $\dfrac{1}{x^2} - \dfrac{2}{x} + 3$ (f) $5 - \dfrac{1}{x} + \dfrac{2}{y}$ (g) $A - \dfrac{A^2-1}{2A}$ (h) $\dfrac{3}{2u-1} + u$

(i) $\dfrac{x+2}{x+1} + \dfrac{1}{x}$ (j) $\dfrac{2}{p+2} - \dfrac{1}{p-3}$ (k) $\dfrac{x+1}{x(x-1)} + \dfrac{1}{x} - x$

Expanding algebraic fractions

You saw on page 33 that if an expression is a sum of several terms, then dividing it by a second expression is the same as dividing *each term* of the expression by the second expression.

This means that if you have an algebraic fraction whose *numerator* is a sum of terms, then you can rewrite it so that each term is individually divided by the denominator. For example,

$$\frac{2x^2 - y + 3}{x} = \frac{2x^2}{x} - \frac{y}{x} + \frac{3}{x} = 2x - \frac{y}{x} + \frac{3}{x}.$$

This procedure is known as **expanding** the algebraic fraction. Like expanding brackets, it's sometimes a useful thing to do, and sometimes not. Expanding an algebraic fraction is essentially the reverse procedure to adding or subtracting algebraic fractions.

Expand the following algebraic fractions.

(a) $\dfrac{a^2 + a^5 - 1}{a^2}$ (b) $\dfrac{2 - 5cd}{c}$ (c) $\dfrac{2a + 3a^2}{6}$

Remember that an algebraic fraction can be expanded only if it has a sum of terms in the *numerator*. The following fraction, which has a sum of terms in the denominator, can't be expanded:

$$\frac{a^2}{a^2 + a^5 - 1}.$$

Multiplying and dividing algebraic fractions

To *multiply* numerical fractions, you multiply the numerators together and multiply the denominators together. For example,

$$\frac{3}{4} \times \frac{2}{3} = \frac{3 \times 2}{4 \times 3} = \frac{6}{12} = \frac{1}{2}.$$

The rule for *dividing* numerical fractions can be conveniently described using the idea of the *reciprocal* of a number. A number and its **reciprocal** multiply together to give 1. So, for example, the reciprocal of $\frac{2}{3}$ is $\frac{3}{2}$, since $\frac{2}{3} \times \frac{3}{2} = 1$. Similarly, the reciprocal of $\frac{1}{2}$ is $\frac{2}{1} = 2$, and the reciprocal of $-\frac{3}{5}$ is $-\frac{5}{3}$. Every number except 0 has a reciprocal.

Since a number and its reciprocal multiply together to give 1, another way to think about the reciprocal of a number is that it is 1 divided by the number.

To find the reciprocal of a fraction, you just swap the numerator and the denominator. For example, the reciprocal of $\frac{3}{5}$ is $\frac{5}{3}$, since $\frac{3}{5} \times \frac{5}{3} = \frac{15}{15} = 1$.

The rule for dividing numerical fractions is as follows: to divide by a numerical fraction, you multiply by its reciprocal. For example,

$$\frac{3}{4} \div \frac{2}{3} = \frac{3}{4} \times \frac{3}{2} = \frac{3 \times 3}{4 \times 2} = \frac{9}{8}.$$

If you don't know *why* fractions are multiplied and divided using the rules described here, have a look at the document *Fraction arithmetic* on the module website.

Algebraic fractions are multiplied and divided in the same way as numerical ones.

> **Strategy:**
> **To multiply or divide algebraic fractions**
>
> - To multiply two or more algebraic fractions, multiply the numerators together and multiply the denominators together.
> - To divide by an algebraic fraction, multiply by its reciprocal.
>
> Simplify the answer if possible.

Here's an example of multiplying algebraic fractions:

$$\frac{4}{7a^3} \times \frac{7a}{2b^3} = \frac{28a}{14a^3b^3} = \frac{2}{a^2b^3}.$$

In this manipulation the two numerators were multiplied and the two denominators were multiplied, and then the answer was simplified by cancelling common factors. However, it's often quicker and easier to cancel any common factors *before* you multiply the numerators and denominators of fractions, like this:

$$\frac{4}{7a^3} \times \frac{7a}{2b^3} = \frac{\overset{2}{\cancel{4}}}{7a^3} \times \frac{7a}{2b^3} = \frac{\overset{2}{\cancel{4}}}{\underset{1}{\cancel{7}a^3}} \times \frac{\overset{1}{\cancel{7}a}}{2b^3} = \frac{\overset{2}{\cancel{4}}}{\underset{1}{\cancel{7}}\underset{a^2}{\cancel{a^3}}} \times \frac{\overset{1}{\cancel{7}}\overset{1}{\cancel{a}}}{2b^3} = \frac{2}{a^2} \times \frac{1}{b^3} = \frac{2}{a^2b^3}.$$

This technique is known as **cross-cancelling**. As with ordinary cancelling, there is no need to show every, or indeed any, stage of the cancelling process.

Example 16 *Multiplying and dividing algebraic fractions*

Simplify the following expressions.

(a) $\dfrac{2x-5}{(x-1)^2} \times \dfrac{x-1}{4}$ (b) $\dfrac{9P^2}{Q^8} \div \dfrac{3P^3}{Q^9}$

Solution

(a) 🔍 To multiply the fractions, multiply the numerators and multiply the denominators. Cross-cancel any common factors first. 💬

$$\frac{2x-5}{(x-1)^2} \times \frac{x-1}{4} = \frac{2x-5}{\underset{x-1}{\cancel{(x-1)^2}}} \times \frac{\overset{1}{\cancel{x-1}}}{4} = \frac{2x-5}{4(x-1)}$$

(b) 🔍 To divide by a fraction, multiply by the reciprocal. Cross-cancel any common factors before doing the multiplication. 💬

$$\frac{9P^2}{Q^8} \div \frac{3P^3}{Q^9} = \frac{9P^2}{Q^8} \times \frac{Q^9}{3P^3} = \frac{\overset{3}{\cancel{9}}P^2}{Q^8} \times \frac{Q^9}{\underset{1}{\cancel{3}}P^3}$$

$$= \frac{\overset{3}{\cancel{9}}\overset{1}{\cancel{P^2}}}{Q^8} \times \frac{Q^9}{\underset{1}{\cancel{3}}\underset{P}{\cancel{P^3}}} = \frac{\overset{3}{\cancel{9}}\overset{1}{\cancel{P^2}}}{\cancel{Q^8}} \times \frac{\overset{Q}{\cancel{Q^9}}}{\underset{1}{\cancel{3}}\underset{P}{\cancel{P^3}}} = \frac{3Q}{P}$$

You can practise multiplying and dividing algebraic fractions in the next activity. Notice that division is indicated in three different ways in this activity, namely with a division sign, with a horizontal line and with a slash symbol.

Activity 28   *Multiplying and dividing algebraic fractions*

Simplify the following expressions.

(a) $\dfrac{40A}{B} \times \dfrac{BC}{16A^4}$ (b) $\dfrac{b}{c^2} \div c^3$ (c) $\left(\dfrac{6y}{x^7}\right) \Big/ \left(\dfrac{15y^{10}}{x^4}\right)$

(d) $\dfrac{a/(a+1)}{a^6/(a+1)^2}$ (e) $\dfrac{3x}{y} \div \dfrac{6}{y^2}$ (f) $g \times \dfrac{5}{k}$

4 Roots and powers

In this section you'll revise how to work with roots and powers of numbers and algebraic expressions.

4.1 Roots of numbers

As you know, a **square root** of a number is a number that when squared (raised to the power 2) gives the original number. For example, both 6 and -6 are square roots of 36, since

$$6^2 = 6 \times 6 = 36 \quad \text{and} \quad (-6)^2 = (-6) \times (-6) = 36.$$

Similarly, a **cube root** of a number is a number that when cubed (raised to the power 3) gives the original number. For example, 4 is a cube root of 64, and -4 is a cube root of -64, because

$$4^3 = 4 \times 4 \times 4 = 64 \quad \text{and} \quad (-4)^3 = (-4) \times (-4) \times (-4) = -64.$$

As you'd expect, a **fourth root** of a number is a number that when raised to the power 4 gives the original number, and **fifth roots**, **sixth roots** and so on are defined in a similar way.

Every positive number has two square roots, a positive one and a negative one. For example, as you saw above, the two square roots of 36 are 6 and -6. When we say *the* square root of a positive number, we mean the positive square root. Every negative number has no real square roots – in other words, it has no square roots that are real numbers. For example, there's no real number that when squared gives -36. (You'll see in Unit 12 that negative numbers do have 'imaginary' square roots.) The number 0 has one square root, namely itself.

The situation for cube roots is simpler: every real number, whether positive, negative or zero, has exactly one real cube root.

The situation for fourth roots, sixth roots and all even-numbered roots is similar to that for square roots, and the situation for fifth roots, seventh roots and all odd-numbered roots is similar to that for cube roots. That is, the following facts hold. For every even natural number n, every positive number has exactly two real nth roots (a positive one and a negative one), every negative number has no real nth roots, and the number 0 has exactly one nth root (itself). For every *odd* natural number n, every real number has exactly one real nth root. For example,

64 has two real sixth roots, 2 and -2;
-64 has no real sixth roots;
243 has one real fifth root, 3;
-243 has one real fifth root, -3.

You can use the symbol '$\pm$', which means 'plus or minus', to write a positive and a negative root together. For example, the two square roots of 36 are ± 6, and the two real sixth roots of 64 are ± 2.

The symbol $\sqrt{}$ is used to denote the positive square root of a positive real number, or the square root of zero. For example,

$$\sqrt{36} = 6 \quad \text{and} \quad \sqrt{0} = 0.$$

Because $\sqrt{}$ means a positive or zero square root, it's incorrect to write, for example,

'if $x^2 = 4$, then $x = \sqrt{4} = \pm 2$'.

What you should write is

'if $x^2 = 4$, then $x = \pm\sqrt{4} = \pm 2$'.

Similarly, the symbol $\sqrt[3]{}$ denotes the cube root of a positive or zero real number, the symbol $\sqrt[4]{}$ denotes the positive or zero fourth root of a positive or zero real number, and so on. For example, $\sqrt[4]{81} = 3$ and $\sqrt[4]{0} = 0$. Note in particular that the number under any of the symbols $\sqrt{}, \sqrt[3]{}, \sqrt[4]{}, \ldots$ must be positive or zero, and the resulting root is always positive or zero.

> The symbol $\sqrt{}$ for roots was introduced by René Descartes, an influential French philosopher and mathematician.

René Descartes (1596–1650)

Most roots of numbers are irrational numbers. In particular, the square root of any natural number that isn't a perfect square is irrational. So, for example, $\sqrt{2}$, $\sqrt{3}$, $\sqrt{5}$ and $\sqrt{6}$ are all irrational numbers.

Because numbers like these can't be written down exactly as fractions or terminating decimals, we often leave them just as they are in calculations and in the answers to calculations. For example, we might say that the answer to a calculation is $1 - 2\sqrt{5}$. The advantage of this approach is that it allows us to work with exact numbers, rather than approximations. This can help to simplify calculations.

An expression such as $1 - 2\sqrt{5}$ is called a *surd*. That is, a **surd** is a numerical expression that contains one or more irrational roots of numbers. Here are some more surds:

$$\sqrt{2}, \quad -\sqrt{2}, \quad 2 + \sqrt[3]{5}, \quad \sqrt{6} + \sqrt{7}, \quad \frac{\sqrt{7}}{3}.$$

Note that in some texts, the word 'surd' means 'irrational root' rather than 'numerical expression containing one or more irrational roots'.

Surds are usually written concisely, in a similar way to algebraic expressions. Multiplication signs are usually omitted – for example, we write $2\sqrt{5}$ rather than $2 \times \sqrt{5}$. However, sometimes it's necessary or helpful to include multiplication signs in a surd. Also, where a number and an irrational root are multiplied together, the number is written first – for example, we write $2\sqrt{5}$ rather than $\sqrt{5}\,2$. This is because, for example, $\sqrt{5}\,2$ could easily be misread as $\sqrt{52}$.

> The word 'surd' is derived from the same Latin word as 'absurd'. The original Latin word is 'surdus', which means deaf or silent.

4.2 Manipulating surds

You sometimes have to manipulate surds, in a similar way to algebraic expressions. In particular, you sometimes have to simplify them. Many calculators can simplify surds, but you should also know how to do this yourself. This is because it is useful to be able to simplify straightforward surds without having to resort to a calculator, and because you'll have to use similar methods to simplify algebraic expressions involving roots.

You can manipulate surds using the usual rules of algebra – you treat the irrational roots in the same way that you treat variables. For example, you can collect like terms. In the expression below, there are two terms with $\sqrt{3}$ in them, which can be collected, and two terms with $\sqrt{7}$ in them, which can also be collected:

$$\sqrt{3} + 2\sqrt{7} + 4\sqrt{3} - \sqrt{7} = (1 + 4)\sqrt{3} + (2 - 1)\sqrt{7}$$
$$= 5\sqrt{3} + \sqrt{7}.$$

There are also several ways to manipulate surds that don't involve treating irrational roots in the same way that you treat variables. In particular, you should keep in mind that an expression of the form $(\sqrt{a})^2$ can be simplified to a. For example,

$$\sqrt{8}\sqrt{8} = (\sqrt{8})^2 = 8.$$

Two further useful rules are given below. The reason why they hold is explained in the next subsection. These rules apply to all appropriate numbers – for example, in the second rule b must be non-zero, because division by zero isn't possible.

The square root of a product of numbers is the same as the product of the square roots of the numbers, and similarly for a quotient:

$$\sqrt{ab} = \sqrt{a}\sqrt{b}, \qquad \sqrt{\frac{a}{b}} = \frac{\sqrt{a}}{\sqrt{b}}.$$

Analogous rules apply to cube roots, fourth roots and so on.

For example,

$$\sqrt{5}\sqrt{3} = \sqrt{5 \times 3} = \sqrt{15} \quad \text{and} \quad \frac{\sqrt{6}}{\sqrt{3}} = \sqrt{\frac{6}{3}} = \sqrt{2}.$$

Similarly,

$$\sqrt[3]{7}\sqrt[3]{2} = \sqrt[3]{7 \times 2} = \sqrt[3]{14} \quad \text{and} \quad \frac{\sqrt[3]{8}}{\sqrt[3]{2}} = \sqrt[3]{\frac{8}{2}} = \sqrt[3]{4}.$$

It's *not true* that, in general, $\sqrt{a + b} = \sqrt{a} + \sqrt{b}$. For example, $\sqrt{9 + 16} = \sqrt{25} = 5$, whereas $\sqrt{9} + \sqrt{16} = 3 + 4 = 7$.

Activity 29 *Simplifying surds*

Simplify the following surds.

(a) $\sqrt{5}\sqrt{6}$ (b) $\dfrac{\sqrt{75}}{\sqrt{15}}$ (c) $3 + \sqrt{10}\sqrt{10}$ (d) $\sqrt{8}\sqrt{2}$ (e) $\dfrac{\sqrt[3]{5}}{\sqrt[3]{15}}$

Here are some more complicated examples.

Example 17 *Manipulating surds*

In parts (a) and (b), multiply out the brackets. In part (c), write the expression as a single fraction. Simplify your answers.

(a) $\sqrt{7}(\sqrt{7} - \sqrt{2})$ (b) $(3 + \sqrt{2})(1 + 5\sqrt{2})$ (c) $\dfrac{1}{\sqrt{2}} + \dfrac{1}{\sqrt{3}}$

Solution

🔍 Use the usual rules of algebra, combining them with the extra rules for manipulating surds. In part (a), start by multiplying each term in the brackets by the multiplier. In part (b), start by using FOIL. In part (c), start by writing the fractions with the same denominator. 💭

(a) $\sqrt{7}(\sqrt{7} - \sqrt{2}) = (\sqrt{7})^2 - \sqrt{7}\sqrt{2} = 7 - \sqrt{14}$

(b) $(3 + \sqrt{2})(1 + 5\sqrt{2}) = 3 + 15\sqrt{2} + \sqrt{2} + 5(\sqrt{2})^2$

$$= 3 + 16\sqrt{2} + 10$$
$$= 13 + 16\sqrt{2}$$

(c) $\dfrac{1}{\sqrt{2}} + \dfrac{1}{\sqrt{3}} = \dfrac{\sqrt{3}}{\sqrt{2}\sqrt{3}} + \dfrac{\sqrt{2}}{\sqrt{2}\sqrt{3}} = \dfrac{\sqrt{3}}{\sqrt{6}} + \dfrac{\sqrt{2}}{\sqrt{6}} = \dfrac{\sqrt{2} + \sqrt{3}}{\sqrt{6}}$

Activity 30   *Manipulating surds*

In parts (a)–(e), multiply out the brackets. In parts (f) and (g), write the expression as a single fraction. Simplify your answers.

(a) $\sqrt{3}(2\sqrt{2} + \sqrt{3})$ (b) $\sqrt{2}(1 + \sqrt{3}) + 9\sqrt{2}$ (c) $(1 - \sqrt{5})(6 - 2\sqrt{5})$

(d) $(6 - \sqrt{7})(6 + \sqrt{7})$ (e) $(\sqrt{3} + 2\sqrt{2})(\sqrt{3} - 2\sqrt{2})$

(f) $3 - \dfrac{1}{\sqrt{2}}$ (g) $\dfrac{4}{\sqrt{5}} + \dfrac{\sqrt{3}}{\sqrt{2}}$

Here's another useful way to simplify surds. If, in an irrational square root (such as $\sqrt{48}$ or $\sqrt{10}$) in a surd, the number under the square root sign has a factor that's a perfect square, then you can simplify this square root.

To do this, you write the number under the square root sign as the product of the perfect square and another number, then you use the rule $\sqrt{ab} = \sqrt{a}\sqrt{b}$. This is illustrated in the next example.

Example 18 *Simplifying square roots in surds*

Simplify the following surds, where possible.

(a) $\sqrt{48}$ (b) $\sqrt{10}$

Solution

(a) 🗨 48 has a factor that's a perfect square, namely 16. 🗨

$$\sqrt{48} = \sqrt{16 \times 3}$$

🗨 Use the rule $\sqrt{ab} = \sqrt{a}\sqrt{b}$. 🗨

$$= \sqrt{16}\sqrt{3} = 4\sqrt{3}.$$

(b) $\sqrt{10}$ doesn't have a factor that's a perfect square, so it can't be simplified.

Note that, as mentioned earlier, the first 15 perfect squares are:

$$1, 4, 9, 16, 25, 36, 49, 64, 81, 100, 121, 144, 169, 196, 225.$$

Activity 31 *Simplifying square roots in surds*

(a) Simplify the following surds, where possible.

(i) $\sqrt{8}$ (ii) $\sqrt{150}$ (iii) $\sqrt{22}$ (iv) $\sqrt{32}$ (v) $5 + \sqrt{108}$
(vi) $\sqrt{12} + \sqrt{4}$ (vii) $\sqrt{27} - \sqrt{3}$

(b) Multiply out the brackets in the following surds, and simplify your answers.

(i) $\sqrt{6}(\sqrt{3} + \sqrt{2})$ (ii) $(\sqrt{10} - \sqrt{5})(2\sqrt{5} + 1)$

Here's a final way to simplify surds. If a surd contains an irrational root in the denominator of a fraction, then it's sometimes useful to rewrite it so that the denominator no longer contains this irrational root. This is called **rationalising** the denominator, and it can make the surd easier to work with. It can often be achieved by multiplying the top and bottom of the fraction by a suitable surd. (As you know, multiplying the top and bottom of a fraction by the same number doesn't change the value of the fraction.)

For example, you can rationalise the denominator of the surd $1/\sqrt{2}$ by multiplying the top and bottom by $\sqrt{2}$:

$$\frac{1}{\sqrt{2}} = \frac{1}{\sqrt{2}} \times \frac{\sqrt{2}}{\sqrt{2}} = \frac{\sqrt{2}}{2}.$$

In more complicated cases, the surd might include a fraction such as

$$\frac{5}{4\sqrt{7} + \sqrt{2}} \quad \text{or} \quad \frac{\sqrt{2}}{5 - 2\sqrt{3}},$$

in which the denominator is a sum of two terms, either or both of which is a rational number multiplied by an irrational square root. You can rationalise a denominator like this by multiplying the top and bottom of the fraction by a **conjugate** of the expression in the denominator. This is the expression that you get when you change the sign of one of the two terms – it's usual to choose the second term.

For example, the expressions in the denominators of the two fractions above have conjugates

$$4\sqrt{7} - \sqrt{2} \quad \text{and} \quad 5 + 2\sqrt{3},$$

respectively.

Part (b) of the next example shows you how to rationalise a denominator by multiplying top and bottom by a conjugate of the denominator. To see why this method works, notice that when you multiply top and bottom of the fraction by the conjugate, in the denominator you obtain a product of the form

$$(A + B)(A - B),$$

where A and B are the terms of the denominator of the original fraction.

As you saw on page 37, when you multiply out this product you get the expression

$$A^2 - B^2.$$

The squaring of the terms A and B gets rid of the irrational square roots, as you can see in the example.

Example 19 *Rationalising denominators*

Rationalise the denominators of the following surds.

(a) $\dfrac{1}{3\sqrt{2}}$ (b) $\dfrac{\sqrt{2}}{5-2\sqrt{3}}$

Solution

(a) $\dfrac{1}{3\sqrt{2}} = \dfrac{1}{3\sqrt{2}} \times \dfrac{\sqrt{2}}{\sqrt{2}} = \dfrac{\sqrt{2}}{3 \times 2} = \dfrac{\sqrt{2}}{6}$

(b) 🔍 A conjugate of $5 - 2\sqrt{3}$ is $5 + 2\sqrt{3}$. 💭

$$\dfrac{\sqrt{2}}{5-2\sqrt{3}} = \dfrac{\sqrt{2}}{5-2\sqrt{3}} \times \dfrac{5+2\sqrt{3}}{5+2\sqrt{3}}$$

$$= \dfrac{\sqrt{2}(5+2\sqrt{3})}{(5-2\sqrt{3})(5+2\sqrt{3})}$$

$$= \dfrac{5\sqrt{2}+2\sqrt{3}\sqrt{2}}{5^2-(2\sqrt{3})^2}$$

$$= \dfrac{5\sqrt{2}+2\sqrt{6}}{5^2-2^2(\sqrt{3})^2}$$

$$= \dfrac{5\sqrt{2}+2\sqrt{6}}{25-4\times3}$$

$$= \dfrac{5\sqrt{2}+2\sqrt{6}}{13}$$

Activity 32 *Rationalising denominators*

Rationalise the denominators of the following surds.

(a) $\dfrac{3}{\sqrt{7}}$ (b) $\dfrac{\sqrt{2}}{\sqrt{6}}$ (c) $\dfrac{5}{\sqrt{5}}$ (d) $\dfrac{2}{1+\sqrt{17}}$ (e) $\dfrac{\sqrt{5}+\sqrt{3}}{\sqrt{5}-\sqrt{3}}$

In general, if the final answer that you've found to a question is a surd, then you should use the methods in this subsection to simplify it as much as possible, except that it isn't always necessary to rationalise a denominator that contains an irrational root. For example, it's acceptable to leave the surd $1/\sqrt{2}$ as it is. However, many calculators rationalise denominators: for example, they display $1/\sqrt{2}$ as $\sqrt{2}/2$.

4.3 Working with powers

As you know, *raising a number to a power* means multiplying the number by itself a specified number of times. For example, raising 2 to the power 3 gives

$$2^3 = 2 \times 2 \times 2 = 8.$$

Here the number 2 is called the **base number** or just **base**, and the superscript 3 is called the **power**, **index** or **exponent**. The word 'power' is also used to refer to the *result* of raising a number to a power – for example, we say that 2^3, or 8, is a **power** of 2. These two alternative meanings of the word 'power' don't normally cause any confusion, as it's usually clear from the context which of them is meant.

Note that the plural of 'index', in the context here, is 'indices'. (With some other meanings of 'index', such as the type of index that you get at the back of a book, the plural is 'indexes'.)

Activity 33 *Calculating powers*

Evaluate the following expressions without using your calculator.

(a) 2^4 (b) $(-2)^4$ (c) -2^4 (d) $(-3)^3$ (e) $\left(\frac{1}{2}\right)^2$ (f) $\left(\frac{1}{3}\right)^3$

There are some useful rules that you can use to manipulate expressions that contain indices. These are known as **index laws**. In this subsection you'll revise these rules, and practise using them.

We'll start with the three most basic index laws. To see where the first of them comes from, suppose that you want to simplify the expression $a^5 \times a^2$.

You could do this as follows:

$$a^5 \times a^2 = \underbrace{a \times a \times a \times a \times a}_{5 \text{ copies of } a} \times \underbrace{a \times a}_{2 \text{ copies of } a}$$

$$= \underbrace{a \times a \times a \times a \times a \times a \times a}_{7 \text{ copies of } a} = a^7.$$

You can see that, in general, to *multiply* two powers with the same base, you *add* the indices. This gives the first index law in the box below.

Now suppose that you want to simplify the expression a^5/a^2. You could do this as follows:

$$\frac{a^5}{a^2} = \frac{\overbrace{a \times a \times a \times a \times a}^{5 \text{ copies of } a}}{\underbrace{a \times a}_{2 \text{ copies of } a}} = \frac{\cancel{a} \times \cancel{a} \times a \times a \times a}{\cancel{a} \times \cancel{a}} = \underbrace{a \times a \times a}_{3 \text{ copies of } a} = a^3.$$

You can see that, in general, to *divide* a power by another power with the same base, you *subtract* the 'bottom' index from the 'top' one. This gives the second index law in the box below.

Finally, suppose that you want to simplify the expression $(a^2)^3$. You could do this as follows:

$$(a^2)^3 = a^2 \times a^2 \times a^2 = (a \times a) \times (a \times a) \times (a \times a) = a^6.$$

You can see that, in general, to *raise* a power *to a power* you *multiply* the indices. This gives the third index law in the box below.

Index laws for a single base

To multiply two powers with the same base, add the indices:

$$a^m a^n = a^{m+n}.$$

To divide two powers with the same base, subtract the indices:

$$\frac{a^m}{a^n} = a^{m-n}.$$

To find a power of a power, multiply the indices:

$$(a^m)^n = a^{mn}.$$

If you think about where the first index law comes from, you'll see that it extends to products of more than two powers of the same base. For example,

$$a^m a^n a^r = a^{m+n+r}.$$

Another way to think about such extensions of the first index law is as two or more applications of the law. For example,

$$a^m a^n a^r = (a^m a^n)a^r = a^{m+n}a^r = a^{m+n+r}.$$

Activity 34   *Using the three basic index laws*

Simplify the following expressions.

(a) $\dfrac{a^{20}}{a^5}$ (b) $(y^4)^5$ (c) $\dfrac{b^4 b^7}{b^3}$ (d) $p^3 p^5 p^3 p$ (e) $(x^3)^3 x^2$

(f) $(m^3 m^2)^5$ (g) $\left(\dfrac{c^5}{c^2}\right)^2$

Activity 35   *Using the three basic index laws again*

Multiply out the brackets or expand the fraction, as appropriate, and simplify your answers.

(a) $(x^3 - 1)(2x^3 + 5)$ (b) $(a^4 + b^4)^2$ (c) $\dfrac{p^8 + p^2}{p^2}$

All the indices in Activities 34 and 35 are positive integers, but you can also have zero or negative indices. It might not be immediately clear to you what it means to raise a number to the power 0, or to the power -3, for example, but if you think about the fact that we want the basic index laws in the box above to work for powers like these, then it soon becomes clear what they must mean.

For example, consider the power 2^0. If the first index law in the box above works for this power, then, for instance,

$$2^3 2^0 = 2^{3+0} = 2^3.$$

This calculation tells you that if you multiply 2^3 by 2^0, then you get 2^3 again. So the value of 2^0 must be 1. You can see that, in general, a non-zero number raised to the power 0 must be 1. Usually we don't give a meaning to 0^0, but in some contexts it's convenient to take it to be equal to 1.

There's no obvious, correct meaning for 0^0. This is because on the one hand you'd expect that if you raise a number to the power 0 then the answer will be 1, but on the other hand you'd expect that if you raise 0 to a power then the answer will be 0. Mathematicians have debated the meaning of 0^0 for several centuries, and in 1821 Augustin-Louis Cauchy included it in a list of undefined forms, along with expressions like $0/0$. Cauchy was a French mathematician, one of the pioneers of mathematical *analysis*, the theory that underlies calculus.

Augustin-Louis Cauchy
(1789–1857)

Now let's consider 2^{-3}, for example. Again, if the first index law in the box above works for this power, then, for example,

$$2^3 2^{-3} = 2^{3+(-3)} = 2^0 = 1.$$

This calculation tells you that if you multiply 2^3 by 2^{-3} then you get 1. So 2^{-3} must be the reciprocal of 2^3; that is, $2^{-3} = 1/2^3$. You can see that, in general, a non-zero number raised to a negative index must be the reciprocal of the number raised to the corresponding positive index.

In summary, the meanings of zero and negative indices are given by the following index laws.

> **More index laws for a single base**
>
> A number raised to the power 0 is 1:
>
> $$a^0 = 1.$$
>
> A number raised to a negative power is the reciprocal of the number raised to the corresponding positive power:
>
> $$a^{-n} = \frac{1}{a^n}.$$

These index laws hold for all appropriate numbers. So, for example, in the second law above, a can be any number except 0; it can't be 0 because division by 0 isn't possible.

The second index law in the box above tells you that, in particular,

$$a^{-1} = \frac{1}{a}.$$

So raising a number to the power -1 is the same as finding its reciprocal. For example,

$$2^{-1} = \tfrac{1}{2}, \quad \left(\tfrac{1}{2}\right)^{-1} = 2 \quad \text{and} \quad \left(\tfrac{2}{3}\right)^{-1} = \tfrac{3}{2}.$$

This fact can help you to evaluate numerical expressions that contain negative indices. For example,

$$\left(\tfrac{1}{2}\right)^{-3} = \left(\tfrac{1}{2}\right)^{-1 \times 3} = \left(\left(\tfrac{1}{2}\right)^{-1}\right)^3 = 2^3 = 8.$$

Activity 36   *Understanding zero and negative indices*

Evaluate the following powers without using your calculator.

(a) 4^{-2} (b) 3^{-1} (c) 5^0 (d) $\left(\frac{2}{7}\right)^{-1}$ (e) $\left(\frac{1}{3}\right)^{-1}$ (f) $\left(\frac{1}{3}\right)^{-2}$

Indices can also be fractions, or any real numbers at all – the meaning of such indices is discussed later in this subsection. All the index laws given in this subsection hold for indices and base numbers that are any real numbers (except that the numbers must be appropriate for the operations – for example, you can't divide by zero).

The index laws that you've seen so far in this subsection involve just one base number, but there are also two index laws that involve two different base numbers. To see where they come from, consider the following algebraic manipulations:

$$(ab)^3 = ab \times ab \times ab = ababab = aaabbb = a^3b^3,$$
$$\left(\frac{a}{b}\right)^3 = \frac{a}{b} \times \frac{a}{b} \times \frac{a}{b} = \frac{aaa}{bbb} = \frac{a^3}{b^3}.$$

In general, the following rules hold.

Index laws for two bases

A power of a product of numbers is the same as the product of the same powers of the numbers, and similarly for a power of a quotient:

$$(ab)^n = a^n b^n,$$
$$\left(\frac{a}{b}\right)^n = \frac{a^n}{b^n}.$$

The first index law above extends to a product of any number of factors. For example,

$$(abc)^n = a^n b^n c^n.$$

You can see why this is if you think about where the law comes from, or you can think of it as more than one application of the law:

$$(abc)^n = (ab)^n c^n = a^n b^n c^n.$$

The next example illustrates how you can use all the index laws that you've seen so far in this subsection to simplify expressions that contain indices. There are several alternative ways to do this. Whichever you use, you should check that you have combined all powers of the same base. For example, you should change $a^2 a^3$ to a^5, and a^2/a^6 to $1/a^4$. It's often best for your final version to include only positive indices, especially if the expression has a denominator. You can change negative indices into positive indices by using the rule $a^{-n} = 1/a^n$. For example, you can change a^{-3} to $1/a^3$, and $1/a^{-3}$ to a^3.

Example 20   *Simplifying expressions containing indices*

Simplify the following expressions, ensuring that the simplified versions contain no negative indices.

(a) $\dfrac{d^2}{d^{-4}}$ (b) $\dfrac{b^{-3}}{b^2 c^{-4}}$ (c) $(2h^{-3}g)^2$

Solution

(a)   Use the law $a^{-n} = 1/a^n$ to change the negative index into a positive index, then use the law $a^m a^n = a^{m+n}$ to combine the powers.

$$\frac{d^2}{d^{-4}} = d^2 \times \frac{1}{d^{-4}} = d^2 d^4 = d^6$$

Alternatively, use the law $a^m/a^n = a^{m-n}$.

$$\frac{d^2}{d^{-4}} = d^{2-(-4)} = d^6$$

(b)   Use the law $a^{-n} = 1/a^n$ to change the negative indices into positive indices, then use the law $a^m a^n = a^{m+n}$ to combine the powers of b.

$$\frac{b^{-3}}{b^2 c^{-4}} = \frac{c^4}{b^2 b^3} = \frac{c^4}{b^5}$$

Alternatively, use the law $a^m/a^n = a^{m-n}$ to combine the powers of b, then use the law $a^{-n} = 1/a^n$ to change the negative indices into positive indices.

$$\frac{b^{-3}}{b^2 c^{-4}} = \frac{b^{-5}}{c^{-4}} = \frac{c^4}{b^5}$$

(c)   Remove the brackets by using the law $(ab)^n = a^n b^n$, then the law $(a^m)^n = a^{mn}$. Then use the law $a^{-n} = 1/a^n$ to change the negative index into a positive index.

$$(2h^{-3}g)^2 = 2^2(h^{-3})^2 g^2 = 4h^{-6}g^2 = \frac{4g^2}{h^6}$$

Alternatively, use the law $a^{-n} = 1/a^n$ to change the negative index into a positive index, then use the law $(a/b)^n = a^n/b^n$, then the laws $(ab)^n = a^n b^n$ and $(a^m)^n = a^{mn}$.

$$(2h^{-3}g)^2 = \left(\frac{2g}{h^3}\right)^2 = \frac{(2g)^2}{(h^3)^2} = \frac{2^2 g^2}{h^6} = \frac{4g^2}{h^6}$$

As mentioned above and illustrated in Example 20, when you're simplifying an expression that contains indices, it's often a good idea to aim for a final version that contains no negative indices. However, sometimes a final form that contains negative indices is simpler, or more useful. As with many algebraic expressions, there's often no 'right answer' for the simplest form of an expression that contains indices. One form might be better for some purposes, and a different form might be better for other purposes.

Activity 37 *Simplifying expressions containing indices*

Simplify the following expressions, ensuring that the simplified versions contain no negative indices. (In parts (l), (n) and (o) you're not expected to multiply out any brackets.)

(a) $5g^{-1}$ (b) $\dfrac{1}{y^{-1}}$ (c) $\dfrac{2}{3x^{-5}}$ (d) $\dfrac{a^{-3}}{b^{-4}}$ (e) $\dfrac{P^2}{Q^{-5}}$

(f) $(3h^2)^2$ (g) $(3h^2)^{-2}$ (h) $\dfrac{(b^{-4})^3}{(3c)^2}$ (i) $\dfrac{(A^{-1}B)^2}{(B^{-3})^3}$

(j) $\left(\dfrac{2y^{-1}}{z^2}\right)^5$ (k) $\dfrac{x^{-5}}{x}$ (l) $\dfrac{(x-1)^{-3}}{(x-1)^2}$ (m) $\left(\dfrac{3}{z^2}\right)^{-3}$

(n) $\dfrac{x}{(2x-3)^3} \times x^{-2}$ (o) $\left(\dfrac{(x+2)^2}{x^5}\right) \Big/ (x+2)^{-4}$

Now let's consider indices that are fractions or any real numbers. To understand what's meant by a fractional index, first consider the power $2^{1/3}$. If the index law for raising a power to a power, $(a^m)^n = a^{mn}$, is to work for fractional indices, then, for example,

$$(2^{1/3})^3 = 2^{(1/3)\times 3} = 2^1 = 2.$$

This calculation tells you that if you raise $2^{1/3}$ to the power 3, then you get 2. So $2^{1/3}$ must be the cube root of 2; that is, $2^{1/3} = \sqrt[3]{2}$. In general, you can see that raising a positive number to the power $1/n$, say, is the same as taking the nth root of the number. So $5^{1/2} = \sqrt{5}$, and $12^{1/4} = \sqrt[4]{12}$, and so on. This is the first rule in the following box.

To understand what's meant by a fractional index when the numerator of the fraction isn't 1, consider, for example, the power $2^{5/3}$. If the index law for raising a power to a power is to work for fractional indices, then we must have

$$2^{5/3} = 2^{(1/3)\times 5} = (2^{1/3})^5 = (\sqrt[3]{2})^5.$$

So $2^{5/3}$ must be the cube root of 2, raised to the power 5. However, by the same index law we must also have

$$2^{5/3} = 2^{5\times(1/3)} = (2^5)^{1/3} = \sqrt[3]{2^5}.$$

So $2^{5/3}$ must be the cube root of 2^5. Luckily these two alternative definitions give the same answer, both in this case and for other fractional powers of a positive real number. This gives the second, more general rule in the following box.

> **Converting between fractional indices and roots**
>
> $$a^{1/n} = \sqrt[n]{a}$$
>
> $$a^{m/n} = \left(\sqrt[n]{a}\right)^m = \sqrt[n]{a^m}$$

Notice that since the notation $\sqrt[n]{a}$ is defined only when a is positive or zero, only positive numbers and zero can be raised to fractional powers. So the notation a^n has no meaning if a is negative and n is not an integer.

Activity 38   *Converting fractional indices to root signs*

Rewrite the following expressions so that they contain root signs (such as $\sqrt{}$ and $\sqrt[3]{}$) instead of fractional indices.

Hint for parts (d), (f) and (g): first rewrite the expression to change the negative index into a positive index.

(a) $t^{1/2}$ (b) $x^{1/3}$ (c) $p^{2/3}$ (d) $x^{-1/2}$ (e) $(2x-3)^{1/2}$

(f) $(1+x^2)^{-1/2}$ (g) $(1+x)x^{-1/2}$

Although you were asked to convert several different fractional indices to root signs in Activity 38, it's often best to avoid using any root signs other than the square root sign $\sqrt{}$ in algebraic expressions. This is because the small numbers in root signs such as $\sqrt[3]{}$ and $\sqrt[4]{}$ can be easily misread, especially when they're handwritten. For example,

$$p\sqrt[3]{q} \quad \text{could be misread as} \quad p^3\sqrt{q},$$

so it is better written as $pq^{1/3}$.

Activity 39   *Converting root signs to fractional indices*

Rewrite the following expressions so that they contain fractional indices instead of root signs.

(a) $\sqrt[4]{y}$ (b) $\sqrt[5]{1-2x}$ (c) $\dfrac{1}{\sqrt[3]{x}}$ (d) $\left(\sqrt[5]{u}\right)^2$ (e) $\dfrac{1}{\sqrt[3]{x^4}}$

(f) $\sqrt[4]{(y+2)^3}$

You should simplify an algebraic expression that contains fractional indices in the same ways as an expression that contains only integer indices – you should combine powers of the same base where possible, and so on. When you've done that, if the expression contains the index $\frac{1}{2}$ or $-\frac{1}{2}$, then you might consider rewriting it so that it contains the square root sign instead. For example, you might prefer to write

$$x^{1/2} \text{ as } \sqrt{x}, \quad \text{and} \quad x^{-1/2} \text{ as } \frac{1}{\sqrt{x}}.$$

You should usually leave any other fractional indices as they are (except that it may be helpful to convert negative indices to positive ones). Here's an example.

Example 21   *Simplifying expressions containing fractional indices*

Simplify the following expressions.

(a) $\dfrac{c^{3/4}}{c^{5/4}}$ (b) $(2h^{1/6})^2$

Solution

(a) 🗨 Use the index laws in the same ways as for integer indices. 🗨

$$\frac{c^{3/4}}{c^{5/4}} = c^{(3/4)-(5/4)} = c^{-2/4} = c^{-1/2}$$

🗨 Usually, change the negative index to a positive one, and perhaps use a square root sign instead of the index $\frac{1}{2}$. 🗨

$$= \frac{1}{c^{1/2}} = \frac{1}{\sqrt{c}}$$

(b) 🗨 Proceed as in part (a). Leave the final fractional index as it is, since it's not $\frac{1}{2}$ or $-\frac{1}{2}$. 🗨

$$(2h^{1/6})^2 = 2^2(h^{1/6})^2 = 4h^{(1/6)\times 2} = 4h^{1/3}$$

Activity 40   *Simplifying expressions containing fractional indices*

Simplify the following expressions. (In part (f) you're not expected to multiply out any brackets.)

(a) $x^{1/3}x^{1/3}$ (b) $\dfrac{a}{a^{1/3}}$ (c) $\dfrac{a}{a^{1/2}}$ (d) $\dfrac{x}{x^{-1/2}}$ (e) $(2x^{1/5})^3$

(f) $\dfrac{(1+x)^2}{\sqrt{1+x}}$ (g) $\left(\dfrac{1}{u}\right)^{1/3}$ (h) $\dfrac{A^{5/2}}{A^3}$ (i) $\dfrac{x^{1/2}y^2}{x^3y^{1/2}}$ (j) $\sqrt{4x}$

It follows from the meaning of fractional indices that the two rules for square roots that you used in the last subsection,

$$\sqrt{ab} = \sqrt{a}\sqrt{b} \quad \text{and} \quad \sqrt{\frac{a}{b}} = \frac{\sqrt{a}}{\sqrt{b}},$$

are just particular cases of the two index laws in the box on page 67. They're these index laws with the index n taken to be $\frac{1}{2}$.

So far in this subsection you've seen what's meant by indices that are rational numbers. However, as mentioned earlier, an index can be any real number. For example, you can raise any positive number to the irrational index $\sqrt{2}$. A precise definition of the meaning of an irrational index is beyond the scope of this module, but the basic idea is that you can work out the value of any positive number raised to any irrational index as accurately as you like, by using as many decimal places of the decimal form of the irrational index as you like. For example, suppose that you're interested in the value of $3^{\sqrt{2}}$. Since

$$\sqrt{2} = 1.414\,213\,562\,373\,09\ldots,$$

one approximation to $3^{\sqrt{2}}$ is

$$3^{1.414} = 4.727\,695\,035\,268\,53\ldots,$$

and a more accurate one is

$$3^{1.414\,213} = 4.728\,801\,466\,241\,14\ldots,$$

and so on. The indices here, 1.414 and $1.414\,213$, and so on, are rational, as they are terminating decimals. It's possible to show that the closer a rational index r is to $\sqrt{2}$, the closer 3^r is to some fixed real number. The value of $3^{\sqrt{2}}$ is defined to be this number.

So an index can be any real number. All the index laws that you've met in this subsection hold for indices and base numbers that are any real numbers (except that the numbers must be appropriate for the operations – for example, you can't divide by zero or apply $\sqrt{\ }$ to a negative number). Here's a summary of them all.

Index laws

$$a^m a^n = a^{m+n} \qquad \frac{a^m}{a^n} = a^{m-n} \qquad (a^m)^n = a^{mn}$$

$$a^0 = 1 \qquad a^{-n} = \frac{1}{a^n}$$

$$(ab)^n = a^n b^n \qquad \left(\frac{a}{b}\right)^n = \frac{a^n}{b^n}$$

$$a^{1/n} = \sqrt[n]{a} \qquad a^{m/n} = \left(\sqrt[n]{a}\right)^m = \sqrt[n]{a^m}$$

Here's an activity involving indices that contain variables as well as numbers. You can deal with these using the index laws in the usual way.

Activity 41   *Simplifying indices that contain variables*

Simplify the following expressions.

(a) $a^{2p} a^{5p}$ (b) $\dfrac{b^{7k}}{b^{4k}}$ (c) $(g^n)^k$ (d) $(2y^{2t})^2 y^{-t}$ (e) $\dfrac{m^{3x}}{m^{-x}}$

(f) $\dfrac{c^{3y}}{c^{5y}}$ (g) $\dfrac{(a^{-3t} b^{3t})^2}{a^{3t} b^t}$ (h) $(d^{1/r})^{2r}$ (i) $(3h)^{2p}(9h)^p$

Scientific notation

One use of indices is in **scientific notation** (also known as **standard form**). This is a way of writing numbers that's particularly helpful when you're dealing with very large or very small numbers. To express a number in scientific notation, you write it in the form

(a number between 1 and 10, but not including 10)

$\times$ (an integer power of ten).

Here are some examples.

$$\begin{array}{llll}
427 & = & 4.27 \times 100 & = & 4.27 \times 10^2 \\
42.7 & = & 4.27 \times 10 & = & 4.27 \times 10^1 \\
4.27 & = & 4.27 \times 1 & = & 4.27 \times 10^0 \\
0.427 & = & 4.27 \times 0.1 & = & 4.27 \times 10^{-1} \\
0.0427 & = & 4.27 \times 0.01 & = & 4.27 \times 10^{-2}
\end{array}$$

(a) Express the following numbers in scientific notation.

(i) 38 800 000   (ii) 4237   (iii) 0.0973   (iv) 1.303

(v) 0.000 000 028

(b) Express the following numbers in ordinary notation.

(i) 2.8×10^4 (ii) 5.975×10^{-1} (iii) 2.78×10^{-7}

(iv) 3.43×10^7

In computer output, scientific notation is sometimes represented with the power of 10 indicated by the letter E (for exponent). For example, 4.27×10^{-2} would be represented as 4.27E−2.

5 Equations

In this section you'll revise how to rearrange and solve equations.

5.1 Terminology for equations

You saw earlier that to indicate that two expressions are equivalent, you put an equals sign between them. However, there's another use of equals signs. You can place an equals sign between *any* two expressions, to form an **equation**. Here's an example:

$$3(d + 1) = 7d - 5. \tag{3}$$

Usually you form an equation like this when you're interested in the values of the variables in the equation that make the equation true. These values are said to **satisfy** the equation, and are called **solutions** of the equation. For example, the value $d = 2$ satisfies equation (3), as shown in Example 22 below, but the equation isn't satisfied by any other value of d.

Notice that equation (3) contains the variable d and no other variable. This fact is expressed by saying that it's an **equation in** d. Similarly, an equation that contains the variables x and y and no other variables is an equation in x and y, and so on.

The next example illustrates how you should set out your working when you're checking whether an equation is satisfied. You should evaluate the left- and right-hand sides *separately*, and check whether each side gives the same answer. If you wish, you can use the abbreviations LHS and RHS for the left-hand side and right-hand side of the equation.

Example 22   *Checking whether an equation is satisfied*

Show that $d = 2$ satisfies the equation

$$3(d + 1) = 7d - 5.$$

Solution

If $d = 2$, then

$$\text{LHS} = 3(2 + 1) = 3 \times 3 = 9$$

and

$$\text{RHS} = 7 \times 2 - 5 = 14 - 5 = 9.$$

Since LHS = RHS, $d = 2$ satisfies the equation.

In the next activity you're asked to check whether another equation is satisfied for particular values of its variables. The right-hand side of this equation is just a number, so to check whether it's satisfied you just need to evaluate the other side to see whether you get this number.

Activity 43   *Checking whether an equation is satisfied*

Show that the equation $2x + 3y = 5$ is

(a) satisfied by $x = 4$ and $y = -1$;

(b) not satisfied by $x = 3$ and $y = -2$.

It's traditional to use letters from near the end of the alphabet, such as x, y and z, to represent unknowns, and letters from near the start of the alphabet, such as a, b and c, to represent known constants. This tradition originates from René Descartes (see page 56). It's thought that x was preferred to y and z because printers tended to have more type for the letter x than for the letters y and z, due to the frequency of occurrence of these letters in the French and Latin languages.

An equation that is satisfied by *all* possible values of its variables is called an **identity**. For example, the equation

$$x(x + y) = x^2 + xy$$

is an identity: it's true no matter what the values of x and y are. However, in this section we'll mostly be concerned with equations that are satisfied by only some values of their variables. (In some texts, an identity is indicated using the symbol $\equiv$, rather than $=$.)

Sometimes the variables in an equation are restricted to numbers of a particular type. For example, if an equation contains a variable that represents the length of an object, then this variable would take only positive values.

This means that the solutions of an equation depend not only on the equation itself, but also on the possible values that its variables can take. For example, if x can be any number, then the equation $x^2 = 4$ has two solutions, namely $x = 2$ and $x = -2$, but if you know that x is a positive number, then the same equation has only one solution, $x = 2$.

It's often clear from the context of an equation what type of values its variables can take. If it isn't, then you should assume that the variables can be any real numbers.

The process of finding the solutions of an equation is called **solving** the equation. When we're trying to solve an equation, the variables in the equation are often referred to as **unknowns**, since they represent particular numbers whose values aren't yet known, rather than any numbers at all. The key to solving equations is the technique of *rearranging* them, which you'll revise in the next subsection.

5.2   Rearranging equations

It's often helpful to transform an equation into a different equation that contains the same variables, and is satisfied by the same values of these variables. This is called **rearranging**, **manipulating** or simply **rewriting** the equation. When you rearrange an equation, the original equation and the new one are said to be **equivalent**, or different **forms** of the same equation. Rewriting an equation as a simpler equation is called **simplifying** the equation.

There are three main ways to transform an equation into an equivalent equation – these are summarised below.

Rearranging equations

Carrying out any of the following operations on an equation gives an equivalent equation.

- Rearrange the expressions on one or both sides.
- Swap the sides.
- Do the same thing to both sides.

Here are some examples.

- The equations $y + y = 2$ and $2y = 2$ are equivalent, because the second equation is the same as the first but with the expression on the left-hand side rearranged.
- The equations $2x = 1$ and $1 = 2x$ are equivalent, because the second equation is the same as the first but with its sides swapped.
- The equations $y = 3x$ and $2y = 6x$ are equivalent, because the second equation is the same as the first but with both sides multiplied by 2.

Some of the things that you can do to both sides of an equation to obtain an equivalent equation are set out below. Note that a **non-negative** number is one that's either positive or zero.

> **Doing the same thing to both sides of an equation**
>
> Doing any of the following things to *both sides* of an equation gives an equivalent equation.
>
> - Add something.
> - Subtract something.
> - Multiply by something (provided that it is non-zero).
> - Divide by something (provided that it is non-zero).
> - Raise to a power (provided that the power is non-zero, and that the expressions on each side of the equation can take only non-negative values).

To understand why doing any of the things in the box above to both sides of an equation gives an equivalent equation, consider, for example, adding 2 to each side of the equation

$$2x - 3 = 9 - x.$$

The value $x = 4$ satisfies the original equation, because with this value of x, each side of the equation is equal to 5. Adding 2 to both sides of the equation gives the new equation

$$2x - 3 + 2 = 9 - x + 2,$$

and the value $x = 4$ also satisfies this new equation, because with this value of x, each side of the new equation is equal to $5 + 2$, that is, 7. Similarly, the value $x = 3$ *doesn't* satisfy the original equation, because it gives LHS $= 3$ and RHS $= 6$, and this value doesn't satisfy the new equation either, because it gives LHS $= 3 + 2 = 5$ and RHS $= 6 + 2 = 8$. In general, doing any of the things in the box above to both sides of an equation doesn't change the values of the variables that satisfy the equation.

Notice that there are some restrictions given in brackets in the box above. For example, the restriction on the third item in the box tells you that multiplying both sides of an equation by something is guaranteed to give an equivalent equation *only if the something is non-zero*. To see why this restriction is needed, notice that if you multiply both sides of any equation by zero, then you obtain the equation $0 = 0$, which will usually not be equivalent to the original equation. There's a more detailed discussion of the restrictions in the next subsection.

There are 'shortcuts' for adding or subtracting something on both sides of an equation, and for multiplying or dividing both sides, which can be useful in particular, common situations. These are described below. Note that some tutors recommend that it's best *not* to use the first shortcut, 'change the side, change the sign', since it can easily lead to mistakes, as detailed below.

Change the side, change the sign

Suppose, for example, that you have the equation

$$7x = 3 - 2y \tag{4}$$

and you want to rewrite it as an equation in which all the variables appear on the left-hand side only. You can achieve this by adding the term $2y$ to each side. This gives the equivalent equation

$$7x + 2y = 3 - 2y + 2y,$$

which can be simplified to

$$7x + 2y = 3. \tag{5}$$

If you compare equations (4) and (5), then you can see that the overall effect on the original equation is that the term $2y$ has been moved to the other side, and its sign has been changed. In general, the technique of adding or subtracting on both sides of an equation leads to the following rule.

> Moving a term of one side of an equation to the other side, and changing its sign, gives an equivalent equation.

This rule is sometimes summarised as 'change the side, change the sign'. Some people find it useful, while others find it just as convenient to stick with thinking about adding or subtracting on both sides. If you do use the rule, then you need to do so carefully, as it can easily lead to mistakes of the kinds explained next.

When you use the rule, you must make sure that the term you're moving is a term *of the whole expression* on one side of the equation, not just a term of a subexpression. For example, the equations

$$3(a + b + c) = d \quad \text{and} \quad 3(a + b) = d - c$$

are *not* equivalent, because the term that's been moved, c, is not a term of the whole expression on the left-hand side, but only of the subexpression $a + b + c$. (The first equation *is* equivalent to $3(a + b) = d - 3c$, which is obtained by moving the term $3c$ that's obtained when you multiply out the left-hand side of the original equation.)

You must also make sure that the term you're moving becomes a term of the whole expression on the other side, not just a term of a subexpression. For example, the equations

$$a + b = \frac{c+d}{2} \quad \text{and} \quad a = \frac{c+d-b}{2}$$

are *not* equivalent, because the term that's been moved, b, has not become a term of the whole expression on the right-hand side, but only of the subexpression $c + d - b$. (The first equation *is* equivalent to $a = \frac{c+d}{2} - b$.)

If you find that you tend to make these types of errors, then it might be better to avoid using the 'change the side, change the sign' rule, and instead think about adding or subtracting on both sides.

Activity 44   *Adding or subtracting on both sides correctly*

Which of the following are pairs of equivalent equations?

(a) $y = \sqrt{x-3}$ and $y + 3 = \sqrt{x}$

(b) $u^2 = \frac{1}{2}v + 7$ and $u^2 - 7 = \frac{1}{2}v$

(c) $\dfrac{x^2 + x}{3} = \dfrac{x+9}{2}$ and $\dfrac{x^2}{3} = \dfrac{9}{2}$

Multiplying or dividing through

Consider the equation

$$a + b = c + d + e,$$

and suppose that you want to multiply both sides by 3. You know (by the box on page 33) that multiplying the left-hand side by 3 is the same as multiplying each individual term of the left-hand side by 3, and the same goes for the right-hand side. So multiplying both sides of the equation by 3 gives

$$3a + 3b = 3c + 3d + 3e.$$

You can see that the overall effect on the original equation is that each individual term on both sides has been multiplied by 3.

Similarly, if you *divide* both sides of the equation by 3, then (by the same box on page 33) the overall effect is that each individual term on both sides is divided by 3:

$$\frac{a}{3} + \frac{b}{3} = \frac{c}{3} + \frac{d}{3} + \frac{e}{3}.$$

It's useful to remember the following rules.

- Multiplying each term on both sides of an equation by something (provided that it is non-zero) gives an equivalent equation.

- Dividing each term on both sides of an equation by something (provided that it is non-zero) gives an equivalent equation.

Multiplying each term on both sides of an equation by something is known as **multiplying through** by the something, and similarly dividing each term on both sides of an equation by something is known as **dividing through** by the something. For example, the equation above was multiplied through by 3, and also divided through by 3.

When you use the rules in the box above, you must make sure that you're multiplying or dividing terms *of the whole expression* on a side, not just terms of a subexpression. For example, multiplying the equation

$$(a + b)^2 = 5$$

through by 3 does *not* give

$$(3a + 3b)^2 = 15.$$

This is because a and b are not terms of the whole expression on the left-hand side of the first equation, but only of the subexpression $a + b$. (Multiplying the first equation through by 3 gives $3(a + b)^2 = 15$.)

One situation where it's often useful to multiply through an equation is when it contains fractions. You can often obtain an equivalent equation with no fractions by multiplying through by an appropriate number or expression. For example, if you have the equation

$$\frac{x}{4} + 1 = x,$$

then you can multiply through by 4 to obtain

$$x + 4 = 4x.$$

This is known as **clearing**, or simply *removing*, the fractions in the equation. When you clear fractions in this way, you should keep in mind that multiplying an equation through by an expression is guaranteed to give an equivalent equation *only if the expression doesn't take the value zero*. There's more about this issue in Subsection 5.3.

Activity 45   *Multiplying and dividing through correctly*

Which of the following are pairs of equivalent equations?

(a) $\dfrac{a}{3} = \dfrac{a^2}{6} - 3$ and $2a = a^2 - 3$

(b) $\dfrac{x^2 - 1}{2x} + x = \dfrac{1}{2x}$ and $x^2 - 1 + x = 1$ $(x \neq 0)$

(c) $hy = x + 2$ and $y = \dfrac{x}{h} + \dfrac{2}{h}$ $(h \neq 0)$

(d) $\sqrt{\dfrac{x}{2y}} = 1$ and $\sqrt{\dfrac{x}{y}} = 2$ $(y \neq 0)$

Cross-multiplying

Suppose that you want to clear the fractions in the equation

$$\frac{x}{2} = \frac{x+1}{3}.$$

You can do this by multiplying through by 2, and then multiplying through by 3. This gives the equation

$$3x = 2(x+1).$$

You can see that the overall effect on the original equation is that you have 'multiplied diagonally across the equals sign', like this:

$$\frac{x}{2} \bowtie \frac{x+1}{3} \quad \text{gives} \quad 3x = 2(x+1).$$

This technique is called **cross-multiplying**. You can use it as a shortcut for multiplying through, whenever you have an equation of the form fraction = fraction. The general rule is summarised in the box below.

Cross-multiplying

If A, B, C and D are any expressions, then the equations

$$\frac{A}{B} = \frac{C}{D} \quad \text{and} \quad AD = BC$$

are equivalent (provided that B and D are never zero).

If only one side of an equation is a fraction, then you can still cross-multiply (the other side can be thought of as a fraction with denominator 1).

For example,

$$\frac{x}{2} = x + 1 \quad \text{is equivalent to} \quad x = 2(x+1).$$

Activity 46   *Cross-multiplying correctly*

Which of the following are pairs of equivalent equations?

(a) $3 = \dfrac{1}{x+4}$ and $3(x+4) = 1$ $(x \neq -4)$

(b) $b + \dfrac{a}{a-3} = 6$ and $b + a = 6(a-3)$ $(a \neq 3)$

(c) $\dfrac{y}{2y-1} = \dfrac{y+1}{y}$ and $y^2 = (y+1)(2y-1)$ $(y \neq \frac{1}{2}, 0)$

(d) $2 + x = \dfrac{9}{2x+5}$ and $2 + x(2x+5) = 9$ $(x \neq -\frac{5}{2})$

5.3 Solving linear equations in one unknown

In this subsection you'll revise how to solve *linear equations in one unknown*. Equations of this type occur frequently, and are straightforward to solve.

A **linear** equation is one in which, after you've expanded any brackets and cleared any fractions, each term is either a constant term or a constant value times a variable. As you'd expect, a linear equation *in one unknown* is a linear equation that contains just one unknown.

For example,

$$2x - 5 = 8x$$

is a linear equation in the single unknown x.

Usually, a linear equation in one unknown has exactly one solution, which can be found by using the following strategy.

Strategy:
To solve a linear equation in one unknown

Use the rules for rearranging equations to obtain successive equivalent equations. Aim to obtain an equation in which the unknown is alone on one side, with only a number on the other side. To achieve that, do the following, in order.

---

1. Clear any fractions and multiply out any brackets. To clear fractions, multiply through by a suitable expression.

2. Add or subtract terms on both sides to get all the terms in the unknown on one side, and all the other terms on the other side. Collect like terms.

3. Divide both sides by the coefficient of the unknown.

This strategy is illustrated in the next example.

Example 23 *Solving linear equations*

Solve the following equations.

(a) $\dfrac{x}{5} - 4 = 3(4 - x)$ (b) $\dfrac{1}{a} - 1 = \dfrac{1}{7a}$

Solution

(a) $\dfrac{x}{5} - 4 = 3(4 - x)$

🔍 There is a fraction with denominator 5, so multiply through by 5 to clear it. 💬

$$x - 20 = 15(4 - x)$$

🔍 Multiply out the brackets. 💬

$$x - 20 = 60 - 15x$$

🔍 Get all the terms in the unknown on one side, and all the other terms on the other side. Collect like terms. 💬

$$x + 15x = 60 + 20$$
$$16x = 80$$

🔍 Divide both sides by 16, the coefficient of the unknown. 💬

$$x = 5$$

The solution is $x = 5$.

🔍 If you wish, check the answer by substituting into the original equation, as follows. 💬

Check: if $x = 5$,

$$\text{LHS} = \tfrac{5}{5} - 4 = 1 - 4 = -3,$$

and

$$\text{RHS} = 3(4 - 5) = 3 \times (-1) = -3.$$

Since LHS = RHS, $x = 5$ satisfies the equation.

(b) $\quad \dfrac{1}{a} - 1 = \dfrac{1}{7a}$

💭 To clear the fractions, multiply through by a common multiple of the denominators, such as the lowest common multiple, $7a$. For this to be guaranteed to give an equivalent equation, you have to assume that $7a \neq 0$, that is, $a \neq 0$. 💭

Assume that $a \neq 0$.

$$\frac{7a}{a} - 7a = \frac{7a}{7a}$$

💭 Simplify, then proceed as in part (a). 💭

$$7 - 7a = 1$$
$$7 - 1 = 7a$$
$$6 = 7a$$
$$\tfrac{6}{7} = a$$

The value $a = \tfrac{6}{7}$ satisfies the assumption $a \neq 0$, so it is the solution.

Notice that before you can multiply the equation in Example 23(b) through by $7a$ to clear the fractions, you have to make the assumption that a never takes the value 0. In other words, you have to assume that the solutions of the equation are restricted to non-zero numbers. It's fine to make this assumption, because it's clear that $a = 0$ isn't a solution of the equation anyway, because it makes the fractions undefined. But because the rearrangements of the equation are based on this assumption, you have to check the solution that you obtain: if you get $a = 0$, then this doesn't count as a valid solution.

Notice also that in Example 23(b) the solution was left as $a = \tfrac{6}{7}$. It wasn't converted to a rounded decimal, such as $a = 0.857$ to three decimal places. In general, in mathematics you should always try to use *exact* numbers, where it's reasonably straightforward to do so. (However, it's often helpful to give answers to practical problems as rounded decimals.)

You can practise solving linear equations in the next activity. When you're solving a linear equation, you don't need to rigidly follow the steps of the strategy above if you can see a better way to proceed. You can do whatever you think will be helpful, as long as you're following the rules for rearranging equations given in the boxes in Subsection 5.2.

Activity 47   *Solving linear equations*

Solve the following equations.

(a) $12 - 5q = q + 3$ (b) $3(x - 1) = 4(1 - x)$ (c) $\dfrac{t - 3}{4} + 5t = 1$

(d) $\dfrac{3}{b} = \dfrac{2}{3b} - \dfrac{1}{3}$ (e) $2(A + 2) = \dfrac{A}{3} + 1$ (f) $\dfrac{1}{z + 1} + \dfrac{1}{5(z + 1)} = 1$

In the next activity, each of the equations is of a form that allows you to clear the fractions by cross-multiplying.

Activity 48   *Solving more linear equations*

Use cross-multiplication to help you solve the following equations.

(a) $h + 1 = \dfrac{4h}{5}$ (b) $\dfrac{2}{y} = \dfrac{3}{y + 2}$ (c) $\dfrac{3}{2x - 1} = \dfrac{2}{3 - x}$

Finally in this subsection, let's have a more detailed look at why the restrictions in the box 'Doing the same thing to both sides of an equation' on page 77 are needed. Remember that this box sets out the things that you can do to both sides of an equation to obtain an equivalent equation, and the restrictions appear in brackets. Take a look back at the box before you read on.

The restrictions don't normally cause problems when you're solving linear equations in one unknown, but they can be an issue when you manipulate other types of equations.

For example, suppose that you want to solve the equation

$$x^2 = x.$$

You might think that you could simplify this equation by dividing both sides by x, to give

$$x = 1.$$

However, something has gone wrong here, because the first equation has two solutions, namely $x = 0$ and $x = 1$, whereas the second equation has only one solution, $x = 1$. So dividing the first equation by x has *not* given an equivalent equation. The problem here is that dividing by the variable x is guaranteed to give an equivalent equation only if you know that x can't take the value 0 (this is the restriction on the fourth item in the box).

If you do know that x can't take the value 0, then the first equation has only one solution, $x = 1$, and dividing the first equation by x does indeed give an equivalent second equation.

As another example, consider the simple equation

$$x = 2.$$

You might think that you could obtain an equivalent equation by raising both sides to the power 2 (that is, squaring both sides). This gives

$$x^2 = 4.$$

Again, something has gone wrong here, because when the variable x has the value -2, it doesn't satisfy the first equation, and yet it does satisfy the second equation. So raising both sides of the first equation to the power 2 has *not* given an equivalent equation. The problem this time is that raising both sides of an equation to a power is guaranteed to give an equivalent equation only if you know that the expression on each side of the equation can take only non-negative values (this is a restriction on the fifth item in the box).

By contrast, if you know that x is positive, then negative values of x such as -2 cannot arise, and squaring both sides of the first equation does give an equivalent second equation (since $x = -2$ no longer counts as a solution).

Similar issues can arise when you're solving an equation involving algebraic fractions. For example, consider the equation

$$\frac{x^2}{x} = 0.$$

This equation has no solutions. To see this, notice that the only way that a fraction can be equal to zero is for its numerator to be equal to zero. So the only possible solution of the equation is $x = 0$, but this value isn't a solution, because it makes the fraction undefined. Now consider what happens when you cancel down the left-hand side of the equation. You obtain the equation

$$x = 0,$$

which has one solution, namely $x = 0$. So cancelling down the fraction on the left-hand side has *not* given an equivalent equation. This is because the fraction x^2/x is valid for all values of x except zero, whereas its cancelled-down version, x, is valid for all values of x, with no exceptions. The two expressions aren't quite the same – this issue was mentioned on page 46. Essentially, the problem is that cancelling down an algebraic fraction in an equation is guaranteed to give an equivalent equation only if the factor that you cancel can't take the value 0.

Activity 49 *Thinking about the restrictions*

What's wrong with the following 'proof' that $1 = 2$?

> Suppose that a and b are non-zero numbers such that $a = b$. Then we have:
>
> $a = b$
>
> $a^2 = ab$ (by multiplying through by a)
>
> $a^2 - b^2 = ab - b^2$ (by subtracting b^2 from both sides)
>
> $(a + b)(a - b) = b(a - b)$ (by using the facts that $a^2 - b^2$ is a difference of two squares, and $ab - b^2$ has a common factor)
>
> $a + b = b$ (by dividing through by $a - b$)
>
> $2b = b$ (since $a = b$)
>
> $2 = 1$ (by dividing through by b)

5.4 Making a variable the subject of an equation

If an equation contains more than one variable, and one side of the equation is just a single variable that doesn't appear at all on the other side, then that variable is called the **subject** of the equation. For example, the equation

$$a = c(c + b) \qquad (6)$$

has a subject, namely a. The subject of an equation is usually written on the left-hand side.

An equation with a subject is called a **formula**. We say that it's a formula *for* whatever the subject is; for example, equation (6) is a formula for a. The word *formula* is often used for the expression to which the subject is equal, as well as for the whole equation. For example, if a, b and c are related by equation (6), then we say that $c(c + b)$ is a formula for a.

The purpose of a formula is usually to allow you to find the value of the subject when you know the values of the other variables. For example, if a, b and c are related by equation (6), and you know that $b = 16$ and $c = 3$, then you can substitute these values of b and c into the equation to find the value of a:

$$a = 3(3 + 16) = 3 \times 19 = 57.$$

If you have an equation relating two or more variables, then it's often useful to rearrange it so that a particular variable becomes its subject. This isn't always possible, but for many equations you can do it by using essentially the same method that you use to solve linear equations, treating the variable that you want to be the subject (which we'll call the *required subject*) as the unknown. This method is summarised in the following strategy.

Strategy:
To make a variable the subject of an equation
(this works for some equations but not all)

Use the rules for rearranging equations to obtain successive equivalent equations. Aim to obtain an equation in which the required subject is alone on one side. To achieve this, do the following, in order.

1. Clear any fractions and multiply out any brackets. To clear fractions, multiply through by a suitable expression.

2. Add or subtract terms on both sides to get all the terms containing the required subject on one side, and all the other terms on the other side. Collect like terms.

3. If more than one term contains the required subject, then take it out as a common factor.

4. Divide both sides by the expression that multiplies the required subject.

This strategy works provided that the equation is 'linear in the required subject'. That is, its form must be such that if you replace every variable other than the required subject by a suitable number (one that doesn't lead to multiplication or division by zero) then the result is a linear equation in the required subject.

As when you're solving equations, you don't need to follow the steps of the strategy rigidly if you can see a better way to proceed. You just have to make sure that you're following the rules for rearranging equations given in the boxes in Subsection 5.2.

Example 24   *Making a variable the subject of an equation*

Rearrange the equation

$$t(h - 1) = \frac{2}{t} + hr$$

to make h the subject.

Solution

$$t(h - 1) = \frac{2}{t} + hr$$

🔍 Multiply through by t to clear the fraction (assume that $t \neq 0$). 💬

$$t^2(h - 1) = 2 + thr \quad \text{(assuming } t \neq 0\text{)}$$

🔍 Multiply out the brackets. 💬

$$t^2h - t^2 = 2 + thr$$

🔍 Get all the terms in the required subject, h, on one side, and all the other terms on the other side. Check for like terms – there are none. 💬

$$t^2h - thr = 2 + t^2$$

🔍 Take the required subject, h, out as a common factor. 💬

$$h(t^2 - tr) = 2 + t^2$$

🔍 Divide both sides by the expression that multiplies the required subject h (assume that $t \neq r$, to ensure that $t^2 - tr \neq 0$). 💬

$$h = \frac{2 + t^2}{t^2 - tr} \quad \text{(assuming } t \neq r)$$

The working in the example above tells you that, provided the variable t does not take the value 0 or the same value as r, then the initial and final equations are equivalent. It tells you nothing about what happens when t does take these values. In the next activity, you should note the assumptions that you make as you carry out the manipulations, as in the example above.

Activity 50   *Making variables the subjects of equations*

(a) Make m the subject of the equation $am = 2a + 3m$.

(b) Make d the subject of the equation $c = \frac{1}{3}(2 + 5d)$.

(c) Make X the subject of the equation $\dfrac{Y}{X} = \dfrac{3Y + 2}{X + 1}$.

(d) Make c the subject of the equation $a = \dfrac{b}{1 - 2c}$.

(e) Make B the subject of the equation $A = \dfrac{2}{B} + AC$.

In the next example, the strategy given earlier for making a variable the subject of an equation doesn't apply, but you can make the required variable the subject simply by raising both sides of the equation to an appropriate power, and simplifying.

Example 25   *Raising both sides of an equation to a power*

Rearrange the equation

$$a^6 = 64bc^6$$

to make a the subject. All the variables in this equation take only positive values.

Solution

$$a^6 = 64bc^6$$

Raise both sides to the power $\frac{1}{6}$ (that is, take the sixth root of both sides). This is okay, because the expressions on both sides of the original equation are always positive – this follows from the fact that all the variables in the equation take only positive values.

$$a = (64bc^6)^{1/6}$$
$$a = 2b^{1/6}c$$

Activity 51   *Raising both sides of equations to powers*

In this activity, all the variables take only positive values.

(a) Make Q the subject of the equation $Q^3 = PR^2$.

(b) Make h the subject of the equation $h^{1/4} = \dfrac{2k^{1/2}}{m}$.

(c) Make u the subject of the equation $u^2 = v + w$.

You can often adapt the strategy given earlier for making a variable the subject of an equation to allow you to deal with equations for which the strategy doesn't quite work. In the next example, the required subject, p, is raised to the power 4 in the original equation, rather than just appearing as p. The strategy doesn't apply directly to situations like this, but you can make p the subject by first 'making p^4 the subject', then raising both sides to the power $\frac{1}{4}$.

Example 26 *Making a variable the subject of an equation, again*

Rearrange the equation

$$\frac{3p^4 - D}{c} = 1$$

to make p the subject. All the variables in this equation take only positive values.

Solution

🔍 First 'make p^4 the subject'. 💬

$$\frac{3p^4 - D}{c} = 1$$
$$3p^4 - D = c$$
$$3p^4 = c + D$$
$$p^4 = \frac{c + D}{3}$$

🔍 Now raise both sides to the power $\frac{1}{4}$. This is fine, because both sides are always positive – this follows from the fact that all the variables in the equation take only positive values. 💬

$$p = \left(\frac{c + D}{3}\right)^{1/4}$$

Activity 52 *Making variables the subjects of equations, again*

In this activity, all the variables take only positive values.

(a) Make a the subject of the equation $a^2 - 2b^2 = 3c^2$.

(b) Make t the subject of the equation $a^2 = \dfrac{bt^2}{N}$.

(c) Make r the subject of the equation $\left(\dfrac{r}{3s}\right)^5 = \sqrt{d}$.

(d) Make y the subject of the equation $(4y)^{1/3} = x$.

6 Writing mathematics

An important part of studying mathematics at university level is learning how to communicate it effectively. In this section you'll make a start on that, by learning how to write good solutions to TMA questions.

Usually you won't be able to write down an answer to a TMA question, or part of a TMA question, immediately. You'll need to carry out some working to find the answer, and it's important that you include this working as part of the solution that you write out to send to your tutor. However, it's not enough to *simply write down your working*. Instead, what you need to do is *clearly explain how you reached your answer*.

To illustrate the difference, let's look at a sample TMA question. This particular question can be answered by using Pythagoras' theorem, so before you see it, here's a reminder about that.

You may remember that Pythagoras' theorem allows you to work out the length of one of the sides of a right-angled triangle, if you know the lengths of the other two sides. The side opposite the right angle in a right-angled triangle is called the **hypotenuse** – this is always the longest side.

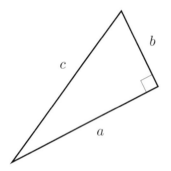

Figure 9   A right-angled triangle

> **Pythagoras' theorem**
>
> For a right-angled triangle, the square of the hypotenuse is equal to the sum of the squares of the other two sides.

For example, applying Pythagoras' theorem to the right-angled triangle in Figure 9 gives

$$c^2 = a^2 + b^2.$$

So if you know the side lengths a and b, for example, then you can substitute them into this equation, and solve it to find the side length c.

Now here's the sample TMA question.

Question 1

A symmetrical, circular circus dais, shown below, has diameter 1.1 m at the top and 1.7 m at the bottom, and is 40 cm high. Find its slant height.

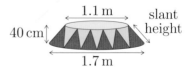

Here are two different solutions to the question.

Poorly-written solution

$1.7 - 1.1 = 0.6 \times \frac{1}{2} \Rightarrow 0.3$

$40 \Rightarrow 0.4$

Pythagoras' theorem

$$a^2 + b^2 = c^2$$
$$= 0.3^2 + 0.4^2 = c^2$$
$$= 0.25 = c^2$$
$$= c = \sqrt{0.25} = \pm 0.5$$

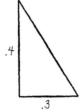

Length $\Rightarrow$ positive.

$\therefore \underline{c = 0.5}$

Well-written solution

A cross-section of the dais is shown below.

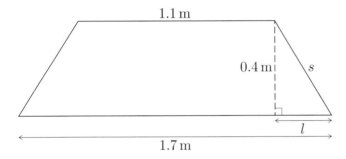

The length l (in metres) shown in the diagram is given by

$l = \frac{1}{2}(1.7 - 1.1) = \frac{1}{2} \times 0.6 = 0.3.$

So, by Pythagoras' theorem, the slant height s (in metres) is given by

$$s^2 = 0.4^2 + l^2$$
$$= 0.4^2 + 0.3^2$$
$$= 0.16 + 0.09$$
$$= 0.25.$$

Therefore, since s is positive,

$$s = \sqrt{0.25} = 0.5.$$

That is, the slant height of the dais is $0.5\,\text{m}$.

Each of the two solutions above uses a correct method, obtains the correct answer and shows all the working. However, the author of the poorly-written solution has done little more than just jot down some working (and has also used notation incorrectly, as explained later), whereas the author of the well-written solution has written out a clear explanation of how he or she has reached the answer. The result is that the well-written solution is much easier for a reader to understand.

Writing mathematics so that it can be easily understood by a reader is an important skill. It will be useful not only when you write TMA solutions for your tutor, but in other situations too. For example, it will be valuable if you need to write mathematical reports, or if you teach mathematics to others, or even when you make notes for yourself to be read at a later date. Also, explaining your thinking clearly can help you to deepen your understanding of the mathematics, identify any errors and remember the techniques.

Here are some things that you should try to do when you write mathematics, to make it easier for a reader to understand. The author of the well-written solution has done all of these things, whereas the author of the poorly-written solution has done few of them.

Write in sentences.

The well-written solution is written as a sequence of sentences. In contrast, the poorly-written solution is just a collection of fragments of English and mathematics, such as 'Pythagoras' theorem' and '40 $\Rightarrow$ 0.4'.

You should always aim to write your mathematics in sentences, though these sentences will often consist mostly of mathematical notation. However, if you're answering a question that simply asks you to carry out a mathematical manipulation, such as rearranging an expression, then you don't need to include any extra words.

Explain your reasoning.

In the well-written solution, the author has explained how each claim that he or she makes follows from something that was calculated earlier in the solution, or is given in the question, or is a known fact (such as Pythagoras' theorem). Notice in particular how he or she has used the link words 'so', 'therefore' and 'that is' to indicate what follows from what. Other examples of useful link words and phrases are 'hence', 'it follows that' and 'since'.

In your answers to TMA questions, you can use any of the facts that are stated in the *Handbook* or in the boxes in the units. You do not need to prove these facts, or state where you saw them.

Use equals signs only between two numbers, quantities or algebraic expressions that are equal.

In the first line of the poorly-written solution, the author has written '$1.7 - 1.1 = 0.6 \times \frac{1}{2}$'. This is incorrect! Whenever you write an equals sign, whatever is on the left of the sign must be equal to whatever is on the right.

There's one situation in which it's sometimes helpful to relax this rule, however. When you're carrying out a calculation that includes units, it's acceptable to omit the units until the end of the calculation.

For example, an alternative solution to the TMA question above might involve the calculation

$$\sqrt{0.3^2 + 0.4^2}\, \text{m} = \sqrt{0.25}\, \text{m} = 0.5\, \text{m}.$$

(You can see such a solution on page 98.) It's acceptable to write this calculation as

$$\sqrt{0.3^2 + 0.4^2} = \sqrt{0.25} = 0.5\, \text{m}.$$

Although strictly it's incorrect to write this, omitting units in this way can help to prevent calculations looking unnecessarily complicated.

Don't use equals signs to link equations.

In the poorly-written solution, the author has solved the equation $0.3^2 + 0.4^2 = c^2$ by writing down a sequence of equivalent equations, ending with $c = \pm 0.5$. This is fine, but he or she has linked the equations in the sequence by writing equals signs between them. Don't do this! Whenever you manipulate an equation in this way, the only equals signs should be the equals signs in the equations themselves.

You can link just two or three equivalent equations by using link words such as 'that is'. When you want to link a longer sequence of equivalent equations, you can begin by making it clear that you're manipulating an equation, and then just write the equivalent equations underneath each other, with no linking symbols, like this:

Solving the equation $0.3^2 + 0.4^2 = c^2$ gives:

$$0.3^2 + 0.4^2 = c^2$$
$$0.25 = c^2$$
$$c = \pm\sqrt{0.25}$$
$$c = \pm 0.5.$$

It's important to appreciate that this point applies to *equations* (which contain equals signs), not *expressions* (which don't). (The definitions of an expression and an equation are given on pages 24 and 74, respectively, and in the *Handbook*.) When you manipulate an *expression*, you *should* link the equivalent expressions with equals signs (often aligned vertically below each other). For example, you can see this done in the well-written solution, at the end of the sentence beginning 'So, by Pythagoras' theorem, . . .'.

If you introduce new variables, explain what they are.

The poorly-written solution includes the line '$a^2 + b^2 = c^2$', with no indication of what a, b and c represent. Don't do this: if you introduce a variable that isn't mentioned in the question, then explain what it represents.

If you introduce a variable that represents a physical quantity, then specify its units. For example, the author of the well-written solution has specified near the beginning that l and s are lengths *in metres*.

Finish with a conclusion that clearly answers the question.

The poorly-written solution finishes with '$c = 0.5$'. This is not a good conclusion, because the TMA question didn't ask, for example, 'What is the value of c?'. Also, it's not clear whether the final answer, 0.5, is in metres, or centimetres, for example, as the author hasn't specified units. The final line of the well-written solution is much more helpful: it's a clear answer to the question that was asked, with units included.

Include enough detail, but no more than is needed.

You need to give enough detail to enable your reader to easily understand what you've done, but try to give no more than this. Excess detail can waste your time and your reader's time, and it can actually make your solution harder to understand.

Sometimes you might be unsure about how much detail you need to include, and indeed as your mathematical experience grows it's appropriate to include less detail of routine procedures, such as solving linear equations. As a general guideline, you should include enough detail to make your solution clear to a reader whose mathematical experience is about the same as yours. Another useful guideline is that the amount of detail should be similar to that in the worked examples and activity solutions in the module units. (Remember that any blue 'thinks' text is not part of the solution, but any other text is.) But, if in doubt, include the extra detail!

If there's a worked example or an activity in the module that's similar to a question that you're answering, then it's fine to use the format of its solution as a guide for the format of your solution. This isn't plagiarism, as it's the format that you're copying, rather than the solution itself.

Make sure that the mathematical symbols you use are appropriate.

Often it's better to use words instead. For example, the author of the poorly-written solution has written

Length $\Rightarrow$ positive.

It would be clearer, and more mathematically correct, to write something like

The variable c represents a length, so its value must be positive.

Similarly, rather than writing

$40 \Rightarrow 0.4,$

it would be better to write, for example,

The height of the dais is $40\,\text{cm} = 0.4\,\text{m}$.

The symbol $\Rightarrow$, which means 'implies', is often used incorrectly, and it's probably best not to use it at all in this module. It isn't used in any of the materials provided (except here!). You can learn about its correct use in the module *Essential mathematics 2* (MST125).

The symbol ∴ means 'therefore' and can be useful when you're short of time, such as in an examination, or in rough or informal work. Usually, however, it's better to use a word, such as 'so', 'hence' or 'therefore', as this makes your mathematical writing more pleasant to read. The symbol ∴ isn't much used in university-level mathematics.

Display larger pieces of mathematical notation on separate lines.

Notice how the author of the well-written solution has done this. For example, the part of the solution immediately below the diagram would be less easy to read if it were written like this:

The length l (in metres) shown in the diagram is given by $l = \frac{1}{2}(1.7 - 1.1) = \frac{1}{2} \times 0.6 = 0.3$. So, by Pythagoras' theorem, ...

Include the digit 0 in numbers such as 0.3.

In the poorly-written solution, the numbers 0.3 and 0.4 are written as .3 and .4 (on the diagram). Don't do this. Whenever you write a decimal point, there should always be a digit on each side of it. This is because, for example, .3 could easily be read as 3 by mistake.

Make sure that diagrams are clear and helpful.

If you include a diagram – and it's often useful to do so, even if the question doesn't explicitly ask for one – then make sure that it's neat, clearly labelled and not too cluttered, and that it's clear how it relates to the question. It's a good idea to use a ruler to draw straight lines. There's usually no need to use graph paper for diagrams or graphs.

A geometric diagram, such as the one in the well-written solution, doesn't need to be an exact scaled-down version of the situation that it represents – an approximate representation is fine.

Any well-written TMA solution will comply with the points above, but there's no single 'correct way' to write a solution to a TMA question. For example, the following alternative solution to the TMA question on page 92 looks quite different from the well-written solution you saw on page 93, but it is just as acceptable.

Notice in particular that the final sentence of this solution consists of some explanation, some mathematical working and a clear final answer, including units, all within a single sentence. This can be appropriate for a straightforward calculation.

Alternative well-written solution

The radius of the top of the dais is

$$\tfrac{1}{2} \times 1.1\,\text{m} = 0.55\,\text{m},$$

and the radius of the bottom is

$$\tfrac{1}{2} \times 1.7\,\text{m} = 0.85\,\text{m}.$$

The diagram on the right shows half of a cross-section of the dais. The base of the right-angled triangle shown is

$$0.85\,\text{m} - 0.55\,\text{m} = 0.3\,\text{m}.$$

Hence, by Pythagoras' theorem, the slant height of the dais is

$$\sqrt{0.3^2 + 0.4^2}\,\text{m} = \sqrt{0.25}\,\text{m} = 0.5\,\text{m}.$$

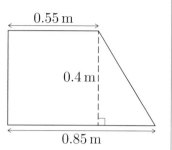

Activity 53 *Improving a TMA solution*

Consider the following TMA question and poorly-written solution.

Question 2

A cold frame is constructed by vertically fixing a pane of glass that is 1.15 m high at a distance of 98 cm from a wall, and then fixing another pane of glass of the same height at an angle between the top of the first pane and the wall, as shown. (Two trapezium-shaped sides are also attached.) Find the height of the cold frame where it meets the wall, to the nearest centimetre.

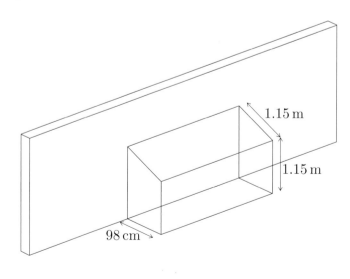

Poorly-written solution

$$h^2 + 98^2 = 1.15^2$$
$$\Rightarrow h^2 + 0.98^2 = 1.15^2$$
$$\Rightarrow h^2 = 1.15^2 - 0.98^2 = 0.3621$$
$$\Rightarrow h = \sqrt{0.3621} = 0.6$$
$$\therefore h = 0.6 + 1.15 \Rightarrow 1.75$$

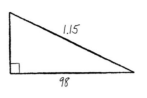

(a) Criticise the solution: list the features that contribute to its being poorly-written and difficult to follow, and describe how it could be improved.

(b) Write out a better solution.

In many of the TMAs for this module, a few marks are allocated for 'good mathematical communication'. The two well-written solutions that you've seen in this subsection (on pages 93 and 98) would merit full marks for their mathematical communication, as well as full marks for their mathematics. On the other hand, although the poorly-written solutions that you've seen (on page 93 and in Activity 53) would achieve some marks for their mathematics, they wouldn't be awarded any marks for mathematical communication. They would also lose an additional mark or half-mark because their final answers don't include units and hence are incomplete.

When you're working on a TMA question, you might find it helpful to first write out a rough solution, and then work on a better version to send to your tutor. This may be especially helpful near the start of the module, while you're learning the basics of mathematical communication. It's also helpful to read through your TMA solutions after you've written them, to try to judge for yourself how easy they are to follow. Then you can improve them where this seems appropriate. If you have time, try to leave them aside for a few days, or even longer, between writing them and reading them through.

You'll find that the feedback that your tutor provides on your TMA solutions will help you to improve your mathematical writing as you progress through the module.

You might be wondering whether you should handwrite your TMA solutions, or type them. The answer is that it's your choice: either is just as acceptable as the other. Remember, though, that you're expected to handwrite your answers in many mathematics exams, so you might find it useful to practise in preparation for that. Another thing to think about is that it can take time to learn to type mathematics, and it can take time to check typed mathematics for typing errors. If you're short of time, then it would be better to concentrate on learning and practising the mathematics in the module rather than typing your TMA solutions.

If you do plan to type your TMA solutions, then you should use an equation editor to format most of the mathematics. The ordinary text features of a word processor aren't adequate for the mathematics that you'll learn in this module. The module *Essential mathematics 2* (MST125) teaches you how to typeset mathematics, using your choice from three different typesetting programs, so if your study programme includes this module, then you may wish to delay learning to type mathematics until you take it. Alternatively, you can access the MST125 teaching materials on this topic via the MST124 website.

Another thing that you might be wondering about is how you should write a solution to a mathematics question in a written examination. The short answer is that you should try to use many of the same writing skills that you use for TMA questions, but you need to adapt them so that you can get the questions done as quickly as possible. For example, you might use abbreviated forms of sentences, and the 'therefore' symbol.

Learning outcomes

After studying this unit, you should be able to:

- work fluently and accurately with different types of numbers, including negative numbers

- understand how to avoid some common types of errors, such as rounding errors, errors arising from incorrect use of the BIDMAS rules and errors in algebraic manipulation

- manipulate and simplify algebraic expressions fluently and accurately, including those involving brackets, algebraic fractions and indices

- manipulate and simplify surds

- solve linear equations, including those involving algebraic fractions

- rearrange equations fluently and accurately

- appreciate some principles of writing mathematics, and begin to apply them.

Solutions to activities

Solution to Activity 1

(a) (i) $\quad 23 - 2 \times 3 + (4 - 2)$
$$= 23 - 2 \times 3 + 2$$
$$= 23 - 6 + 2$$
$$= 19$$

(ii) $\quad 2 - \frac{1}{2} \times 4 = 2 - 2 = 0$

(iii) $\quad 4 \times 3^2 = 4 \times 9 = 36$

(iv) $\quad 2 + 2^2 = 2 + 4 = 6$

(v) $\quad \dfrac{1+2}{1+3^2} = \dfrac{3}{1+9} = \dfrac{3}{10}$

(vi) $\quad 1 - 2/3^2 = 1 - 2/9 = 7/9$

(b) (i) $\quad 3(b-a)^2 = 3(5-3)^2$
$$= 3 \times 2^2 = 3 \times 4 = 12$$

(ii) $\quad a + b(2a+b) = 3 + 5(2 \times 3 + 5)$
$$= 3 + 5(6+5)$$
$$= 3 + 5 \times 11$$
$$= 3 + 55$$
$$= 58$$

(iii) $\quad a + 9\left(\dfrac{b}{a}\right) = 3 + 9 \times \dfrac{5}{3}$
$$= 3 + 15$$
$$= 18$$

(iv) $\quad 30/(ab) = 30/(3 \times 5)$
$$= 30/15$$
$$= 2$$

Solution to Activity 2

(a) $41.394 = 41.4$ (to 1 d.p.)

(b) $22.325 = 22.3$ (to 3 s.f.)

(c) $80\,014 = 80\,000$ (to 3 s.f.)

(d) $0.056\,97 = 0.057$ (to 2 s.f.)

(e) $0.006\,996 = 0.007\,00$ (to 3 s.f.)

(f) $56\,311 = 56\,300$ (to the nearest 100)

(g) $72\,991 = 73\,000$ (to the nearest 100)

(Notice that rounding $80\,014$ gives the same answer, $80\,000$, whether you're rounding to 1, 2 or 3 significant figures. Also, rounding $0.006\,996$ gives the same answer whether you're rounding it to 3 or 4 significant figures, but in the first case you'd express the answer as $0.007\,00$, and in the second case you'd express it as $0.007\,000$.)

Solution to Activity 3

(a) Let the radius of the circle be r (in cm). Then
$$77.2 = 2\pi r,$$
so
$$r = \frac{77.2}{2\pi} = 12.286\,761\,60\ldots = 12.3 \text{ (to 3 s.f.)}.$$
That is, the radius of the circle is 12.3 cm (to 3 s.f.).

(b) Let the area of the circle be A (in cm^2). Then
$$A = \pi r^2$$
$$= \pi \times (12.286\,761\,60\ldots)^2$$
$$= 474.268\,998\ldots$$
$$= 470 \text{ (to 2 s.f.)}.$$
That is, the area of the circle is 470 cm^2 (to 2 s.f.).

Solution to Activity 4

(a) $-3 + (-4) = -3 - 4 = -7$

(b) $2 + (-3) = 2 - 3 = -1$

(c) $2 - (-3) = 2 + 3 = 5$

(d) $-1 - (-5) = -1 + 5 = 4$

(e) $5 \times (-4) = -20$

(f) $\dfrac{-15}{-3} = 5$

(g) $(-2) \times (-3) \times (-4) = 6 \times (-4) = -24$

(h) $6(-3 - (-1)) = 6(-3 + 1) = 6 \times (-2) = -12$

(i) $20 - (-5) \times (-2) = 20 - 10 = 10$

(j) $-5 + (-3) \times (-1) - 2 \times (-2) = -5 + 3 + 4 = 2$

(k) $\dfrac{-2 - (-1) \times (-2)}{-8} = \dfrac{-2 - 2}{-8} = \dfrac{-4}{-8} = \dfrac{1}{2}$

Unit 1 Algebra

Solution to Activity 5

(a) $-5^2 = -25$

(b) $(-5)^2 = 25$

(c) $-(-8) = 8$

(d) $-(-8)^2 = -64$

(e) $-2^2 + 7 = -4 + 7 = 3$

(f) $-(-5) - (-1) = 5 + 1 = 6$

(g) $-4^2 - (-4)^2 = -16 - 16 = -32$

(h) $-3 \times (-2^2) = -3 \times (-4) = 12$

Solution to Activity 6

(a) $-b = -(-3) = 3$

(b) $-a - b = -(-2) - (-3) = 2 + 3 = 5$

(c) $-b^2 = -(-3)^2 = -9$

(d) $a^2 + ab = (-2)^2 + (-2) \times (-3) = 4 + 6 = 10$

(e) $\dfrac{3 - a^2}{b} = \dfrac{3 - (-2)^2}{-3} = \dfrac{3 - 4}{-3} = \dfrac{-1}{-3} = \dfrac{1}{3}$

(f) $\begin{aligned} a^2 - 2a + 5 &= (-2)^2 - 2 \times (-2) + 5 \\ &= 4 + 4 + 5 = 13 \end{aligned}$

(g) $\begin{aligned} (6 - a)(2 + b) &= (6 - (-2)) \times (2 + (-3)) \\ &= (6 + 2) \times (2 - 3) \\ &= 8 \times (-1) = -8 \end{aligned}$

(h) $a^3 = (-2)^3 = -8$

(i) $-b^3 = -(-3)^3 = -(-27) = 27$

Solution to Activity 7

(a) (i) The positive factor pairs of 28 are

$1, 28; \quad 2, 14; \quad 4, 7.$

The positive factors of 28 are

$1, \ 2, \ 4, \ 7, \ 14, \ 28.$

(ii) The positive factor pairs of 25 are

$1, 25; \quad 5, 5.$

The positive factors of 25 are

$1, \ 5, \ 25.$

(iii) The positive factor pairs of 36 are

$1, 36; \quad 2, 18; \quad 3, 12; \quad 4, 9; \quad 6, 6.$

The positive factors of 36 are

$1, \ 2, \ 3, \ 4, \ 6, \ 9, \ 12, \ 18, \ 36.$

(b) (i) The factor pairs of 28 are

$1, 28; \quad 2, 14; \quad 4, 7;$
$-1, -28; \quad -2, -14; \quad -4, -7.$

(ii) The factor pairs of -28 are

$1, -28; \quad 2, -14; \quad 4, -7;$
$-1, 28; \quad -2, 14; \quad -4, 7.$

Solution to Activity 8

(a) $594 = 2 \times 3^3 \times 11$

(b) $525 = 3 \times 5^2 \times 7$

(c) $221 = 13 \times 17$

(d) $223 = 223$

(The number 223 is prime.)

Solution to Activity 9

The prime factorisations are

$\begin{aligned} 9 &= 3^2 \\ 18 &= 2 \times 3^2 \\ 24 &= 2^3 \times 3 \end{aligned}$

(a) The LCM of 18 and 24 is $2^3 \times 3^2 = 72$.

The HCF of 18 and 24 is $2 \times 3 = 6$.

(b) The LCM of 9, 18 and 24 is $2^3 \times 3^2 = 72$.

The HCF of 9, 18 and 24 is 3.

(c) The LCM and HCF of -18 and -24 are the same as the LCM and HCF of 18 and 24 found in part (a). That is, the LCM is 72 and the HCF is 6.

Solution to Activity 10

(a) $-(-uv) = +uv = uv$

(b) $+(-9p) = -9p$

(c) $-(-4r^2) = +4r^2 = 4r^2$

(d) $-(8z) = -8z$

(The expression in part (d) can be simplified by deleting the brackets, as shown. These brackets aren't necessary, as the multiplication is done before taking the negative, anyway, by the BIDMAS rules.)

(e) $2x^2y^2 \times 5xy^4 = 10x^3y^6$

(f) $-P(-PQ) = P^2Q$

(g) $5m \times (-\frac{2}{5}n) = -2mn$

(h) $(-a^3)(-2b^3)(-2a^3) = -4a^6b^3$

(i) $(cd)^2 = cd \times cd = c^2d^2$

(j) $(-3x)^2 = (-3x) \times (-3x) = 9x^2$

(k) $-(3x)^2 = -(3x) \times (3x) = -9x^2$

(l) $-(-3x)^2 = -(-3x) \times (-3x) = -9x^2$

(m) $(-2x)^3 = (-2x) \times (-2x) \times (-2x) = -8x^3$

(n) $-(-2x)^3 = -(-2x) \times (-2x) \times (-2x) = 8x^3$

Solution to Activity 11

(a) $3a \times 3b - 2b \times 3b = 9ab - 6b^2$

(b) $5x \times 8x - 3x(-3x)$
$\quad = 40x^2 + 9x^2 = 49x^2$

(c) $3x^2 - (-3y^2) + (-x^2) + (2y^2)$
$\quad = 3x^2 + 3y^2 - x^2 + 2y^2 = 2x^2 + 5y^2$

(d) $\quad - 3cd + (-5c \times 2d^2) - (-cd^2)$
$\quad = -3cd - 10cd^2 + cd^2$
$\quad = -3cd - 9cd^2$

(e) $\quad - 6p(-\frac{1}{3}p) + (-5p \times p) - 2(-\frac{1}{2}p^2)$
$\quad = 2p^2 - 5p^2 + p^2$
$\quad = -2p^2$

(f) $\quad A(-B) + (-AB) - (-AB) + (-A)(-B)$
$\quad = -AB - AB + AB + AB = 0$

Solution to Activity 12

(a) $a(a^4 + b) = a^5 + ab$

(b) $-x(6x - x^2) = -6x^2 + x^3 = x^3 - 6x^2$

(c) $3pq(2p + 3q - 1) = 6p^2q + 9pq^2 - 3pq$

(d) $(C^3 - C^2 - C)C^2 = C^5 - C^4 - C^3$

(e) $-\frac{1}{2}x \left(\frac{1}{3}x^2 + \frac{2}{3}x \right) = -\frac{1}{6}x^3 - \frac{1}{3}x^2$

Solution to Activity 13

(a) $-(-2x^2 + x - 1) = 2x^2 - x + 1$

(b) $+(2x - 3y + z) = 2x - 3y + z$

(c) $-(p - 2q) = -p + 2q$

Solution to Activity 14

(a) $\underline{x} + \underline{x^2(1 + 3x)} = x + x^2 + 3x^3$

(b) $\quad \underline{7ab} - \underline{b(a + 2b)} = 7ab - ab - 2b^2$
$\quad\quad\quad\quad\quad\quad = 6ab - 2b^2$

(c) $\quad \underline{-6(c + d)} + \underline{3(c - d)}$
$\quad = -6c - 6d + 3c - 3d$
$\quad = -3c - 9d$

(d) $\underline{2X} - \underline{5Y(-4X + 2Y)} = 2X + 20XY - 10Y^2$

(e) $\quad \underline{(1 - p^4)p} + \underline{p^2} - \underline{p} = p - p^5 + p^2 - p$
$\quad\quad\quad\quad\quad\quad = -p^5 + p^2$
$\quad\quad\quad\quad\quad\quad = p^2 - p^5$

Solution to Activity 15

(a) $\quad (a + b)(c + d + e)$
$\quad = a(c + d + e) + b(c + d + e)$
$\quad = ac + ad + ae + bc + bd + be$

(b) $\quad (x + 3)(x + 5)$
$\quad = x(x + 5) + 3(x + 5)$
$\quad = x^2 + 5x + 3x + 15$
$\quad = x^2 + 8x + 15$

(c) $\quad (x^2 - 2x + 3)(3x^2 - x - 1)$
$\quad = x^2(3x^2 - x - 1) - 2x(3x^2 - x - 1)$
$\quad\quad + 3(3x^2 - x - 1)$
$\quad = 3x^4 - x^3 - x^2 - 6x^3 + 2x^2 + 2x$
$\quad\quad + 9x^2 - 3x - 3$
$\quad = 3x^4 - 7x^3 + 10x^2 - x - 3$

Solution to Activity 16

(a) $\quad (x + 5)(x - 7) = x^2 - 7x + 5x - 35$
$\quad\quad\quad\quad\quad\quad = x^2 - 2x - 35$

(b) $\quad (x - 3)(x - 1) = x^2 - x - 3x + 3$
$\quad\quad\quad\quad\quad\quad = x^2 - 4x + 3$

(c) $\quad (2x - 1)(8x + 3) = 16x^2 + 6x - 8x - 3$
$\quad\quad\quad\quad\quad\quad = 16x^2 - 2x - 3$

(d) $\quad (2 - 5x)(x - 9) = 2x - 18 - 5x^2 + 45x$
$\quad\quad\quad\quad\quad\quad = -5x^2 + 47x - 18$

(e) $\quad (c - 2d)(1 + c) = c + c^2 - 2d - 2cd$

(f) $(A - B)(2A - 3B^2)$
$$= 2A^2 - 3AB^2 - 2AB + 3B^3$$

(g) $(a - 1)(a + 1) = a^2 + a - a - 1 = a^2 - 1$

(h) $(2 + 3x)(2 - 3x) = 4 - 6x + 6x - 9x^2$
$$= 4 - 9x^2$$

(i) $x(1 + x) + (x - 1)(2 - x)$
$$= x + x^2 + 2x - x^2 - 2 + x$$
$$= 4x - 2$$

Solution to Activity 17

(a) $(x + 1)^2 = (x + 1)(x + 1)$
$$= x^2 + x + x + 1$$
$$= x^2 + 2x + 1$$

(b) $(3x - 2)^2 = (3x - 2)(3x - 2)$
$$= 9x^2 - 6x - 6x + 4$$
$$= 9x^2 - 12x + 4$$

(c) $(2p + 3q)^2 = (2p + 3q)(2p + 3q)$
$$= 4p^2 + 6pq + 6pq + 9q^2$$
$$= 4p^2 + 12pq + 9q^2$$

Solution to Activity 18

(a) $(x + 6)^2 = x^2 + 2 \times x \times 6 + 6^2$
$$= x^2 + 12x + 36$$

(b) $(x - 2)^2 = x^2 - 2 \times x \times 2 + 2^2$
$$= x^2 - 4x + 4$$

(c) $(1 + m)^2 = 1^2 + 2 \times 1 \times m + m^2$
$$= 1 + 2m + m^2$$

(d) $(1 - 2u)^2 = 1^2 - 2 \times 1 \times (2u) + (2u)^2$
$$= 1 - 4u + 4u^2$$

(e) $(2x - 3)^2 = (2x)^2 - 2 \times (2x) \times 3 + 3^3$
$$= 4x^2 - 12x + 9$$

(f) $(3c + d)^2 = (3c)^2 + 2 \times (3c) \times d + d^2$
$$= 9c^2 + 6cd + d^2$$

Solution to Activity 19

(a) (i) $4a^2 = 2a \times 2a$ and $2ab = 2a \times b$

   (ii) $x^3 = x^2 \times x$ and $x^5 = x^2 \times x^3$

   (iii) $18z^2 = 6z \times 3z$, $6z^2 = 6z \times z$ and
$6z = 6z \times 1$

(b) (i) $10cd^2 = 5c \times 2d^2$ and $10cd^2 = 2cd \times 5d$

   (ii) $p^7 = p^2 \times p^5$ and $p^7 = p^3 \times p^4$

   (iii) $9y^2 = 3 \times 3y^2$, $9y^2 = 9y^2 \times 1$ and
$9y^2 = 3y \times 3y$

Solution to Activity 20

(a) (i)   The highest common factor is $3x$.
$3x^2 = 3x \times x$ and $9xy = 3x \times 3y$

   (ii)   The lowest common multiple is $9x^2y$.
$9x^2y = 3x^2 \times 3y$ and $9x^2y = 9xy \times x$

(b) (i)   The highest common factor is $2pq$.
$6p^2q^3 = 2pq \times 3pq^2$, $4pq^2 = 2pq \times 2q$ and
$2pq = 2pq \times 1$

   (ii)   The lowest common multiple is $12p^2q^3$.
$12p^2q^3 = 6p^2q^3 \times 2$, $12p^2q^3 = 4pq^2 \times 3pq$
and $12p^2q^3 = 2pq \times 6pq^2$

Solution to Activity 21

(a) $pq + 12qr = q(p + 12r)$

(b) $14cd - 7cd^2 = 7cd(2 - d)$

(c) $m^3 - m^7 - 8m^2 = m^2(m - m^5 - 8)$

(d) $-6AB + 3A^2B - 12A^3B^2$
$$= 3AB(-2 + A - 4A^2B)$$
$$= 3AB(A - 4A^2B - 2)$$

(e) $\sqrt{T} - s\sqrt{T} = \sqrt{T}(1 - s)$

(f) $5x^2 - 10x = 5x(x - 2)$

(g) $18y^2 + 6 = 6(3y^2 + 1)$

Solution to Activity 22

(a) $-2x^3 + 3x^2 - x - 5 = -(2x^3 - 3x^2 + x + 5)$

(b) $-ab - a - b = -(ab + a + b)$

(c) $5cd^2 - 10c^2d - 5cd$
$$= -5cd(-d + 2c + 1)$$
$$= -5cd(2c - d + 1)$$

Solution to Activity 23

(a) $\frac{1}{2}a^2 + \frac{3}{2}a = \frac{1}{2}(a^2 + 3a) = \frac{1}{2}a(a+3)$

(b) $\frac{1}{3}x - \frac{1}{6} = \frac{1}{6}(2x - 1)$

(c) $2x^2 - \frac{1}{2}x + \frac{1}{4} = \frac{1}{4}(8x^2 - 2x + 1)$

(d) $\frac{2}{3}u^2v^2 + \frac{1}{2}u^3v = \frac{1}{6}(4u^2v^2 + 3u^3v)$
$$= \frac{1}{6}u^2v(4v + 3u)$$

Solution to Activity 24

(a) $\dfrac{8xy^3}{6x^2y^2} = \dfrac{4y}{3x}$

(b) $\dfrac{2(3x-1)}{10(3x-1)^3} = \dfrac{1}{5(3x-1)^2}$

(c) $\dfrac{(x-1)^2(x-2)}{(x-1)(x-2)^2} = \dfrac{x-1}{x-2}$

(The fraction in part (c) can't be cancelled down any further. There's an x in both the numerator and the denominator, but x isn't a *factor* of either the numerator or the denominator.)

Solution to Activity 25

(a) $\dfrac{ab+a}{a^2+a} = \dfrac{b+1}{a+1}$

(b) $\dfrac{3}{9+6y^2} = \dfrac{1}{3+2y^2}$

(c) $\dfrac{u^2-u^3}{u^5} = \dfrac{1-u}{u^3}$

(d) $\dfrac{2x^2-4x^3}{6x^4-2x^2} = \dfrac{x^2-2x^3}{3x^4-x^2} = \dfrac{1-2x}{3x^2-1}$

(e) $\dfrac{x^3+x^2}{2x+2} = \dfrac{x^2(x+1)}{2(x+1)} = \dfrac{x^2}{2}$

(f) $\dfrac{1-n}{n^2-n} = \dfrac{1-n}{n(n-1)} = \dfrac{-(n-1)}{n(n-1)} = \dfrac{-1}{n} = -\dfrac{1}{n}$

Solution to Activity 26

(a) $\dfrac{1}{x} + \dfrac{y}{x} = \dfrac{1+y}{x}$

(b) $\dfrac{c+2}{c^2+c} - \dfrac{1}{c^2+c} = \dfrac{c+2-1}{c^2+c} = \dfrac{c+1}{c(c+1)} = \dfrac{1}{c}$

(c) $\dfrac{1}{ab} - \dfrac{1}{bc} = \dfrac{c}{abc} - \dfrac{a}{abc} = \dfrac{c-a}{abc}$

(d) $\dfrac{2}{3a} + \dfrac{1}{2a} = \dfrac{4}{6a} + \dfrac{3}{6a} = \dfrac{7}{6a}$

(e) $\dfrac{1}{x^2} - \dfrac{2}{x} + 3 = \dfrac{1}{x^2} - \dfrac{2x}{x^2} + \dfrac{3x^2}{x^2}$
$$= \dfrac{1-2x+3x^2}{x^2}$$

(f) $5 - \dfrac{1}{x} + \dfrac{2}{y} = \dfrac{5}{xy} - \dfrac{y}{xy} + \dfrac{2x}{xy}$
$$= \dfrac{5-y+2x}{xy}$$

(g) $A - \dfrac{A^2-1}{2A} = \dfrac{2A^2}{2A} - \dfrac{A^2-1}{2A}$
$$= \dfrac{2A^2 - (A^2-1)}{2A}$$
$$= \dfrac{A^2+1}{2A}$$

(h) $\dfrac{3}{2u-1} + u = \dfrac{3}{2u-1} + \dfrac{u(2u-1)}{2u-1}$
$$= \dfrac{3 + u(2u-1)}{2u-1}$$
$$= \dfrac{2u^2-u+3}{2u-1}$$

(i) $\dfrac{x+2}{x+1} + \dfrac{1}{x} = \dfrac{x(x+2)}{x(x+1)} + \dfrac{x+1}{x(x+1)}$
$$= \dfrac{x(x+2)+x+1}{x(x+1)}$$
$$= \dfrac{x^2+2x+x+1}{x(x+1)}$$
$$= \dfrac{x^2+3x+1}{x(x+1)}$$

(j) $\dfrac{2}{p+2} - \dfrac{1}{p-3}$

$\quad = \dfrac{2(p-3)}{(p+2)(p-3)} - \dfrac{p+2}{(p+2)(p-3)}$

$\quad = \dfrac{2(p-3) - (p+2)}{(p+2)(p-3)}$

$\quad = \dfrac{2p - 6 - p - 2}{(p+2)(p-3)}$

$\quad = \dfrac{p-8}{(p+2)(p-3)}$

(k) $\dfrac{x+1}{x(x-1)} + \dfrac{1}{x} - x$

$\quad = \dfrac{x+1}{x(x-1)} + \dfrac{x-1}{x(x-1)} - \dfrac{x^2(x-1)}{x(x-1)}$

$\quad = \dfrac{x+1 + (x-1) - x^2(x-1)}{x(x-1)}$

$\quad = \dfrac{x+1 + x - 1 - x^3 + x^2}{x(x-1)}$

$\quad = \dfrac{-x^3 + x^2 + 2x}{x(x-1)}$

$\quad = \dfrac{-x^2 + x + 2}{x-1}$

$\quad = \dfrac{x^2 - x - 2}{1-x}$

$\quad = \dfrac{(x-2)(x+1)}{1-x}$

(Equivalent answers such as

$\quad -\dfrac{(x-2)(x+1)}{x-1}$

or

$\quad \dfrac{2 + x - x^2}{x-1}$

are fine.)

Solution to Activity 27

(a) $\dfrac{a^2 + a^5 - 1}{a^2} = \dfrac{a^2}{a^2} + \dfrac{a^5}{a^2} - \dfrac{1}{a^2}$

$\qquad = 1 + a^3 - \dfrac{1}{a^2}$

(b) $\dfrac{2 - 5cd}{c} = \dfrac{2}{c} - \dfrac{5cd}{c} = \dfrac{2}{c} - 5d$

(c) $\dfrac{2a + 3a^2}{6} = \dfrac{2a}{6} + \dfrac{3a^2}{6} = \dfrac{a}{3} + \dfrac{a^2}{2}$

Solution to Activity 28

(a) $\dfrac{40A}{B} \times \dfrac{BC}{16A^4} = \dfrac{5C}{2A^3}$

(b) $\dfrac{b}{c^2} \div c^3 = \dfrac{b}{c^2} \times \dfrac{1}{c^3} = \dfrac{b}{c^5}$

(c) $\left(\dfrac{6y}{x^7}\right) \Big/ \left(\dfrac{15y^{10}}{x^4}\right) = \dfrac{6y}{x^7} \times \dfrac{x^4}{15y^{10}} = \dfrac{2}{5x^3y^9}$

(d) $\dfrac{a/(a+1)}{a^6/(a+1)^2} = \dfrac{a}{a+1} \div \dfrac{a^6}{(a+1)^2}$

$\qquad = \dfrac{a}{a+1} \times \dfrac{(a+1)^2}{a^6} = \dfrac{a+1}{a^5}$

(e) $\dfrac{3x}{y} \div \dfrac{6}{y^2} = \dfrac{3x}{y} \times \dfrac{y^2}{6} = \dfrac{xy}{2}$

(f) $g \times \dfrac{5}{k} = \dfrac{g}{1} \times \dfrac{5}{k} = \dfrac{5g}{k}$

Solution to Activity 29

(a) $\sqrt{5}\sqrt{6} = \sqrt{5 \times 6} = \sqrt{30}$

(b) $\dfrac{\sqrt{75}}{\sqrt{15}} = \sqrt{\dfrac{75}{15}} = \sqrt{5}$

(c) $3 + \sqrt{10}\sqrt{10} = 3 + 10 = 13$

(d) $\sqrt{8}\sqrt{2} = \sqrt{8 \times 2} = \sqrt{16} = 4$

(e) $\dfrac{\sqrt[3]{5}}{\sqrt[3]{15}} = \sqrt[3]{\dfrac{5}{15}} = \sqrt[3]{\dfrac{1}{3}} = \dfrac{\sqrt[3]{1}}{\sqrt[3]{3}} = \dfrac{1}{\sqrt[3]{3}}$

Solution to Activity 30

(a) $\sqrt{3}(2\sqrt{2} + \sqrt{3}) = 2\sqrt{2}\sqrt{3} + \sqrt{3}\sqrt{3}$

$\qquad\qquad\qquad\quad = 2\sqrt{6} + 3$

$\qquad\qquad\qquad\quad = 3 + 2\sqrt{6}$

(It's slightly tidier to write the term containing the irrational root as the last term.)

(b) $\sqrt{2}(1 + \sqrt{3}) + 9\sqrt{2} = \sqrt{2} + \sqrt{2}\sqrt{3} + 9\sqrt{2}$

$\qquad\qquad\qquad\qquad = \sqrt{6} + 10\sqrt{2}$

(c) $(1 - \sqrt{5})(6 - 2\sqrt{5}) = 6 - 2\sqrt{5} - 6\sqrt{5} + 2\sqrt{5}\sqrt{5}$

$\qquad\qquad\qquad\qquad = 6 - 8\sqrt{5} + 10$

$\qquad\qquad\qquad\qquad = 16 - 8\sqrt{5}$

(d) $(6 - \sqrt{7})(6 + \sqrt{7}) = 36 + 6\sqrt{7} - 6\sqrt{7} - \sqrt{7}\sqrt{7}$

$\qquad\qquad\qquad\qquad = 36 - 7$

$\qquad\qquad\qquad\qquad = 29$

(You can shorten your working in part (d) by noticing that the given expression has the form that

gives a difference of two squares when multiplied out. So
$(6 - \sqrt{7})(6 + \sqrt{7}) = 6^2 - (\sqrt{7})^2 = 36 - 7 = 29.)$

(e) $\quad (\sqrt{3} + 2\sqrt{2})(\sqrt{3} - 2\sqrt{2})$

$\qquad = \sqrt{3}\sqrt{3} - 2\sqrt{3}\sqrt{2} + 2\sqrt{3}\sqrt{2} - 4\sqrt{2}\sqrt{2}$

$\qquad = 3 - 4 \times 2$

$\qquad = -5$

(Again, you can shorten your working in part (e) by noticing that the given expression has the form that gives a difference of two squares when multiplied out. So $(\sqrt{3} + 2\sqrt{2})(\sqrt{3} - 2\sqrt{2}) = (\sqrt{3})^2 - (2\sqrt{2})^2$
$= 3 - 4 \times 2 = -5.)$

(f) $\quad 3 - \dfrac{1}{\sqrt{2}} = \dfrac{3\sqrt{2}}{\sqrt{2}} - \dfrac{1}{\sqrt{2}} = \dfrac{3\sqrt{2} - 1}{\sqrt{2}}$

(g) $\quad \dfrac{4}{\sqrt{5}} + \dfrac{\sqrt{3}}{\sqrt{2}} = \dfrac{4\sqrt{2}}{\sqrt{2}\sqrt{5}} + \dfrac{\sqrt{3}\sqrt{5}}{\sqrt{2}\sqrt{5}} = \dfrac{4\sqrt{2} + \sqrt{15}}{\sqrt{10}}$

Solution to Activity 31

(a) (i) $\quad \sqrt{8} = \sqrt{4 \times 2} = \sqrt{4} \times \sqrt{2} = 2\sqrt{2}$

(ii) $\quad \sqrt{150} = \sqrt{25 \times 6} = \sqrt{25} \times \sqrt{6} = 5\sqrt{6}$

(iii) $\quad \sqrt{22}$ can't be simplified.

(iv) $\quad \sqrt{32} = \sqrt{16 \times 2} = \sqrt{16} \times \sqrt{2} = 4\sqrt{2}$

(v) $\quad 5 + \sqrt{108} = 5 + \sqrt{36 \times 3}$

$\qquad = 5 + \sqrt{36}\sqrt{3}$

$\qquad = 5 + 6\sqrt{3}$

(vi) $\quad \sqrt{12} + \sqrt{4} = \sqrt{4 \times 3} + 2$

$\qquad = 2\sqrt{3} + 2$

$\qquad = 2 + 2\sqrt{3}$

$\qquad = 2(1 + \sqrt{3})$

(It's slightly tidier to write the term containing the irrational root as the last term. It's not essential to take out the common factor 2.)

(vii) $\quad \sqrt{27} - \sqrt{3} = \sqrt{9 \times 3} - \sqrt{3}$

$\qquad = \sqrt{9}\sqrt{3} - \sqrt{3}$

$\qquad = 3\sqrt{3} - \sqrt{3}$

$\qquad = 2\sqrt{3}$

(b) (i) $\quad \sqrt{6}(\sqrt{3} + \sqrt{2}) = \sqrt{3}\sqrt{6} + \sqrt{2}\sqrt{6}$

$\qquad = \sqrt{3}\sqrt{3 \times 2} + \sqrt{2}\sqrt{2 \times 3}$

$\qquad = \sqrt{3}\sqrt{3}\sqrt{2} + \sqrt{2}\sqrt{2}\sqrt{3}$

$\qquad = 3\sqrt{2} + 2\sqrt{3}$

(ii) $\quad (\sqrt{10} - \sqrt{5})(2\sqrt{5} + 1)$

$\qquad = 2\sqrt{5}\sqrt{10} + \sqrt{10} - 2\sqrt{5}\sqrt{5} - \sqrt{5}$

$\qquad = 2\sqrt{5}\sqrt{5}\sqrt{2} + \sqrt{10} - 10 - \sqrt{5}$

$\qquad = 10\sqrt{2} + \sqrt{10} - 10 - \sqrt{5}$

Solution to Activity 32

(a) $\quad \dfrac{3}{\sqrt{7}} = \dfrac{3}{\sqrt{7}} \times \dfrac{\sqrt{7}}{\sqrt{7}} = \dfrac{3\sqrt{7}}{\sqrt{7}\sqrt{7}} = \dfrac{3\sqrt{7}}{7}$

(b) $\quad \dfrac{\sqrt{2}}{\sqrt{6}} = \dfrac{\sqrt{2}}{\sqrt{6}} \times \dfrac{\sqrt{6}}{\sqrt{6}}$

$\qquad = \dfrac{\sqrt{2}\sqrt{6}}{\sqrt{6}\sqrt{6}}$

$\qquad = \dfrac{\sqrt{2}\sqrt{2}\sqrt{3}}{6}$

$\qquad = \dfrac{2\sqrt{3}}{6}$

$\qquad = \dfrac{\sqrt{3}}{3}$

(c) $\quad \dfrac{5}{\sqrt{5}} = \dfrac{5}{\sqrt{5}} \times \dfrac{\sqrt{5}}{\sqrt{5}} = \dfrac{5\sqrt{5}}{\sqrt{5}\sqrt{5}} = \dfrac{5\sqrt{5}}{5} = \sqrt{5}$

(d) $\quad \dfrac{2}{1 + \sqrt{17}} = \dfrac{2}{1 + \sqrt{17}} \times \dfrac{1 - \sqrt{17}}{1 - \sqrt{17}}$

$\qquad = \dfrac{2(1 - \sqrt{17})}{1^2 - (\sqrt{17})^2}$

$\qquad = \dfrac{2(1 - \sqrt{17})}{1 - 17}$

$\qquad = \dfrac{2(1 - \sqrt{17})}{-16}$

$\qquad = \dfrac{1 - \sqrt{17}}{-8}$

$\qquad = \dfrac{\sqrt{17} - 1}{8}$

(Remember that $\sqrt{17} - 1$ is the negative of $1 - \sqrt{17}$; see page 32.)

Unit 1 Algebra

(e) $\dfrac{\sqrt{5}+\sqrt{3}}{\sqrt{5}-\sqrt{3}} = \dfrac{\sqrt{5}+\sqrt{3}}{\sqrt{5}-\sqrt{3}} \times \dfrac{\sqrt{5}+\sqrt{3}}{\sqrt{5}+\sqrt{3}}$

$= \dfrac{(\sqrt{5}+\sqrt{3})(\sqrt{5}+\sqrt{3})}{(\sqrt{5})^2 - (\sqrt{3})^2}$

$= \dfrac{(\sqrt{5})^2 + 2\sqrt{3}\sqrt{5} + (\sqrt{3})^2}{5 - 3}$

$= \dfrac{5 + 2\sqrt{15} + 3}{5 - 3}$

$= \dfrac{8 + 2\sqrt{15}}{2}$

$= 4 + \sqrt{15}$

Solution to Activity 33

(a) $2^4 = 2 \times 2 \times 2 \times 2 = 16$

(b) $(-2)^4 = (-2) \times (-2) \times (-2) \times (-2) = 16$

(c) $-2^4 = -(2 \times 2 \times 2 \times 2) = -16$

(d) $(-3)^3 = (-3) \times (-3) \times (-3) = -27$

(e) $\left(\frac{1}{2}\right)^2 = \frac{1}{2} \times \frac{1}{2} = \frac{1}{4}$

(f) $\left(\frac{1}{3}\right)^3 = \frac{1}{3} \times \frac{1}{3} \times \frac{1}{3} = \frac{1}{27}$

Solution to Activity 34

(a) $\dfrac{a^{20}}{a^5} = a^{15}$

(b) $(y^4)^5 = y^{20}$

(c) $\dfrac{b^4 b^7}{b^3} = \dfrac{b^{11}}{b^3} = b^8$

(d) $p^3 p^5 p^3 p = p^{12}$

(e) $(x^3)^3 x^2 = x^9 x^2 = x^{11}$

(f) $(m^3 m^2)^5 = (m^5)^5 = m^{25}$

(g) $\left(\dfrac{c^5}{c^2}\right)^2 = (c^3)^2 = c^6$

Solution to Activity 35

(a) $(x^3 - 1)(2x^3 + 5) = 2x^6 + 5x^3 - 2x^3 - 5$

$= 2x^6 + 3x^3 - 5$

(b) $(a^4 + b^4)^2 = (a^4 + b^4)(a^4 + b^4)$

$= a^8 + 2a^4 b^4 + b^8$

(c) $\dfrac{p^8 + p^2}{p^2} = p^6 + 1$

Solution to Activity 36

(a) $4^{-2} = \dfrac{1}{4^2} = \frac{1}{16}$

(b) $3^{-1} = \frac{1}{3}$

(c) $5^0 = 1$

(d) $\left(\frac{2}{7}\right)^{-1} = \frac{7}{2}$

(e) $\left(\frac{1}{3}\right)^{-1} = 3$

(f) $\left(\frac{1}{3}\right)^{-2} = \left(\left(\frac{1}{3}\right)^{-1}\right)^2 = 3^2 = 9$

$\left(\text{or } \left(\frac{1}{3}\right)^{-2} = \dfrac{1}{\left(\frac{1}{3}\right)^2} = \dfrac{1}{\left(\frac{1}{9}\right)} = 9\right)$

Solution to Activity 37

(a) $5g^{-1} = \dfrac{5}{g}$

(b) $\dfrac{1}{y^{-1}} = y$

(c) $\dfrac{2}{3x^{-5}} = \dfrac{2x^5}{3}$

(d) $\dfrac{a^{-3}}{b^{-4}} = \dfrac{b^4}{a^3}$

(e) $\dfrac{P^2}{Q^{-5}} = P^2 Q^5$

(f) $(3h^2)^2 = 3^2 (h^2)^2 = 9h^4$

(g) $(3h^2)^{-2} = \dfrac{1}{(3h^2)^2} = \dfrac{1}{3^2(h^2)^2} = \dfrac{1}{9h^4}$

(h) $\dfrac{(b^{-4})^3}{(3c)^2} = \dfrac{b^{-12}}{3^2 c^2} = \dfrac{1}{9b^{12}c^2}$

(i) $\dfrac{(A^{-1}B)^2}{(B^{-3})^3} = \dfrac{(A^{-1})^2 B^2}{(B^{-3})^3}$

$= \dfrac{A^{-2}B^2}{B^{-9}} = \dfrac{B^2 B^9}{A^2} = \dfrac{B^{11}}{A^2}$

(j) $\left(\dfrac{2y^{-1}}{z^2}\right)^5 = \dfrac{(2y^{-1})^5}{(z^2)^5} = \dfrac{2^5 y^{-5}}{z^{10}} = \dfrac{32}{y^5 z^{10}}$

(k) $\dfrac{x^{-5}}{x} = \dfrac{1}{x^5 x} = \dfrac{1}{x^6}$

(l) $\dfrac{(x-1)^{-3}}{(x-1)^2} = \dfrac{1}{(x-1)^3(x-1)^2} = \dfrac{1}{(x-1)^5}$

(m) $\left(\dfrac{3}{z^2}\right)^{-3} = \left(\dfrac{3}{z^2}\right)^{-1 \times 3}$

$= \left(\dfrac{z^2}{3}\right)^3 = \dfrac{(z^2)^3}{3^3} = \dfrac{z^6}{27}$

$\left(\text{or } \left(\dfrac{3}{z^2}\right)^{-3} = \dfrac{1}{(3/z^2)^3}\right.$

$\left. = \dfrac{1}{3^3/(z^2)^3} = \dfrac{1}{27/z^6} = \dfrac{z^6}{27}\right)$

(n) $\dfrac{x}{(2x-3)^3} \times x^{-2} = \dfrac{x}{x^2(2x-3)^3} = \dfrac{1}{x(2x-3)^3}$

(o) $\left(\dfrac{(x+2)^2}{x^5}\right) \Big/ (x+2)^{-4}$

$= \dfrac{(x+2)^2}{x^5} \times \dfrac{1}{(x+2)^{-4}}$

$= \dfrac{(x+2)^2}{x^5(x+2)^{-4}}$

$= \dfrac{(x+2)^2(x+2)^4}{x^5}$

$= \dfrac{(x+2)^6}{x^5}$

Solution to Activity 38

(a) $t^{1/2} = \sqrt{t}$

(b) $x^{1/3} = \sqrt[3]{x}$

(c) $p^{2/3} = \sqrt[3]{p^2} \quad \left(\text{or } \left(\sqrt[3]{p}\right)^2\right)$

(d) $x^{-1/2} = \dfrac{1}{x^{1/2}} = \dfrac{1}{\sqrt{x}}$

(e) $(2x-3)^{1/2} = \sqrt{2x-3}$

(f) $(1+x^2)^{-1/2} = \dfrac{1}{(1+x^2)^{1/2}} = \dfrac{1}{\sqrt{1+x^2}}$

(g) $(1+x)x^{-1/2} = \dfrac{1+x}{x^{1/2}} = \dfrac{1+x}{\sqrt{x}}$

Solution to Activity 39

(a) $\sqrt[4]{y} = y^{1/4}$

(b) $\sqrt[5]{1-2x} = (1-2x)^{1/5}$

(c) $\dfrac{1}{\sqrt[3]{x}} = \dfrac{1}{x^{1/3}}$

(d) $\left(\sqrt[5]{u}\right)^2 = u^{2/5}$

(e) $\dfrac{1}{\sqrt[3]{x^4}} = \dfrac{1}{x^{4/3}}$

(f) $\sqrt[4]{(y+2)^3} = (y+2)^{3/4}$

Solution to Activity 40

(a) $x^{1/3}x^{1/3} = x^{2/3}$

(b) $\dfrac{a}{a^{1/3}} = a^{2/3}$

(c) $\dfrac{a}{a^{1/2}} = a^{1/2} = \sqrt{a}$

(It's fine to leave the answer as $a^{1/2}$.)

(d) $\dfrac{x}{x^{-1/2}} = x^{3/2}$

(e) $(2x^{1/5})^3 = 8x^{3/5}$

(f) $\dfrac{(1+x)^2}{\sqrt{1+x}} = \dfrac{(1+x)^2}{(1+x)^{1/2}} = (1+x)^{3/2}$

(g) $\left(\dfrac{1}{u}\right)^{1/3} = \dfrac{1}{u^{1/3}}$

(It's fine to leave the answer as $u^{-1/3}$.)

(h) $\dfrac{A^{5/2}}{A^3} = A^{(5/2)-3} = A^{-1/2} = \dfrac{1}{A^{1/2}} = \dfrac{1}{\sqrt{A}}$

(It's fine to write the answer as $\dfrac{1}{A^{1/2}}$, or as $A^{-1/2}$.)

(i) $\dfrac{x^{1/2}y^2}{x^3y^{1/2}} = \dfrac{y^{3/2}}{x^{5/2}} \quad \left(\text{or } \sqrt{\dfrac{y^3}{x^5}}\right)$

(j) $\sqrt{4x} = \sqrt{4}\sqrt{x} = 2\sqrt{x}$

Solution to Activity 41

(a) $a^{2p}a^{5p} = a^{7p}$

(b) $\dfrac{b^{7k}}{b^{4k}} = b^{3k}$

(c) $(g^n)^k = g^{nk}$

Unit 1   Algebra

(d) $(2y^{2t})^2 y^{-t} = 2^2(y^{2t})^2 y^{-t}$
$$= 4y^{4t}y^{-t}$$
$$= 4y^{3t}$$

(e) $\dfrac{m^{3x}}{m^{-x}} = m^{3x}m^{x}$
$$= m^{4x}$$

(f) $\dfrac{c^{3y}}{c^{5y}} = \dfrac{1}{c^{2y}}$

(g) $\dfrac{(a^{-3t}b^{3t})^2}{a^{3t}b^t} = \dfrac{(a^{-3t})^2(b^{3t})^2}{a^{3t}b^t}$
$$= \dfrac{a^{-6t}b^{6t}}{a^{3t}b^t}$$
$$= \dfrac{b^{5t}}{a^{9t}}$$

(h) $(d^{1/r})^{2r} = d^2$

(i) $(3h)^{2p}(9h)^p = 3^{2p}h^{2p}9^p h^p$
$$= 3^{2p}h^{3p}(3^2)^p$$
$$= 3^{2p}h^{3p}3^{2p}$$
$$= 3^{4p}h^{3p}$$

Solution to Activity 42

(a) (i) $38\,800\,000 = 3.88 \times 10^7$

  (ii) $4237 = 4.237 \times 10^3$

  (iii) $0.0973 = 9.73 \times 10^{-2}$

  (iv) $1.303 = 1.303 \times 10^0$

  (v) $0.000\,000\,028 = 2.8 \times 10^{-8}$

(b) (i) $2.8 \times 10^4 = 28\,000$

  (ii) $5.975 \times 10^{-1} = 0.5975$

  (iii) $2.78 \times 10^{-7} = 0.000\,000\,278$

  (iv) $3.43 \times 10^7 = 34\,300\,000$

Solution to Activity 43

(a) If $x = 4$ and $y = -1$, then
  LHS $= 2 \times 4 + 3 \times (-1) = 8 - 3 = 5 = $ RHS.
  So the equation is satisfied.

(b) If $x = 3$ and $y = -2$, then
  LHS $= 2 \times 3 + 3 \times (-2) = 6 - 6 = 0 \neq$ RHS.
  So the equation is not satisfied.

Solution to Activity 44

(a) These equations are not equivalent. The term in the first equation that's been moved, -3, isn't a term of the whole expression on the right-hand side, but only of the subexpression $x - 3$.

(b) These equations are equivalent.

(c) These equations are not equivalent. The second equation is obtained from the first by subtracting $x/3$ from the left-hand side and $x/2$ from the right-hand side, but this does not give an equivalent equation.

Solution to Activity 45

(a) These equations are not equivalent. Multiplying the first equation through by 6 gives
$$2a = a^2 - 18.$$

(b) These equations are not equivalent. Multiplying the first equation through by $2x$ gives
$$x^2 - 1 + 2x^2 = 1.$$

(c) These equations are equivalent.

(d) These equations are not equivalent. Multiplying the first equation through by 2 gives $\sqrt{\dfrac{2x}{y}} = 2$.

Solution to Activity 46

(a) These equations are equivalent.

(b) These equations are not equivalent. Multiplying both sides of the first equation by $a - 3$ gives
$$b(a - 3) + a = 6(a - 3).$$
Alternatively, you can rearrange the first equation to give
$$\frac{a}{a - 3} = 6 - b,$$
and cross-multiply to give
$$a = (6 - b)(a - 3).$$

(c) These equations are equivalent.

(d) These equations are not equivalent. Cross-multiplying in the first equation gives
$$(2 + x)(2x + 5) = 9.$$

Solution to Activity 47

(a)
$$12 - 5q = q + 3$$
$$12 - 3 = q + 5q$$
$$9 = 6q$$
$$\tfrac{3}{2} = q$$
The solution is $q = \tfrac{3}{2}$.

(b)
$$3(x - 1) = 4(1 - x)$$
$$3x - 3 = 4 - 4x$$
$$3x + 4x = 4 + 3$$
$$7x = 7$$
$$x = 1$$
The solution is $x = 1$.

(c)
$$\frac{t - 3}{4} + 5t = 1$$
$$\frac{4(t - 3)}{4} + 4 \times 5t = 4$$
$$t - 3 + 20t = 4$$
$$t + 20t = 4 + 3$$
$$21t = 7$$
$$t = \tfrac{1}{3}$$
The solution is $t = \tfrac{1}{3}$.

(d)
$$\frac{3}{b} = \frac{2}{3b} - \frac{1}{3}$$
$$\frac{3 \times 3b}{b} = \frac{2 \times 3b}{3b} - \frac{3b}{3} \quad \text{(assuming } b \neq 0\text{)}$$
$$9 = 2 - b$$
$$7 = -b$$
$$-7 = b$$
The solution is $b = -7$.

(e)
$$2(A + 2) = \frac{A}{3} + 1$$
$$6(A + 2) = \frac{3A}{3} + 3$$
$$6A + 12 = A + 3$$
$$6A - A = 3 - 12$$
$$5A = -9$$
$$A = -\tfrac{9}{5}$$
The solution is $A = -\tfrac{9}{5}$.

(f)
$$\frac{1}{z + 1} + \frac{1}{5(z + 1)} = 1,$$
so assuming that $z \neq -1$,
$$\frac{5(z + 1)}{z + 1} + \frac{5(z + 1)}{5(z + 1)} = 5(z + 1)$$
$$5 + 1 = 5z + 5$$
$$1 = 5z$$
$$\tfrac{1}{5} = z$$
The solution is $z = \tfrac{1}{5}$.

(The fourth equation above is obtained by subtracting 5 from each side of the third equation.)

Solution to Activity 48

(a)
$$h + 1 = \frac{4h}{5}$$
$$5(h + 1) = 4h$$
$$5h + 5 = 4h$$
$$5h - 4h = -5$$
$$h = -5$$
The solution is $h = -5$.

(b)
$$\frac{2}{y} = \frac{3}{y + 2}$$
$$2(y + 2) = 3y \quad \text{(assuming } y \neq -2, 0\text{)}$$
$$2y + 4 = 3y$$
$$4 = 3y - 2y$$
$$4 = y$$
The solution is $y = 4$.

(c)
$$\frac{3}{2x - 1} = \frac{2}{3 - x}$$
$$3(3 - x) = 2(2x - 1) \quad \text{(assuming } x \neq \tfrac{1}{2}, 3\text{)}$$
$$9 - 3x = 4x - 2$$
$$9 + 2 = 4x + 3x$$
$$11 = 7x$$
$$\tfrac{11}{7} = x$$
The solution is $x = \tfrac{11}{7}$.

Solution to Activity 49

The problem with the 'proof' is that it involves dividing by $a - b$, which is equal to zero, since $a = b$.

Unit 1 Algebra

Solution to Activity 50

(a)
$$am = 2a + 3m$$
$$am - 3m = 2a$$
$$m(a - 3) = 2a$$
$$m = \frac{2a}{a - 3} \quad \text{(assuming } a \neq 3)$$

(b)
$$c = \tfrac{1}{3}(2 + 5d)$$
$$3c = 2 + 5d$$
$$3c - 2 = 5d$$
$$5d = 3c - 2$$
$$d = \tfrac{1}{5}(3c - 2)$$

(The alternative form $d = \dfrac{3c - 2}{5}$ is fine.)

(c)
$$\frac{Y}{X} = \frac{3Y + 2}{X + 1}$$
$$Y(X + 1) = X(3Y + 2) \quad \text{(assuming } X \neq 0, -1)$$
$$XY + Y = 3XY + 2X$$
$$Y = 3XY - XY + 2X$$
$$Y = 2XY + 2X$$
$$Y = 2X(Y + 1)$$
$$\frac{Y}{2(Y + 1)} = X \quad \text{(assuming } Y \neq -1)$$
$$X = \frac{Y}{2(Y + 1)}$$

(d)
$$a = \frac{b}{1 - 2c}$$
$$a(1 - 2c) = b \quad \text{(assuming } c \neq \tfrac{1}{2})$$
$$a - 2ac = b$$
$$a - b = 2ac$$
$$2ac = a - b$$
$$c = \frac{a - b}{2a} \quad \text{(assuming } a \neq 0)$$

(e)
$$A = \frac{2}{B} + AC$$
$$A - AC = \frac{2}{B}$$
$$B(A - AC) = 2 \quad \text{(assuming } B \neq 0)$$
$$AB(1 - C) = 2$$
$$B = \frac{2}{A(1 - C)} \quad \text{(assuming } A \neq 0, C \neq 1)$$

Solution to Activity 51

(a)
$$Q^3 = PR^2$$
$$Q = (PR^2)^{1/3}$$
$$Q = P^{1/3} R^{2/3}$$

(The forms $Q = (PR^2)^{1/3}$ and $Q = \sqrt[3]{PR^2}$ are also suitable final answers.)

(b)
$$h^{1/4} = \frac{2k^{1/2}}{m}$$
$$h = \left(\frac{2k^{1/2}}{m}\right)^4$$
$$h = \frac{16k^2}{m^4}$$

(c)
$$u^2 = v + w$$
$$u = \sqrt{v + w}$$

Solution to Activity 52

(a)
$$a^2 - 2b^2 = 3c^2$$
$$a^2 = 2b^2 + 3c^2$$
$$a = \sqrt{2b^2 + 3c^2}$$

(b)
$$a^2 = \frac{bt^2}{N}$$
$$a^2 N = bt^2$$
$$\frac{a^2 N}{b} = t^2$$
$$t^2 = \frac{a^2 N}{b}$$
$$t = \sqrt{\frac{a^2 N}{b}}$$
$$t = a\sqrt{\frac{N}{b}}$$

(c)
$$\left(\frac{r}{3s}\right)^5 = \sqrt{d}$$
$$\left(\frac{r}{3s}\right)^5 = d^{1/2}$$
$$\frac{r}{3s} = (d^{1/2})^{1/5}$$
$$r = 3sd^{1/10}$$

(d)
$$(4y)^{1/3} = x$$
$$4y = x^3$$
$$y = \tfrac{1}{4}x^3$$

(The alternative form $y = \dfrac{x^3}{4}$ is fine.)

Solution to Activity 53

(a) Here are some ways in which the solution could have been improved.

- It should be written in sentences.
- It needs some words of explanation.
- The three $\Rightarrow$ symbols at the left should be omitted.
- The fourth $\Rightarrow$ symbol (the one just before the number 1.75) should be replaced by an equals sign. Here, the author of the solution has worked out that $0.6 + 1.15$ is *equal* to 1.75, so an equals sign is the correct symbol.
- The equation
$$\sqrt{0.3621} = 0.6$$
should be changed to
$$\sqrt{0.3621} = 0.60 \text{ (to 2 d.p.)}$$
or
$$\sqrt{0.3621} \approx 0.60.$$

  The reason why either '(to 2 d.p.)' should be appended or the equals sign changed to '$\approx$' is that, without such a change, the equals sign is used incorrectly. This is because $\sqrt{0.3621}$ is *not equal* to 0.6. These numbers are only approximately equal.

  The reason why the rounded answer 0.6 should be written as 0.60 is to indicate that it has been rounded to *two* decimal places.

- The solution should explain what the variable h represents.
- The first equation, $h^2 + 98^2 = 1.15^2$, should not have been written at all. It is incorrect, because it has been obtained from Pythagoras' theorem by substituting in one length expressed in centimetres and another expressed in metres. Any lengths substituted into Pythagoras' theorem must be in the same units.
- Ideally the letter h should not be used to represent two different quantities, and it should certainly not be used in this way without explanation. (In most of the solution the letter h seems to represent the vertical height of the sloping pane of glass,

but in the final line it seems to represent the total height of the cold frame. This makes the solution difficult to understand.)

- The solution should finish with a clear answer to the question, including units.
- The lengths in the diagram should include units (or they should be expressed in the same units and it should be made clear what the units are).
- The diagram should relate more clearly to the question.
- Ideally, the $\therefore$ symbol should be replaced by a word, such as 'So'.

(b) Here is a better solution.

A side view of the cold frame is shown below.

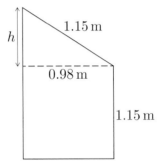

By Pythagoras' theorem, the vertical height h (in metres) of the slant pane of glass is given by
$$h^2 + 0.98^2 = 1.15^2.$$
Solving this equation (and using the fact that h is positive) gives
$$h^2 = 1.15^2 - 0.98^2$$
$$h^2 = 0.3621$$
$$h = \sqrt{0.3621}$$
$$h = 0.601\,747\ldots$$
Hence the height of the cold frame where it meets the wall is
$$(1.15 + 0.601\,747\ldots)\,\text{m}$$
$$= 1.751\,747\ldots\,\text{m}$$
$$= 1.75\,\text{m (to the nearest cm)}.$$

Acknowledgements

Grateful acknowledgement is made to the following sources:

Page 3: Tobin Copley / www.flickr.com

Page 3: Michael Maggs / This file is licensed under the Creative Commons Attribution-Share Alike Licence http://creativecommons.org/licenses/by-sa/3.0/

Page 13: Jeremy Norman's 'From Cave Paintings to the Internet', www.historyofinformation.com

Every effort has been made to contact copyright holders. If any have been inadvertently overlooked the publishers will be pleased to make the necessary arrangements at the first opportunity.

Graphs and equations

Introduction

Mathematics is often used to represent and analyse the relationship between two quantities. For example, consider a car travelling along a road from some starting point. There is a relationship between the time that has elapsed since the start of the journey and the distance the car has travelled. This relationship can be investigated mathematically.

The use of mathematics to represent and study real-life situations is known as **mathematical modelling**. When creating a **mathematical model**, we usually simplify the real-life situation in order to concentrate on the aspects that we think are the most important. This often allows the relationship between the quantities of interest to be expressed as an equation.

In the example of the travelling car, if the variable t is used to represent the time in hours since the car left its starting point, and the variable s is used to represent the distance in kilometres that the car has travelled since the start, then there is a relationship between the variables t and s. In this unit you will consider some cases where the relationship between the variables s and t is modelled by using a relatively simple equation. Note that mathematicians often use s to represent distance.

Every equation in two variables, whether it models a practical situation or not, represents a relationship between those variables. For example, the equation

$$y = 2x - 1 \tag{1}$$

represents a relationship between the variables x and y. Each particular value of x corresponds to a particular value of y.

A useful way to visualise a relationship between two variables is to draw its *graph*. If the relationship is specified by an equation, then this graph is called the graph of the equation. Figure 1 shows the graph of equation (1).

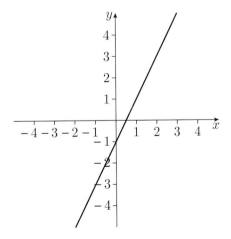

Figure 1 The graph of $y = 2x - 1$

Each point on the graph corresponds to a pair of values of x and y that are related by the equation. The graph of an equation in two variables can give new insights into the relationship between the variables. These complement those that you can obtain by using an algebraic approach.

In this unit you will revise two particular types of equation and their graphs. You have probably met these in your previous study of mathematics. They are covered here because they occur frequently in the later units of this module and you need to be confident in working with them, both graphically and algebraically. If you are familiar with them, then you may not wish to spend long reading the sections about them, but you should try the activities and ensure that you are not missing anything new to you, particularly in Subsection 2.4, which is important for the calculus that you'll study later. You will also begin to learn how to use the module computer algebra system to help you investigate mathematical problems.

In Section 1 you will revise the concepts of coordinates and graphs, and then in Sections 2 and 3 you will consider equations of the form

$$y = mx + c,$$

where x and y are variables, and m and c are constants. Equation (1) is of this form, with $m = 2$ and $c = -1$. The graph of every equation of this form is a straight line. You will see how such equations can be used to model some real-life situations, and revise how to solve pairs of such equations *simultaneously*.

In Section 4, you will consider equations of the form

$$y = ax^2 + bx + c,$$

where again x and y are variables, and a, b and c are constants, with $a \neq 0$. For example, the equation

$$y = x^2 - 2 \tag{2}$$

is of this form, with $a = 1$, $b = 0$ and $c = -2$. The graph of every equation of this form has a particular curved shape called a *parabola*. Figure 2 shows the parabola that is the graph of equation (2).

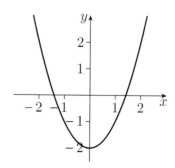

Figure 2   The graph of $y = x^2 - 2$

Equations of this form can be used to model some types of real-life situations, such as the motion of an object falling under the influence of gravity. To find the values of x where a graph such as that in Figure 2 crosses the x-axis you have to solve a *quadratic equation*, and you will revise various techniques for solving equations of this type.

Finally, in Section 5 you will learn how to use the module computer algebra system to plot the graphs of various equations in two variables, manipulate expressions and solve equations.

1 Plotting graphs

In this section you'll revise the idea of the graph of an equation, and practise plotting graphs using tables of values. We begin with a brief reminder about *coordinates*.

1.1 Coordinates

The location of each point in a plane (that is, on a flat surface) can be specified using a pair of **coordinates** that give the position of the point relative to two *axes* at right angles to each other, as illustrated in Figure 3.

The horizontal and vertical axes are usually labelled x and y, respectively, and are referred to as the **x-axis** and the **y-axis**. The point where the axes intersect is called the **origin**, and is sometimes labelled O. Each axis is drawn with an arrowhead to indicate the positive direction (the direction in which the numbers increase), and is usually marked with numbers to show the scale.

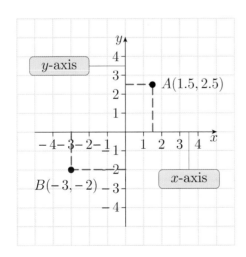

Figure 3   Coordinates

The coordinates of a point are written in brackets, separated by a comma, like this: $(1, 2)$. The first number is the number on the x-axis directly below or above the point, and is called the **x-coordinate**. The second number is the number on the y-axis directly to the left or right of the point, and is called the **y-coordinate**. For example, Figure 3 shows two points, A and B, with coordinates $(1.5, 2.5)$ and $(-3, -2)$, respectively.

This method of specifying the position of points is known as a *rectangular* or *Cartesian* coordinate system. The plane in which the axes and the points lie is sometimes called the **Cartesian plane**, the **x,y-plane**, the **coordinate plane** or, when there is no ambiguity, simply the **plane**. The axes are sometimes referred to as the **coordinate axes**.

> The adjective *Cartesian* comes from the surname of the French mathematician and philosopher René Descartes (1596–1650). He is credited with being the first person to realise that the shapes of curves and surfaces can be studied using algebra. Poor health at school led to his life-long habit of never rising from bed until 11 o'clock in the morning. He later suggested this was an essential requirement for doing good mathematics!

Although x and y are the standard labels for graph axes, other labels can be used. For example, if a graph represents the relationship between the variables s and t, then these letters are used to label the axes. You can also refer to the horizontal and vertical axes, and the horizontal and vertical coordinates, and adjust the way you describe other quantities accordingly. Whatever the axis labels are, the first number in a pair of coordinates is always the position along the horizontal axis, and the second number is always the position along the vertical axis.

The position of a point in a plane can be marked with a dot, as in Figure 3, or with a small cross. It can be left unlabelled, or it can be labelled in any of various ways: with its coordinates, or with a letter, or with both, as in Figure 3.

1.2   Graphs of equations

Suppose that you have an equation in x and y, such as

$$y = 2x - 1, \quad y = x^2 + x + 3 \quad \text{or} \quad x^2 + y^2 = 1.$$

A point (x, y) is said to **satisfy** the equation if the equation is true for the point's values of x and y.

Example 1   *Checking whether a point satisfies an equation*

Show that the point $(3, 2)$ satisfies the equation $y = x^2 - 2x - 1$.

Solution

🔍 Substitute the x- and y-coordinates of the point into the left-hand side and right-hand side of the equation, and check that the two sides are equal. 💬

When $x = 3$ and $y = 2$,

$$\text{LHS} = y = 2$$

and

$$\text{RHS} = x^2 - 2x - 1 = 3^2 - 2 \times 3 - 1 = 9 - 6 - 1 = 2.$$

The LHS and RHS are equal, so the point $(3, 2)$ satisfies the equation.

The method in Example 1 is the same as that in Example 22 in Unit 1.

Activity 1   *Checking whether points satisfy an equation*

Determine whether the following points satisfy the equation $y - 2 = 3x$.

(a) $(6, 20)$ (b) $(-2, 8)$

You know from Unit 1 that if a pair of values of x and y satisfy an equation in x and y, then they also satisfy any rearranged version of the equation. This means that the collection of points that satisfy an equation does not change when the equation is rearranged. For example, the points that satisfy the equation $y - 2x = -1$ are the same as the points that satisfy the equation $y = 2x - 1$.

Usually, for any particular equation in x and y, the points that satisfy the equation are the points that lie on a particular line or curve. If the equation has the property that it can be rearranged to express y as a formula in terms of x (so each value of x determines just one value of y), then the line or curve is called the **graph** of the equation. The word 'graph' is also used to refer to the whole diagram, including the line or curve and the coordinate axes.

A simple way to get an idea of the shape of the graph of an equation is to choose a few values for x, substitute them into the equation to find the corresponding values of y, plot the resulting points, and draw a smooth line or curve through them. This is illustrated in the next example. It is convenient to use a *table of values* to record the values of x and y.

Example 2 *Plotting the graph of an equation*

Plot the graph of the equation $y = \dfrac{x}{2} + 2$.

Solution

🔍 Construct a table of values. Choose some equally-spaced values of x, and work out the corresponding values of y by substituting into the equation. For example, substituting $x = -2$ into the equation gives $y = (-2)/2 + 2 = -1 + 2 = 1$. 💬

A table of values for the equation $y = x/2 + 2$ is as follows.

x	-2	-1	0	1	2
y	1	1.5	2	2.5	3

🔍 Draw the axes and plot the points. They seem to lie in a straight line, so draw the straight line through them. Label the line with its equation, either on the graph or in a title. 💬

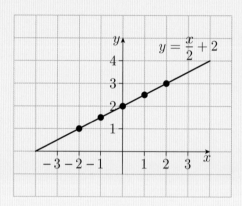

We will consider why the points in Example 2 lie on a straight line in Subsection 2.2.

Notice that the graph drawn in Example 2 has been extended beyond the points that were calculated. This is because every straight line continues infinitely far in each direction. A graph can show only a small, finite part of a line. A finite part of a line, such as the part between two particular points, is called a **line segment**. Also notice that the graph was plotted with x on the horizontal axis and y on the vertical axis. When you plot the graph of an equation in which one variable y is expressed in terms of another variable x, the variable x is always on the horizontal axis and the variable y on the vertical axis.

You can practise using a table of values to plot a graph in the next activity. Remember that whenever you draw a graph, you should label it with its equation, either on the graph or in a title.

Activity 2   *Plotting the graph of an equation*

Complete the table of values below for the equation

$$y = x^2 + 2x + 2,$$

and hence plot the graph of this equation.

x	−2	−1	0	1	2
y					

When you plot the graph of an equation using a table of values alone, you cannot be absolutely sure that the graph is correct. This is because you do not know what happens between the points that you plotted and to each side of them. For example, consider the equation $y = 5x^3 - x^5$. A table of values for this equation, using integer values of x from −2 to 2, is given in Table 1.

Table 1   A table of values for $y = 5x^3 - x^5$

x	−2	−1	0	1	2
y	−8	−4	0	4	8

These points lie on a straight line, as shown in Figure 4(a). However this line is *not* the graph of the equation $y = 5x^3 - x^5$. A correct graph is shown in Figure 4(b).

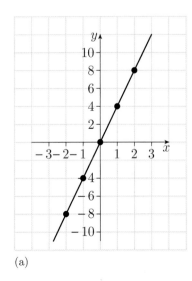

(a)

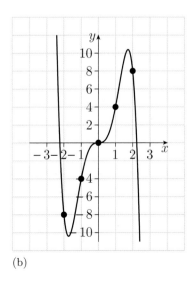

(b)

Figure 4   (a) The straight line through the points in Table 1
(b) the graph of $y = 5x^3 - x^5$, which goes through the same points

123

Because you can get the wrong idea about the shape of a graph from an unfortunate choice of plotted points, it's helpful to get to know the general shapes of the graphs of some standard types of equation, and learn how to sketch such graphs without using tables of values. You'll do this for various types of equation throughout this module, starting in Subsection 2.2 with equations whose graphs are straight lines.

2 Straight-line graphs

In this section you'll revise how to recognise equations that have straight-line graphs, and how to sketch such graphs from their equations. First, it's helpful to revise some basic properties of lines. Note that, in mathematics, the word 'line' is generally used to mean a straight line.

2.1 Gradients and intercepts of straight lines

Gradients

The *gradient* of a straight line is a measure of how steep it is. To understand what gradient means, imagine tracing your pen tip along a straight line. The **gradient** (or **slope**) of the line is the number of units that your pen tip moves *up* for every one unit that it moves *to the right*. For example, you can see that the line in Figure 5(a) has gradient 2.

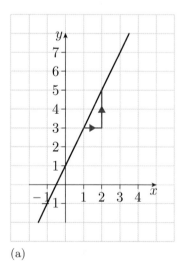

(a)

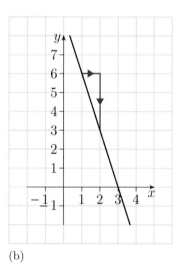

(b)

Figure 5 Straight lines with gradients (a) 2 (b) −3

If you imagine tracing your pen tip along the line in Figure 5(b), you can see that it will move *down*, rather than up, as it moves to the right. It will move down by 3 units for every one unit that it moves to the right. A movement of 3 units down can be thought of as a movement of −3 units *up.* So your pen tip moves up by -3 units for every one unit that it moves to the right, and hence the gradient of this line is -3.

It's helpful to remember the following facts.

> A line that slopes *up* from left to right has a positive gradient.
>
> A line that slopes *down* from left to right has a negative gradient.

Activity 3   *Thinking about gradients*

By thinking about moving your pen tip along each of the lines below, and counting how many units it would move up or down for each unit it moves to the right, write down the gradients of the following lines.

(a)
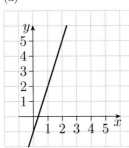

(b)
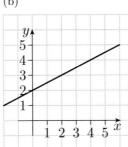

(c)
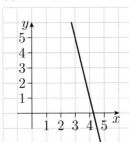

(d)
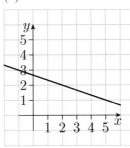

(e)
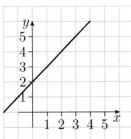

(f)
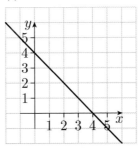

Lines with large positive or negative gradients, such as $10, 50, -10$ or -50, are steeper than those with smaller positive or negative gradients, such as $1, 0.5, -0.5$ or -1. This fact can be expressed more neatly by using the idea of the **magnitude** of a number, which is its value without its minus sign, if it has one. For example, the magnitudes of 5 and -5 are both 5. The magnitude of a number is also called its **modulus** or its **absolute value**. The greater the magnitude of the gradient of a line, the steeper the line.

When the coordinate axes have *equal scales* (that is, when the distance representing one unit is the same for both the horizontal and vertical axes), a line with gradient 1 or -1 makes an angle of $45°$ with the horizontal axis, as shown in Figure 6. So a line whose gradient has magnitude greater than 1 makes an angle of more than $45°$ with the horizontal axis, and a line whose gradient has magnitude less than 1 makes an angle of less than $45°$ with the horizontal axis. Remember, though, that these facts are true *only if the coordinate axes have equal scales*.

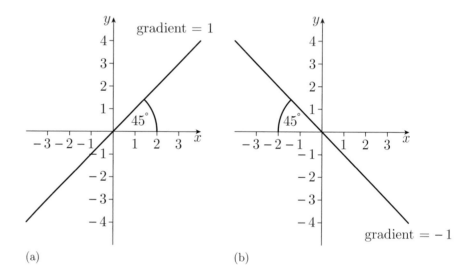

(a)   (b)

Figure 6   Lines with gradient (a) 1 (b) -1

Calculating gradients

You can calculate the gradient of a straight line by choosing any two points on the line, and proceeding as follows.

First you choose one of the two points (it doesn't matter which) to be the 'first point', and the other point to be the 'second point'. Then you find the number of units by which x increases as you trace your pen tip from the first point to the second point. This is known as the **run** from the first point to the second point. You also find the number of units by which y increases as you trace your pen tip from the first point to the second point. This is known as the **rise** from the first point to the second point. If x or y (or both) actually *decreases* as you trace your pen tip from the first point to the second point, then the run or rise (or both) is negative.

For example, in Figure 7(a) the run is 4 and the rise is 2, whereas in Figure 7(b) the run is -1 and the rise is 3.

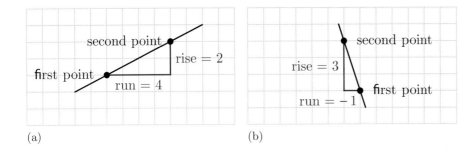

(a)   (b)

Figure 7   The run and rise from one point to another

Once you have found the run and rise from the first point to the second point, you can calculate the gradient as follows:

$$\text{gradient} = \frac{\text{rise}}{\text{run}}.$$

For example, the gradient of the line in Figure 7(a) is

$$\frac{\text{rise}}{\text{run}} = \frac{2}{4} = \frac{1}{2},$$

and the gradient of the line in Figure 7(b) is

$$\frac{\text{rise}}{\text{run}} = \frac{3}{-1} = -3.$$

This method for calculating the gradient of a line can be expressed as a formula in terms of the coordinates of the two points on the line. Let's denote the first and second points by (x_1, y_1) and (x_2, y_2), respectively.

Here x_1 and x_2 are particular values of x, and y_1 and y_2 are particular values of y. Mathematicians often use subscripts in this way to indicate particular values of variables. When you work with subscripts, be careful not to confuse x_2 with x^2, for example.

With this notation,

$$\text{run} = x_2 - x_1 \quad \text{and} \quad \text{rise} = y_2 - y_1.$$

So

$$\text{gradient} = \frac{\text{rise}}{\text{run}} = \frac{y_2 - y_1}{x_2 - x_1}.$$

The gradient of a straight line

The gradient of the straight line through the points (x_1, y_1) and (x_2, y_2), where $x_1 \neq x_2$, is given by

$$\text{gradient} = \frac{y_2 - y_1}{x_2 - x_1}.$$

Although it doesn't matter which point on the line you choose to be (x_1, y_1) and which to be (x_2, y_2) when you use the formula above, it is important to take them the same way round in both the numerator and the denominator.

Activity 4   *Using the formula for gradient*

Consider the following diagram.

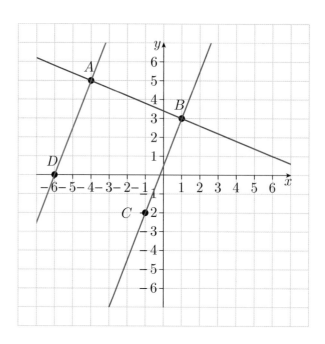

(a) Write down the coordinates of the points A, B, C and D.

(b) Use the formula for gradient to calculate the gradients of the lines that pass through the following pairs of points.

(i) A and B (ii) A and D (iii) B and C

Gradients of horizontal and vertical lines

The gradient of a horizontal line is zero. This is because the gradient is the rise divided by the run, and the rise between any two points on a horizontal line is zero, as illustrated in Figure 8(a). On the other hand, the gradient of a vertical line is *undefined*. This is because, again, the gradient is the rise divided by the run, but the run between any two points on a vertical line is zero, as illustrated in Figure 8(b). Since it is not possible to divide by zero, the gradient of a vertical line does not exist.

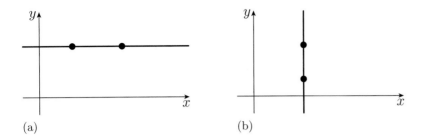

(a)   (b)

Figure 8   (a) The rise between two points on a horizontal line is zero
(b) the run between two points on a vertical line is zero

Intercepts

The value of x where a line crosses the x-axis is called its **x-intercept**, and the value of y where it crosses the y-axis is called its **y-intercept**. For example, in Figure 9 the x-intercept is -3 and the y-intercept is 2.

Some mathematicians use the word 'intercept' to describe the *point* at which a line crosses an axis, rather than the value of the x- or y-coordinate there. They would say that the x- and y-intercepts in Figure 9 are $(-3, 0)$ and $(0, 2)$.

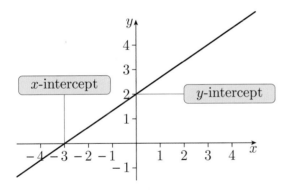

Figure 9   The x- and y-intercepts of a line

2.2 Straight lines and their equations

Let's now consider which equations in x and y are the equations of straight lines. First consider the simple equation $y = 2x$. The points that satisfy this equation are those whose y-coordinate is twice their x-coordinate. These are the points that lie on the straight line through the origin with gradient 2, as illustrated in Figure 10(a).

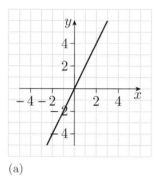

(a)

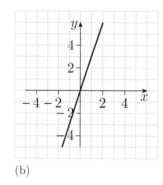

(b)

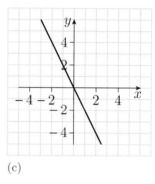

(c)

Figure 10   Lines through the origin with gradient (a) 2 (b) 3 (c) -2

Similarly, the points (x, y) that satisfy the equations $y = 3x$ and $y = -2x$ are the points that lie on the straight lines through the origin with gradients 3 and -2, respectively, as you can see in Figure 10(b) and (c).

In general, for any value of m, the points (x, y) that satisfy the equation $y = mx$ are the points that lie on the straight line through the origin with gradient m.

It is traditional in the UK to use the letter m to represent gradient, though the reason is no longer known! Some countries traditionally use other letters, such as s or k. The earliest known use of the letter m for gradient is by the Italian mathematician Vincenzo Riccati in 1757. In addition to making important contributions to several areas of mathematics, Riccati taught Italian literature and Latin, and was responsible for developing flood control measures around Venice and Bologna.

Vincenzo Riccati (1707–75)

Now consider the equation $y = 2x + 1$. Note that if a point satisfies $y = 2x$, then adding 1 to its y-coordinate gives a point that satisfies $y = 2x + 1$.

So the points that satisfy the equation $y = 2x + 1$ are all the points on the line that is obtained by moving the line in Figure 10(a) vertically up by

1 unit, as shown in Figure 11. Moving the line up by this amount changes its y-intercept from 0 to 1.

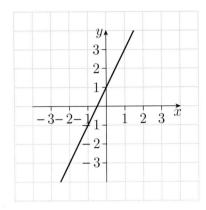

Figure 11   The line with equation $y = 2x + 1$

In general, for any constant c the graph of the equation $y = mx + c$ is obtained by moving the graph of the equation $y = mx$ vertically by c units. So we have the following fact.

Graphs of equations of the form $y = mx + c$

The graph of the equation $y = mx + c$ is the straight line with gradient m and y-intercept c.

It follows that the graph of any equation that can be rearranged into the form $y = mx + c$ is a straight line. For example, the graph of the equation $3x + 2y - 4 = 0$ is a straight line, since this equation can be rearranged as $y = -\frac{3}{2}x + 2$. Any equation that's of the form $y = mx + c$, or that can be rearranged into this form, is called a **linear equation** in the variables x and y. (You met the general definition of *linear equation* in Unit 1, where you revised how to solve linear equations in one unknown.)

When the equation of a line is written in the form $y = mx + c$, it's straightforward to 'read off' the gradient and the y-intercept. The gradient is the coefficient of x, and the y-intercept is the constant term. For example, the line $y = -\frac{3}{2}x + 2$ has gradient $-\frac{3}{2}$ and y-intercept 2.

To find the x-intercept of a line, you need to find the value of x for which $y = 0$. Here is an example.

Example 3   *Finding the x-intercept of a line from its equation*

Find the x-intercept of the line with equation $y = 4x - 3$.

Solution

🔍 The x-intercept is the value of x when $y = 0$. 💬

Putting $y = 0$ gives

$$4x - 3 = 0.$$

Solving this equation gives

$$4x = 3$$
$$x = \tfrac{3}{4}.$$

Hence the x-intercept is $\tfrac{3}{4}$.

🔍 Leave the answer as a fraction. 💬

(Check: substituting $x = \tfrac{3}{4}$ into $y = 4x - 3$ gives $y = 4 \times \tfrac{3}{4} - 3 = 0$, as expected.)

As illustrated in Example 3, if the x-intercept, y-intercept or gradient of a straight line is a fraction, then there is no need to express it as a decimal.

Activity 5   *Finding the gradients and intercepts from equations of lines*

Find the gradient, and x- and y-intercepts, of each of the following lines.

(a) $y = -4x + 3$ (b) $3y - x + 2 = 0$

Equations of horizontal and vertical lines

You saw earlier that the gradient of a horizontal line is zero. So the horizontal line with x-intercept c has equation $y = 0x + c$; that is, $y = c$. For example, the horizontal line in Figure 12(a) has y-intercept 3, so its equation is $y = 3$.

An alternative way to think of this fact is to notice that every point on the line in Figure 12(a) has y-coordinate 3, so the equation $y = 3$ describes each point on the line. It is therefore the equation of the line.

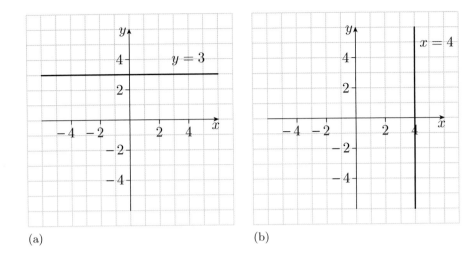

(a)   (b)

Figure 12   (a) A horizontal line (b) a vertical line

What about vertical lines? A vertical line has no gradient, so it doesn't have an equation of the form $y = mx + c$. Vertical lines are the only lines that do not have equations of this form.

However, every point on a vertical line has the same x-coordinate, so the line has an equation of the form $x = d$. The constant d is the x-intercept. For example, consider the vertical line shown in Figure 12(b). Every point on this line has x-coordinate 4, so the equation $x = 4$ describes each point on the line and is therefore the equation of the line.

> **Equations of horizontal and vertical lines**
>
> The horizontal line with y-intercept c has equation $y = c$.
>
> The vertical line with x-intercept d has equation $x = d$.

In particular, the equation of the x-axis is $y = 0$, and the equation of the y-axis is $x = 0$.

Drawing a line from its equation

In Section 1 you saw how to plot the graph of an equation by finding several points that satisfy the equation, and drawing a smooth line or curve through them. If you can recognise an equation as the equation of a straight line, then to draw this line you just need to find *two* points that satisfy the equation, and draw the straight line through them.

One way to find two suitable points is to choose two values of x, and use the equation to find the corresponding values of y. You should try to choose values of x that are reasonably far apart and that lead to simple calculations. For example, if the equation is $y = \frac{1}{3}x + 2$ then you might choose $x = 0$ and $x = 3$, to avoid fractions. An alternative way to find two suitable points is to find the x- and y-intercepts.

Drawing a horizontal or vertical line from its equation is even more straightforward. To draw the line with equation $y = c$, you just mark the y-intercept c and draw the horizontal line through it. Similarly, to draw the line with equation $x = d$, you just mark the x-intercept d and draw the vertical line through it.

Activity 6   *Drawing lines from their equations*

Draw the straight lines with the following equations.

(a) $y = \frac{1}{3}x + 2$ (b) $y = -2x + 4$ (c) $y = \frac{7}{2}$ (d) $x = -3$

Finding the equation of a straight line

Every straight line that you can draw in a plane, with the exception of any vertical line, has a gradient and a y-intercept, and hence has an equation of the form $y = mx + c$.

If you know the gradient and the y-intercept of the line, then you can immediately write down the equation of the line. For example, the line with gradient 3 and y-intercept -5 has equation $y = 3x - 5$.

Sometimes, however, you might know different information about a line. The next example demonstrates a method for finding the equation of a line when you know its gradient and a point on it.

Example 4   *Finding the equation of a line from its gradient and a point on it: Method 1*

Find the equation of the line that has gradient -6 and passes through the point $(-1, 4)$.

Solution

🔍 A straight line has an equation of the form $y = mx + c$, where m is the gradient. 💬

The equation is of the form $y = -6x + c$.

🔍 The point $(-1, 4)$ lies on the line, so this point must satisfy the equation. 💬

Substituting $x = -1$ and $y = 4$ into the equation gives

$$4 = -6 \times (-1) + c$$
$$4 = 6 + c.$$

Solve this equation to find c.

$$-2 = c$$

So the equation of the line is $y = -6x - 2$.

(Check: substituting $x = -1$ into the equation $y = -6x - 2$ gives $y = -6 \times (-1) - 2 = 4$, so the point $(-1, 4)$ lies on the line, as expected.)

Here's an alternative way to find the equation of a straight line from its gradient and a point on it. Suppose that the gradient is m and the point is (x_1, y_1). If (x, y) is any other point on the line, then, by the formula for the gradient on page 127,

$$m = \frac{y - y_1}{x - x_1}. \tag{3}$$

Rearranging this equation gives

$$y - y_1 = m(x - x_1). \tag{4}$$

Equation (3) does not hold when $(x, y) = (x_1, y_1)$, since that would require division by zero, but it does hold for all other points (x, y) on the line. However, the rearranged equation, equation (4), holds for *all* points (x, y) on the line, including $(x, y) = (x_1, y_1)$, since for this point both sides are equal to zero. So equation (4) is the equation of the line. This fact is summarised below.

> The equation of the straight line with gradient m that passes through the point (x_1, y_1) is
>
> $$y - y_1 = m(x - x_1).$$

Example 5   *Finding the equation of a line from its gradient and a point on it: Method 2.*

Find the equation of the line that has gradient -2 and passes through the point $(1, 4)$.

Solution

Substitute $m = -2$, $x_1 = 1$ and $y_1 = 4$ into the equation in the box above, and simplify it.

The equation of the line is

$$y - 4 = -2(x - 1).$$

It can be simplified as follows:

$$y - 4 = -2x + 2$$
$$y = -2x + 6.$$

So the equation of the line is $y = -2x + 6$.

(Check: substituting $x = 1$ into $y = -2x + 6$ gives
$y = -2 \times 1 + 6 = 4$, so the point $(1, 4)$ lies on the line, as expected.)

Sometimes you might want to find the equation of a line from the coordinates of two points on it. If the two points have the same x-coordinate or the same y-coordinate, then you can immediately write down the equation of the horizontal or vertical line that they lie on. Otherwise, you can use the coordinates of the two points to calculate the gradient of the line, and then apply the method of Example 4 or Example 5.

Activity 7   *Finding the equations of lines*

Find the equations of the following lines.

(a) The line through the point $(2, 1)$ with gradient 3

(b) The line through the points $(2, 3)$ and $(4, 5)$

(c) The line with y-intercept 3 and gradient 2

(d) The line with x-intercept 2 and gradient -3

(e) The vertical line that passes through the point $(1, 0)$

(f) The line through the points $(-2, 3)$ and $(4, 3)$

2.3 Parallel and perpendicular lines

Two straight lines are **parallel** if they never cross, even when extended infinitely far in each direction, as illustrated in Figure 13.

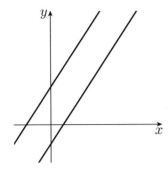

Figure 13   Two parallel lines

In Activity 4 on page 128, the line through the points A and D is parallel to the line through the points B and C. You may have noticed from your solution to this activity that these two lines have the same gradient. In general, saying that two non-vertical lines are parallel means the same as saying that they have the same gradient. Any two vertical lines are also parallel.

Two lines are **perpendicular** if they are at right angles to each other. You'd expect the gradients of two perpendicular lines to be related in some way – but how? To work this out, consider any two perpendicular lines that are not parallel to the axes, as illustrated in Figure 14.

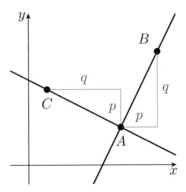

Figure 14   Two perpendicular lines

Let A be the point where the lines cross, let B be any point that lies on one of the lines and is above and to the right of A, and let C be the point on the other line that is obtained by rotating B anticlockwise through a quarter turn about A, as shown in Figure 14.

Let's denote the run from A to B by p, and the rise from A to B by q. Both p and q are positive numbers. If you rotate the right-angled triangle with hypotenuse AB in Figure 14 anticlockwise through a quarter turn about A, then it will lie exactly on top of the right-angled triangle with hypotenuse AC. It follows that the run from A to C is $-q$ (it's negative because C lies to the left of A), and the rise from A to C is p.

Hence

$$\text{gradient of the line through } A \text{ and } B = \frac{q}{p},$$

and

$$\text{gradient of the line through } A \text{ and } C = \frac{p}{-q} = -\frac{p}{q}.$$

Multiplying these two gradients together gives

$$\frac{q}{p} \times \left(-\frac{p}{q}\right) = -1.$$

So we have the following fact.

> **Gradients of perpendicular lines**
>
> The gradients of any two perpendicular lines (not parallel to the axes) have product -1.

Note that if two perpendicular lines are parallel to the axes, then one of them is parallel to the y-axis and hence has undefined gradient.

> **Activity 8**   *Finding the equation of a line perpendicular to another line*
>
> (a) Find the gradient of a line perpendicular to the line $y = 3x + 5$.
> (b) Hence find the equation of the line that is perpendicular to $y = 3x + 5$ and passes through the point $(2, 1)$.

2.4   Applications of straight-line graphs

As mentioned in the introduction to this unit, the relationship between two real-life quantities can often be modelled by an equation in two variables. If the equation representing this relationship is of the form $y = mx + c$, and hence has a straight-line graph, then we say that the model is **linear**.

In this subsection, you'll look at some examples of linear models, and practise working with them. It's particularly important that you work carefully through this subsection, as it underpins *calculus*, which you'll start studying in Unit 6.

First, consider the graph in Figure 15, which represents the journey of a car along a road. It shows the relationship between the time that has elapsed since the car began its journey, and the distance that it has travelled since the start of the journey. The axes of the graph are labelled with 'time' and 'distance', as well as with t and s, the letters chosen to represent these quantities. The units in which each quantity is measured, kilometres (abbreviated to km) and hours (abbreviated to h), are also included. A graph like this, in which distance is plotted against time, is known as a **distance–time graph**.

The variables s and t are often used for distance and time, respectively, so you need to be careful to avoid possible confusion if the unit s (seconds) is used for time.

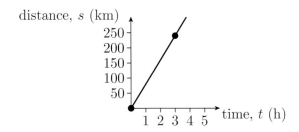

Figure 15   A distance–time graph for the journey of a car

This graph includes only non-negative values of t and s, as the times elapsed and the distances travelled since the start of the journey are all non-negative.

You can calculate the gradient of the graph in Figure 15 by choosing two points on it in the usual way. The two points marked on the graph have coordinates $(0, 0)$ and $(3, 240)$, so

$$\text{gradient} = \frac{(240 - 0)\,\text{km}}{(3 - 0)\,\text{h}} = 80\,\text{km/h}.$$

Notice that, because the numbers on the axes of the graph have units, the gradient also has units. Since the rise is measured in kilometres (km) and the run is measured in hours (h), the units of the gradient are kilometres divided by hours, that is, kilometres per hour (km/h). In general, the units of the gradient of a graph are the units on the vertical axis divided by the units on the horizontal axis.

The units are shown in the calculation above to demonstrate this fact, but in general it's not necessary to include units in the calculation of a gradient. You just need to state the units in the final answer.

Units such as km/h, which are obtained by combining simpler units (in this case km and h), are called **derived units**.

The fact that the gradient of the graph in Figure 15 is 80 km/h tells you that the distance travelled by the car changes by 80 kilometres for each hour of the journey. That is, it tells you that the car travels 80 kilometres in each hour, or, in other words, that the speed of the car is 80 kilometres per hour. The fact that the graph is a straight line tells you that the car is travelling at a *constant* speed.

In general, if a graph is a straight line, then it means that the quantity on the vertical axis is changing at a *constant rate* with respect to the quantity on the horizontal axis. The gradient of the graph tells you how many units the quantity on the vertical axis changes for every one unit that the quantity on the horizontal axis changes. In other words, the gradient of the graph is the **rate of change** of the quantity on the vertical axis **with respect to** the quantity on the horizontal axis. So, for example, the gradient of a distance–time graph is the rate of change of distance with respect to time, which is speed.

Here's another example of a linear model. Consider the graph in Figure 16. It represents the change in the concentration of a chemical as it undergoes a chemical reaction over time. The concentration is denoted by c and measured in a unit called the *molar* (M), and time is denoted by t and measured in seconds (s). A chemical reaction in which the concentration falls linearly, as in Figure 16, is called a *zero-order* reaction.

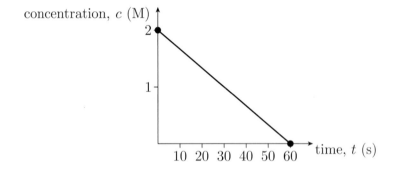

Figure 16 The relationship between the concentration of a reacting chemical and time

The gradient of the graph in Figure 16 is negative, because the concentration of the chemical *decreases* as time goes on. Notice that the graph includes values of t only between 0 and 60, and the corresponding values of c. This is because the times since the beginning of the reaction are all positive, and after 60 seconds the concentration of the chemical has decreased to 0, so the model does not apply for later times.

The gradient of the graph in Figure 16 can be calculated as follows. The two points marked in Figure 16 are $(0, 2)$ and $(60, 0)$, so

$$\text{gradient} = \frac{0 - 2}{60 - 0} = \frac{-2}{60} = -\frac{1}{30} \text{ M/s}.$$

This tells you that the rate of change of the concentration with respect to time is approximately -0.03 M/s. In other words, in each second that passes, the concentration of the chemical decreases by approximately 0.03 M.

In the next activity, you're asked to find and interpret the gradients of two straight-line graphs.

Activity 9   *Calculating gradients of real-life graphs*

For each of the graphs below, find the gradient in appropriate units and explain what the gradient represents.

Graph (a) represents the relationship between the number n of people attending a meeting and the cost C (in £) of hiring the meeting room (including lunch and refreshments for the attendees).

Graph (b) represents the relationship between the price p (in £/kg) charged for building sand and the quantity q (in kg) purchased by a customer.

(a)   (b)

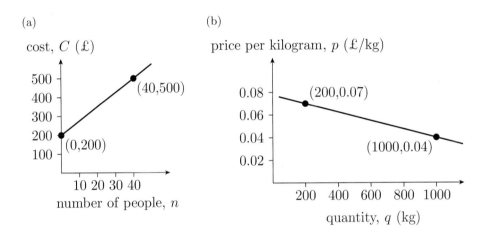

The intercepts of real-life graphs often have practical interpretations too. For example, look back at the graph in Figure 16, which represents the decrease in the concentration of a reacting chemical over time. The intercept on the c-axis is $2\,\mathrm{M}$, which is the concentration of the chemical at the start of the chemical reaction. The intercept on the t-axis is $60\,\mathrm{s}$, which is the time at which the concentration of the chemical falls to zero.

Activity 10   *Interpreting intercepts of real-life graphs*

Look back at the graph in Activity 9(a). State the vertical intercept, and explain what it means.

The intercepts of real-life graphs don't always have useful meanings. For example, look back at the graph in Activity 9(b). Notice that it has been drawn as a line segment that doesn't cross either of the axes. This is because the model isn't valid for the values of q and p that don't correspond to points on this line segment. In particular, it isn't valid when $q = 0$ and $p = 0$, so the intercepts have no meaning in this case.

When you're working with a linear model, it's usually helpful to use the equation of the associated straight-line graph. You can often find the equation using the methods that you practised earlier in this section – you use the variables that represent the real-life quantities in place of the standard variables x and y. For example, for the distance–time graph in Figure 15, the variables on the horizontal and vertical axes are t and s, respectively, so you use t in place of x and s in place of y. The gradient of this graph is $80\,\text{km/h}$ and the y-intercept is $0\,\text{km}$, so the equation of the graph is

$$s = 80t. \tag{5}$$

An alternative way to obtain the equation of the graph in this case is to simply use the familiar relationship

distance travelled = constant speed × time elapsed.

When you use relationships like this, it's important to remember that they're valid only if the units in which the quantities are measured are *consistent*. For example, for the relationship above, the units in which time is measured must be the same as the units of time contained within the derived units in which speed is measured. Here are some examples of consistent sets of units:

- time in seconds, speed in metres per second, distance in metres
- time in minutes, speed in metres per minute, distance in metres
- time in hours, speed in kilometres per hour, distance in kilometres.

The units used for the quantities in equation (5) are consistent since the number 80 represents the speed of the car in km/h, the variable t represents time in hours, and the variable s represents distance in km.

As another example of consistent units, consider the equation representing the line in Figure 16 on page 140, which is

$$c = -\frac{1}{30}t + 2. \tag{6}$$

The units used for the quantities in this equation are consistent since all three terms, c, $-\frac{1}{30}t$ and 2, have the same units, namely molars (M). Note that the gradient $-\frac{1}{30}$ is measured in M/s, and the time t in seconds.

Activity 11 *Finding equations of real-life graphs*

(a) Using your answers to Activity 9, find the equations of the graphs in Activity 9.

(b) Use these equations to find the following.

   (i) The maximum number of people that can be accommodated in the meeting room, if the maximum budget for the meeting is £560.

   (ii) The price per kilogram of building sand that corresponds to a quantity of 500 kg.

Displacement and velocity

When you're considering a moving object, such as a car travelling along a road, it's often helpful to consider not the *distance* that the object has travelled, but its *displacement* from a particular point.

To see what this means, consider any object that's moving along a straight line – we'll consider only motion along a straight line here, for simplicity. We choose any point on the straight line to be a reference point and we choose one of the two directions along the line to be the positive direction. Then the object's **displacement** from the reference point is its distance from that point, with a positive or negative sign to indicate the direction from that point.

For example, consider the straight line in Figure 17. The reference point has been chosen to be the point marked R, and the positive direction has been chosen to be rightwards. An object at position A has a displacement of 3 cm, while an object at position B has a displacement of -5 cm.

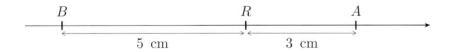

Figure 17 Positions along a straight line

Imagine placing your pen tip at R, moving it to A, and then to B. The *distance moved* by the pen tip is the distance from R to A, plus the distance from A to B, which is $3\,\text{cm} + 8\,\text{cm} = 11\,\text{cm}$. However, the final *displacement* of the pen tip is -5 cm, since it is at B.

To see how the idea of displacement works in practice, suppose that a car is travelling along a straight road, and that a particular reference point R

on the road and direction along it have been chosen, as illustrated in
Figure 18.

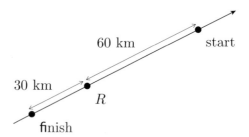

Figure 18   A reference point and a direction on a straight road

The graph in Figure 19 shows the relationship between the time that has
elapsed since the start of the car's journey, and the car's displacement
from the reference point. You can see that the car has displacements of
60 km and −30 km at the start and end of its journey, respectively, and
that it drives past the reference point 1 hour after the start of its journey.
A graph like the one in Figure 19, in which displacement is plotted against
time, is known as a **displacement–time graph**.

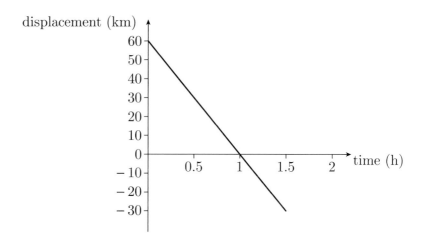

Figure 19   A displacement–time graph for a car's journey

The gradient of the graph in Figure 19 is −60 km/h. This tells you that in
each hour the displacement of the car changes by −60 km. In other words,
the car is moving at a speed of 60 km/h in the negative direction, that is,
in the direction opposite to the direction chosen as the positive direction in
Figure 18.

The gradient of the displacement–time graph of an object moving in a
straight line is called the *velocity* of the object. In other words, the
velocity of an object is its *rate of change of displacement with respect to
time*. So the velocity of an object that's moving along a straight line is the

same as its speed, except that it has a positive or negative sign to indicate the direction in which the object is moving along the line.

Activity 12   *Working with a displacement–time graph*

The displacement–time graph below, which consists of three line segments, represents a woman's walk along a straight path. The woman walks at a constant speed to a bench, sits there for some minutes, and then returns, again at a constant speed, to her starting point. The reference point has been chosen to be the point where she begins her walk, the positive direction has been chosen to be the direction in which she first walks, and time is measured from the time when she begins her walk.

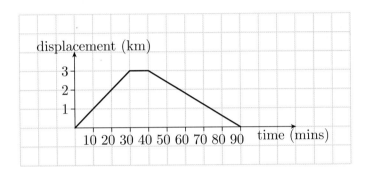

(a) What is the displacement of the bench from the woman's starting point?

(b) How long does the woman remain at the bench?

(c) Calculate the woman's velocity as she walks to the bench.

(d) Calculate her velocity as she walks back to her starting point.

(e) What is the woman's speed as she walks to the bench, and what is her speed as she walks back?

(f) Find the equation of the line segment that represents the first part of the woman's walk.

(g) Use the equation that you found in part (f) to find what the woman's displacement would be after 50 minutes if she hadn't stopped at the bench but had instead carried on walking at the same speed and in the same direction.

Derived units, such as km/h, are often written using *index notation*. For example, the unit km/h can be written as $\mathrm{km\,h^{-1}}$, since $1/\mathrm{h} = \mathrm{h^{-1}}$. This way of writing derived units makes no difference to the way that you read them: for example, $\mathrm{km\,h^{-1}}$ is read as 'kilometres per hour'. Derived units are often written in index notation throughout the rest of this module.

3 Intersection of lines

In this section you'll revise how to find the point at which two lines cross. This point is called the **point of intersection** of the lines.

3.1 Simultaneous equations

Here is an example where we want to find the point of intersection of two lines. Consider Figure 20, which shows the displacement–time graphs for two cars travelling on the same road, drawn on the same coordinate axes. Both graphs are straight lines. Notice that, as time goes on, the displacement of one car increases and the displacement of the other car decreases, which tells you that they're travelling in opposite directions. At the point of intersection of the lines, the displacements of the two cars are equal at the same time.

So this point corresponds to the time and displacement when the two cars pass each other. How can we find this point of intersection?

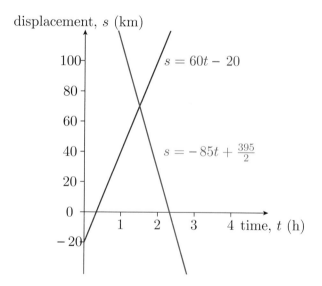

Figure 20   Displacement–time graphs for two cars travelling in opposite directions on the same road

You could find approximate values for the time at which the two cars pass each other, and the displacement at which this happens, by reading off the point of intersection from the graph. Alternatively, you can find accurate values by working with the equations of the lines and using algebra.

The equation of the displacement–time graph of the first car is

$$s = 60t - 20, \tag{7}$$

where s is the displacement in km and t is the time in hours. The corresponding equation for the second car is

$$s = -85t + \frac{395}{2}. \tag{8}$$

The coordinates (t, s) of the point of intersection must satisfy equation (7), since the point lies on the graph of that equation, and must also satisfy equation (8), since it also lies on the graph of this equation.

So to find the point of intersection you have to find a pair of values of t and s that satisfy *both* equations. The process of finding these values is known as solving the equations **simultaneously**, and in this context the two equations are called **simultaneous equations**. Since the equations are *linear* equations, they're **simultaneous linear equations**. The variables t and s are unknowns, and any pair of values of t and s that satisfy both equations is called a **solution** of the simultaneous equations.

Simultaneous equations are not restricted to two equations and two unknowns; systems containing larger numbers of equations and unknowns frequently arise in practical situations.

In the next subsection you'll revise two methods for solving simultaneous linear equations in two unknowns. You'll meet a third method in Unit 9.

3.2 Solving simultaneous equations

In this subsection we'll assume that the simultaneous equations that you want to solve are linear and have been rearranged so that the terms in the unknowns are on the left, and the constant terms are on the right. This is a standard way to present simultaneous equations.

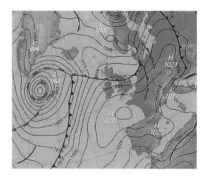

The calculation of weather forecasts requires the solution of millions of simultaneous equations.

For example, rearranging equations (7) and (8) in this way, and also clearing the fractions in equation (8), gives the pair of equations

$$s - 60t = -20,$$
$$2s + 170t = 395.$$

Here's the first method for solving simultaneous linear equations.

Substitution method

This is described in the following strategy and illustrated in Example 6.

> **Strategy:**
> **To solve simultaneous equations: substitution method**
>
> 1. Rearrange one of the equations, if necessary, to obtain a formula for one unknown in terms of the other.
>
> 2. Use this formula to substitute for this unknown in the other equation.
>
> 3. You now have an equation in one unknown. Solve it to find the value of that unknown.
>
> 4. Substitute this value into an equation involving both unknowns to find the value of the other unknown.
>
> (Check: confirm that the two values satisfy the original equations.)

Example 6   *Solving simultaneous equations by substitution*

Use the substitution method to solve the following simultaneous equations.

$$s - 60t = -20$$
$$2s + 170t = 395$$

Solution

🔍 Label the equations, so you can refer to them easily. 💭

The equations are

$$s - 60t = -20, \tag{9}$$
$$2s + 170t = 395. \tag{10}$$

🔍 Rearrange one of the equations to express one unknown in terms of the other. The simplest choice here is to rearrange equation (9) to express s in terms of t. Any other choice of equation or unknown leads to fractions. 💭

Rearranging equation (9) gives

$$s = 60t - 20. \tag{11}$$

🔍 Use this formula to substitute for s in the other equation. 💭

Substituting in equation (10) gives

$$2(60t - 20) + 170t = 395.$$

🔍 Solve this equation to find t. 💬

$$120t - 40 + 170t = 395$$
$$290t = 435$$
$$t = \frac{435}{290} = \frac{3}{2}$$

🔍 Substitute this value of t into an equation containing s, and solve it to find s. 💬

Substituting into equation (11) gives

$$s = 60t - 20$$
$$= 60 \times \tfrac{3}{2} - 20$$
$$= 90 - 20$$
$$= 70.$$

So the solution is $s = 70$, $t = \frac{3}{2}$.

🔍 It's a good idea to check that these values are correct by substituting them into the original equations. 💬

When you solve simultaneous equations, it's fine to label them (1) and (2), every time. If you want to refer to another equation in your working, then you can label it (3), and so on. (The simultaneous equations in Example 6 are labelled (9) and (10) just so that they're in sequence with the other labelled equations in this unit.)

Activity 13   *Solving simultaneous equations by substitution*

Use the substitution method to solve the following pairs of simultaneous equations.

(a) $s - 5t = -3$ (b) $x + 4y = 2$
      $s + 3t = 13$ $2x + 5y = 3$

Here's a variation of the substitution method that's sometimes useful. You've seen that the first step of the method is to rearrange one of the equations to express one unknown in terms of the other. If instead you start by rearranging *both* equations to obtain *two* formulas, each of which expresses one unknown (the same in both cases) in terms of the other unknown, then you can obtain an equation in one unknown by equating the right-hand sides of both formulas. You can then proceed in the usual way.

For example, notice that both the equations of the lines in Figure 20 were obtained originally in equations (7) and (8) as formulas for s in terms of t:

$$s = 60t - 20,$$
$$s = -85t + \frac{395}{2}.$$

You can equate the two right-hand sides to give the following equation in t:

$$60t - 20 = -85t + \frac{395}{2}.$$

You can then solve this equation to find t, and substitute this value into one of the original equations to find s.

Elimination method

Often when you want to solve a pair of simultaneous equations, it's difficult to use the substitution method without introducing fractions. In most cases it's better to use the method described in the following strategy, which is illustrated in Example 7.

Strategy:
To solve simultaneous equations: elimination method

1. Multiply one or both of the equations by suitable numbers, if necessary, to obtain two equations that can be added or subtracted to eliminate one of the unknowns.

2. Add or subtract the equations to eliminate this unknown.

3. You now have an equation in one unknown. Solve it to find the value of that unknown.

4. Substitute this value into an equation involving both unknowns to find the value of the other unknown.

(Check: confirm that the two values satisfy the original equations.)

Example 7   *Solving simultaneous equations by elimination*

Use the elimination method to solve the following simultaneous equations.

$$5u - 40v = 155$$
$$2u + 9v = 12$$

Solution

🔍 Label the equations. 💬

The equations are

$$5u - 40v = 155, \tag{12}$$
$$2u + 9v = 12. \tag{13}$$

🔍 Multiply the first equation by 2, and multiply the second equation by 5, to obtain two equations in which u has the same coefficient. (Alternatively, you could multiply the first equation by 9 and the second equation by 40, to obtain two equations in which v can be eliminated, but that involves harder arithmetic.) 💬

Multiplying equation (12) by 2 and equation (13) by 5 gives

$$10u - 80v = 310, \tag{14}$$
$$10u + 45v = 60. \tag{15}$$

🔍 Subtract equation (14) from equation (15) to eliminate u. 💬

Subtracting equation (14) from equation (15) gives

$$10u - 10u + 45v + 80v = 60 - 310$$

🔍 Solve this equation to find v. 💬

$$125v = -250$$
$$v = -2.$$

🔍 Substitute this value of v into an equation containing u, say equation (12), and solve it to find u. 💬

Hence

$$5u = 40v + 155$$
$$= 40 \times (-2) + 155$$
$$= -80 + 155$$
$$= 75$$
$$u = \tfrac{1}{5} \times 75 = 15.$$

So the solution is $u = 15$, $v = -2$.

The 'check' referred to in the strategy has not been included in the solution to Example 7. You should check your answers wherever possible, but you don't have to write the check down as part of your solution.

The aim of the first step in the solution to Example 7 was to find two equations in which u has the *same* coefficient. This was so that *subtracting* the equations will eliminate u. An alternative strategy in the first step is to find two equations in which the coefficients of u are *negatives of each other*, such as

$$-10u + 80v = -310,$$
$$10u + 45v = 60.$$

(These equations are obtained by multiplying the first of the original equations by -2 and the second by 5.) Then *adding* the equations will eliminate u.

Activity 14   *Solving simultaneous equations by elimination*

Use the elimination method to solve the following pairs of simultaneous equations.

(a) $s + 6t = 20$
      $2s + 7t = 35$

(b) $2x + 3y = -5$
      $3x - 2y = 12$

(c) $3u - v = -\dfrac{5}{2}$
      $2u + 5v = 21$

3.3 The number of solutions of simultaneous equations

Each pair of simultaneous linear equations in the last subsection had exactly one solution, but it's also possible for a pair of simultaneous linear equations to have no solutions, or infinitely many solutions.

To see this, consider the lines that are the graphs of the two equations. They might intersect in a single point, or they might be parallel, or they might be the same line. The three possibilities are illustrated in Figure 21.

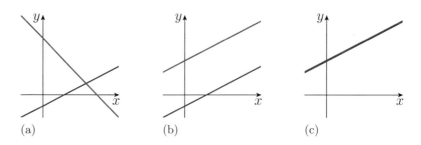

(a)   (b)   (c)

Figure 21   Three possible configurations of two lines

If the two lines have different gradients, as illustrated in Figure 21(a), then they intersect at a single point. So there is exactly one solution.

If the two lines have the same gradient but different y-intercepts, as illustrated in Figure 21(b), then they are parallel and hence do not intersect. In this case, you will not be able to solve the simultaneous equations. For example, the simultaneous equations

$$y - 2x = 3,$$
$$y - 2x = 4$$

have no solution; no matter what values of x and y are chosen, it is impossible for $y - 2x$ to be equal to both 3 and 4.

If the two lines have the same gradient and the same y-intercept, as illustrated in Figure 21(c), then the graphs of the two equations are identical. So every point that satisfies the first equation also satisfies the second equation, and hence there are infinitely many solutions. This situation occurs if one equation can be obtained by rearranging the other. For example, consider the simultaneous equations

$$y - 2x = 3,$$
$$2y - 4x = 6.$$

The second equation is obtained by multiplying the first equation by 2, so they represent the same line, and hence they have infinitely many solutions.

Activity 15   *Finding the number of solutions of simultaneous equations*

Determine whether each of the following pairs of simultaneous equations has one, infinitely many or no solutions. If there is one solution, find it.

(a) $y - 3x = -2$ (b) $y = 4x - 5$ (c) $4y = 2x + 6$
     $2y + x = 10$ $2y - 8x = 10$ $2y - x = 3$

In practice, when you're solving simultaneous equations there's no need to start by investigating the number of solutions. You can just try to solve the equations, and see what happens!

4   Quadratics

In this section we turn our attention to equations of the form

$$y = ax^2 + bx + c, \tag{16}$$

where a, b and c are constants and $a \neq 0$. An expression of the form of the right-hand side of this equation is called a **quadratic expression**, or simply a **quadratic**. An equation of the form

$$ax^2 + bx + c = 0, \tag{17}$$

where a, b and c are constants and $a \neq 0$, is called a **quadratic equation**. Since equation (17) is obtained by putting $y = 0$ in equation (16), its solutions are the x-intercepts of the graph of equation (16).

In the first subsection of this section, you'll revise the shapes of the graphs of equations of form (16). Then in the next few subsections you'll revise two useful techniques for rearranging quadratic expressions, namely *factorisation* and *completing the square*. You'll see how each of these techniques leads to a method for solving quadratic equations. You'll also revise a third method for solving quadratic equations, the *quadratic formula*.

It's important to make sure that you're familiar with all three of these methods for solving quadratic equations, as they're all used later in the module. You'll also need to use the techniques of factorisation of quadratics and completing the square for purposes other than solving quadratic equations.

Finally in this section you'll learn how to sketch the graphs of equations of form (16), and you'll see a few applications of quadratics.

Note that the reason for the condition '$a \neq 0$' in the definitions above is that, if $a = 0$, then the expression $ax^2 + bx + c$ reduces to $bx + c$, which is a *linear* expression.

4.1   Quadratic graphs

You have already seen one quadratic graph in this unit. In Activity 2 on page 123 you were asked to draw the graph of $y = x^2 + 2x + 2$ by first plotting points. In the next activity you can explore the shape of the graph of the equation $y = ax^2 + bx + c$ for various values of a, b and c.

Activity 16   *Investigating quadratic graphs*

Use the *Quadratic graphs* applet to investigate how the shape of the graph of the equation $y = ax^2 + bx + c$ changes as you vary the values of a, b and c.

In Activity 16, you should have seen that no matter what the values of a, b and c are (as long as $a \neq 0$), the graph of the equation $y = ax^2 + bx + c$ always has the same type of shape, which is called a **parabola**. If a is positive, then the parabola is **u-shaped**, as shown in Figure 22(a). If a is negative, then it is **n-shaped**, as shown in Figure 22(b). In both cases, the parabola has a vertical *axis of symmetry*.

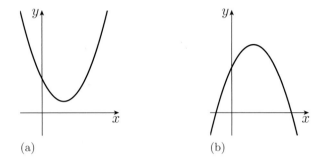

(a)   (b)

Figure 22   Typical graphs of $y = ax^2 + bx + c$ when (a) a is positive (b) a is negative

The word 'parabola' was first used for curves like these by the Greek geometer and astronomer Apollonius of Perga (262BC–190BC), though the shape itself was discovered even earlier.

You should have seen that changing the values of a, b and c can change the position of the parabola, and can stretch or squash it in a direction parallel to one of the axes. In particular, as you might have expected from your study of straight lines, changing the value of c on its own moves the parabola vertically, but keeps the shape the same.

The lowest point on a u-shaped parabola, or the highest point on an n-shaped parabola, is called the **vertex** of the parabola. The parabola gets steeper and steeper on each side of the vertex, but never becomes vertical.

A u-shaped or n-shaped parabola can have two, one or no x-intercepts, as illustrated for u-shaped parabolas in Figure 23. It always has exactly one y-intercept, because there is exactly one value of y for each value of x, including $x = 0$.

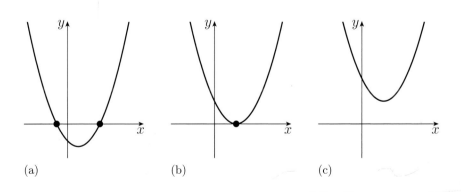

(a)   (b)   (c)

Figure 23   A quadratic graph can have two, one or no x-intercepts

Parabolas have many practical uses, mainly due to the reflecting properties of surfaces with parabolic cross-sections. If such a surface is made of a suitable reflecting material, then all light waves or radio waves that arrive at it by travelling along a direction parallel to its axis of symmetry are reflected to pass through a single point, known as the *focus*. Similarly, any wave that travels from the focus to the surface is reflected to travel along a line parallel to the axis of symmetry. Parabolic reflecting surfaces can be found in car headlights, reflecting and radio telescopes, and satellite dishes. The path of a ball thrown through the air is also parabolic (as long as the effects of air resistance are negligible).

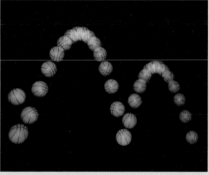

The parabolic dish of a radio telescope and the parabolic path of a ball

4.2 Factorising quadratic expressions

In this subsection you'll revise how to *factorise* a quadratic expression. This usually involves more than simply taking out a common factor, which you revised in Unit 1.

If you take any two linear expressions and multiply them together, then you get a quadratic expression. For example,

$$(2x + 3)(x - 2) = 2x^2 - x - 6.$$

Factorisation of a quadratic is the reverse of this process – it means writing the quadratic as the product of two linear expressions. For example, factorising the quadratic $2x^2 - x - 6$ means writing it as $(2x + 3)(x - 2)$ or, equivalently, as $(x - 2)(2x + 3)$.

Here, you'll see how to factorise certain quadratics *with integer coefficients*. For example, the quadratic $2x^2 - x - 6$ is of this type, as its coefficients 2, -1 and -6 are integers.

You'll see how to factorise such a quadratic into a product of two linear expressions *whose coefficients are also integers*, where this is possible. We'll refer to factorisation of this sort as factorisation *using integers*. For example, you've just seen that the quadratic $2x^2 - x - 6$ can be factorised using integers, since all the coefficients in the expression $(2x+3)(x-2)$ are integers. However, many quadratics with integer coefficients can't be factorised using integers.

Factorising quadratics in which x^2 has coefficient 1

We'll begin by looking at quadratics in which x^2 has coefficient 1, such as

$$x^2 - 2x - 15 \quad \text{and} \quad x^2 - 8x + 12.$$

These are usually easier to factorise than other quadratics.

If it's possible to factorise a quadratic of this type using integers, then the factorisation must be of the form

$$(x \quad)(x \quad), \tag{18}$$

where the two gaps are filled by constant terms. Such an arrangement of brackets with gaps for the constants is called a 'framework' in this unit.

To factorise the quadratic, you have to find two numbers (each a positive or negative integer, or zero) to fill the gaps in the framework (18), such that when you multiply out the brackets you get the quadratic that you started with. For example, if your quadratic is $x^2 - 2x - 15$, then the two numbers that you're looking for are $+3$ and -5, because

$$(x+3)(x-5) = x^2 - 5x + 3x - 15 = x^2 - 2x - 15.$$

You can use two facts to work out what the two numbers must be.

First, the two numbers must multiply together to give the constant term in the quadratic. To see why, consider what happens when you multiply out an expression of form (18). For example,

$$(x \boxed{+3})(x \boxed{-5}) = x^2 - 5x + 3x \boxed{-15} = x^2 - 2x \boxed{-15}.$$

The two numbers are multiplied to give
the constant term in the quadratic.

Second, the two numbers must add together to give the coefficient of x in the quadratic. To see why, again consider what happens when you multiply out an expression of form (18).

For example,

$$(x \boxed{+3})(x \boxed{-5}) = x^2 \boxed{-5}x \boxed{+3}x - 15 = x^2 \boxed{-2}x - 15.$$

The two numbers become   They are added to give the
coefficients of x.   overall coefficient of x.

The next example demonstrates an efficient strategy for using these facts to find the two numbers.

This strategy is quick to use once you've had some practice with it, and it can be adapted to deal with quadratics in which x^2 does *not* have coefficient 1, as you'll see shortly. However, there are other strategies – there's a different one in the document *An alternative strategy for factorising quadratics* on the website that you might like to look at, and you may have learned another one elsewhere. It's fine to use any strategy that works for you.

You might find it easier to understand the strategy if you hear someone explain it to you, so it's a good idea to watch the tutorial clip for Example 8. The strategy is summarised after the example.

Example 8   *Factorising quadratics in which x^2 has coefficient 1*

Factorise the following quadratics.

(a) $x^2 - 8x + 12$ (b) $x^2 + 2x - 15$

Solution

(a) Start by writing out the framework.

$$x^2 - 8x + 12 = (x \quad)(x \quad)$$

The numbers to go in the gaps must have product 12 (the constant term) and sum -8 (the coefficient of x). List the factor pairs of 12:

$$1, 12; \quad -1, -12; \quad 2, 6; \quad -2, -6; \quad 3, 4; \quad -3, -4.$$

Find a pair in this list with sum -8. The only such pair is $-2, -6$.

$$x^2 - 8x + 12 = (x - 2)(x - 6)$$

You can check the answer by multiplying out the brackets.

(b) Write out the framework.

$$x^2 + 2x - 15 = (x \quad)(x \quad)$$

The numbers to go in the gaps must have product -15 and sum 2.
List the factor pairs of -15:

$$1, -15; \quad -1, 15; \quad 3, -5; \quad -3, 5.$$

The only pair with sum 2 is $-3, 5$.

$$x^2 + 2x - 15 = (x - 3)(x + 5)$$

The strategy demonstrated in Example 8 is summarised below.

> **Strategy:**
> **To factorise a quadratic of the form** $x^2 + bx + c$
>
> 1. Start by writing
>
> $$x^2 + bx + c = (x \quad)(x \quad).$$
>
> 2. Find the factor pairs of c (including both positive and negative factors).
>
> 3. Choose a factor pair with sum b.
>
> 4. Write your factor pair p, q in position:
>
> $$x^2 + bx + c = (x + p)(x + q).$$

For some quadratics, this strategy doesn't give a factorisation. When this happens, it means that the quadratic can't be factorised using integers. For example, if you try to apply the strategy to the quadratic $x^2 + 2x + 3$, then you find that neither of the factor pairs of 3, namely $1, 3$ and $-1, -3$, have sum 2. So this quadratic can't be factorised using integers.

As you become more familiar with factorising quadratics, you'll find ways to apply the strategy above more efficiently. For example, rather than writing down *all* the factor pairs before considering their sums, you can consider the sum of each pair as you go along, and stop once you've found a pair with the required sum. Similarly, if you're trying to factorise a quadratic $x^2 + bx + c$ where both b and c are *positive*, then you need consider only *positive* factor pairs of c, since the sum of two negative numbers can't be the positive number b.

Activity 17   *Factorising quadratics of the form* $x^2 + bx + c$

Factorise the following quadratics. (They *can* all be factorised.)

(a) $x^2 + 5x + 6$ (b) $x^2 - 8x + 15$ (c) $x^2 + 4x - 5$

(d) $x^2 - 2x - 35$ (e) $x^2 - 6x + 9$ (f) $x^2 - 6x + 8$

(g) $y^2 - 7y - 18$ (h) $u^2 + 4u + 4$ (i) $p^2 - 4p - 12$

(j) $s^2 + s - 30$ (k) $v^2 + 5v - 50$ (l) $r^2 - 10r + 16$

Factorising quadratics in which x^2 doesn't have coefficient 1

We'll now look at how to factorise quadratics in which x^2 doesn't have coefficient 1, such as $6x^2 - 11x - 35$.

The first thing to do when you want to factorise a quadratic like this is to check whether there are any numerical common factors. If there are, then take them out. For example, if the quadratic is $4x^2 + 2x - 2$, then write it as

$$4x^2 + 2x - 2 = 2(2x^2 + x - 1).$$

Also, if the coefficient of x^2 is negative, then take out a factor of -1. For example, if the quadratic is $-3x^2 + x + 2$, then write it as

$$-3x^2 + x + 2 = -(3x^2 - x - 2).$$

Once you've done these things, you can focus on factorising the simpler quadratic inside the brackets.

Because you can take out a factor of -1 if necessary, you only ever need to factorise quadratics in which the coefficient of x^2 is positive. You can do that by using the strategy that you saw earlier, with two adaptations when the coefficient of x^2 is not 1.

The first adaptation is needed to deal with the fact that there can be more than one possibility for the initial framework that you write out. Each pair of positive factors of the coefficient of x^2 gives you a possible framework. For example, if the quadratic that you want to factorise is

$$6x^2 + 11x - 35,$$

then there are two possible frameworks, namely

$$(6x \quad)(x \quad) \quad \text{and} \quad (2x \quad)(3x \quad).$$

To deal with this, you apply the factorisation strategy to each of the possible frameworks in turn, until you find one that gives you a factorisation. If none of the possibilities gives you a factorisation, then it means that the quadratic can't be factorised using integers.

The second adaptation is a little more complicated. In the earlier strategy, once you've written out the framework, you consider the factor pairs of the constant term, and for each factor pair you consider whether its sum is equal to the coefficient of x. In the adapted strategy, you still consider the factor pairs of the constant term, but you don't consider the sum of each factor pair, as this doesn't tell you anything useful when the coefficient of x^2 isn't 1. Instead, you consider directly whether each factor pair leads to the correct term in x when you multiply out. This process is explained more fully in the following example.

The adapted strategy might seem quite complicated when you first meet it, but it should seem more straightforward after you've practised it a few times. Again, you might find it easier to understand if you hear someone explain it to you, so it's a good idea to watch the tutorial clip for Example 9.

Example 9   *Factorising a quadratic in which x^2 doesn't have coefficient 1*

Factorise the quadratic $2x^2 - 7x - 15$.

Solution

There are no numerical common factors that can be taken out. The coefficient of x^2 is a prime number, so there's only one possible framework.

$$2x^2 - 7x - 15 = (2x \quad)(x \quad)$$

Consider the factor pairs of the constant term -15:

$$1, -15; \quad -1, 15; \quad 3, -5; \quad -3, 5.$$

Each factor pair can go in the brackets in two different ways, giving eight possible cases, as follows.

$$(2x + 1)(x - 15) \qquad (2x - 15)(x + 1)$$
$$(2x - 1)(x + 15) \qquad (2x + 15)(x - 1)$$
$$(2x + 3)(x - 5) \qquad (2x - 5)(x + 3)$$
$$(2x - 3)(x + 5) \qquad (2x + 5)(x - 3)$$

For each case, calculate the term in x that you obtain when you multiply out the brackets.

$$(2x + 1)(x - 15) \quad -29x \qquad (2x - 15)(x + 1) \quad -13x$$
$$(2x - 1)(x + 15) \quad 29x \qquad (2x + 15)(x - 1) \quad 13x$$
$$(2x + 3)(x - 5) \quad -7x \qquad (2x - 5)(x + 3) \quad x$$
$$(2x - 3)(x + 5) \quad 7x \qquad (2x + 5)(x - 3) \quad -x$$

Identify the case that gives $-7x$.

$$2x^2 - 7x - 15 = (2x + 3)(x - 5)$$

You can check the answer to Example 9 by multiplying out the brackets.

The solution to Example 9 includes some working to help with finding the factorisation. You might find it helpful to write down working like this while you're getting used to factorising quadratics, but after a while you'll probably find that you can usually do it in your head. So, when you factorise a quadratic, you don't need to write down any working – it's fine to just write down the quadratic and its factorisation, like this:

$$2x^2 - 7x - 15 = (2x + 3)(x - 5).$$

Here's a summary of the method demonstrated in the example above.

> **Strategy:**
> **To factorise a quadratic of the form** $ax^2 + bx + c$
>
> 1. Take out any numerical common factors. If the coefficient of x^2 is negative, also take out the factor -1. Then apply the steps below to the quadratic inside the brackets.
>
> 2. Find the positive factor pairs of a, the coefficient of x^2. For each such factor pair d, e write down a framework $(dx \quad)(ex \quad)$.
>
> 3. Find all the factor pairs of c, the constant term (including both positive and negative factors).
>
> 4. For each framework and each factor pair of c, write the factor pair in the gaps in the framework in both possible ways.
>
> 5. For each of the resulting cases, calculate the term in x that you obtain when you multiply out the brackets.
>
> 6. Identify the case where this term is bx, if there is such a case. This is the required factorisation.

As with the earlier strategy, if this strategy doesn't lead to a factorisation, then the quadratic can't be factorised using integers.

Activity 18   *Factorising quadratics of the form* $ax^2 + bx + c$

Factorise the following quadratics. (They *can* all be factorised.)

(a) $5x^2 + 13x - 6$ (b) $3x^2 + 16x + 5$ (c) $6x^2 - 11x + 3$

(d) $5x^2 - 8x - 21$ (e) $18x^2 + 9x - 2$ (f) $4x^2 - 8x + 3$

(g) $4p^2 - 19p - 5$ (h) $6u^2 + 11u - 35$ (i) $4t^2 + 4t + 1$

(j) $9v^2 - 12v + 4$ (k) $-4s^2 + 4s + 3$ (l) $12y^2 - 10y - 2$

There are two special types of quadratic that can be factorised more easily than those that you have seen so far in this subsection. You should always check whether your quadratic is one of these before you embark on either of the two strategies above.

Quadratics with no constant term

These can be factorised by taking x out as a common factor. For example,
$$x^2 + 4x = x(x + 4),$$
$$3x^2 - 6x = 3(x^2 - 2x) = 3x(x - 2).$$

Differences of two squares

As you saw in Unit 1, a **difference of two squares** is any expression of the form

$$A^2 - B^2,$$

where A and B are subexpressions. You can check, by multiplying out the brackets, that

$$A^2 - B^2 = (A + B)(A - B). \tag{19}$$

If you can recognise a quadratic as a difference of two squares, then you can use equation (19) to factorise it immediately. For example,

$$x^2 - 9 = x^2 - 3^2 = (x + 3)(x - 3),$$
$$x^2 - 1 = x^2 - 1^2 = (x + 1)(x - 1),$$
$$4x^2 - 1 = (2x)^2 - 1^2 = (2x + 1)(2x - 1).$$

Activity 19 *Factorising special quadratics*

Factorise the following quadratics.

(a) $x^2 - 4$ (b) $x^2 - 4x$ (c) $2x^2 + 5x$ (d) $x^2 - 25$

(e) $9y^2 - 4$ (f) $25t^2 - 1$ (g) $9u^2 - u$ (h) $p^2 + p$

4.3 Solving quadratic equations by factorisation

In this subsection you'll see how you can use the method of factorisation to solve quadratic equations. Remember that a quadratic equation is an equation of the form $ax^2 + bx + c = 0$, where a, b and c are constants with $a \neq 0$.

Whenever you have a quadratic equation to solve, the first thing to do is to check whether it can be simplified, as this will make it easier to deal with. Here are some things that you might be able to do.

Simplifying a quadratic equation

- If necessary, rearrange the equation so that all the non-zero terms are on the same side.

- If the coefficient of x^2 is negative, then multiply the equation through by -1 to make this coefficient positive.

- If the coefficients have a common factor, then divide the equation through by this factor.

- If any of the coefficients are fractions, then multiply the equation through by a suitable number to clear them.

Once you've simplified the quadratic equation as much as you can, you can go on to solve it, using one of the three methods covered in this section.

The method of solving quadratic equations by *factorisation* depends on the techniques that you practised in the last subsection, together with the following crucial fact.

> If the product of two or more numbers is 0, then at least one of the numbers must be 0.

You can see how this fact is used in the example below.

Example 10   *Solving a quadratic equation by factorisation*

Solve the equation
$$6x^2 + 14x - 12 = 0.$$

Solution

Simplify the equation if possible. Here you can divide through by 2.
$$3x^2 + 7x - 6 = 0$$

Factorise the quadratic expression.
$$(3x - 2)(x + 3) = 0$$

Use the fact in the box above.
$$3x - 2 = 0 \quad \text{or} \quad x + 3 = 0$$

Solve these linear equations for x.
$$x = \tfrac{2}{3} \quad \text{or} \quad x = -3$$

So the solutions are $x = \tfrac{2}{3}$ and $x = -3$.

You can check the answers to Example 10 by substituting each of the solutions into the original equation.

Some quadratic equations can't be solved using the method of Example 10, because it's not possible to factorise their associated quadratic expressions using integers. You'll see another method for solving quadratic equations later in this section.

Activity 20 *Solving quadratic equations by factorisation*

Solve the following quadratic equations by factorisation. (They *can* all be solved in this way.)

(a) $x^2 + 4x - 21 = 0$ (b) $3x^2 - 18x + 24 = 0$ (c) $-t^2 - 6t - 9 = 0$

(d) $8x + 4x^2 - 5 = 0$ (e) $3x^2 - x = 0$ (f) $x^2 - 16 = 0$

(g) $\frac{3}{2}u^2 + u - \frac{1}{2} = 0$ (h) $x^2 + \frac{9}{4}x + \frac{1}{2} = 0$ (i) $10(x^2 + 1) = 29x$

In part (c) of the activity above, you'll have noticed that when you factorised the quadratic, the two linear factors were the same, which led to only one solution. A quadratic equation with only one solution is said to have a **repeated solution**.

4.4 Expressing a quadratic in completed-square form

In this subsection you'll revise how to *complete the square* in a quadratic expression, and in the next subsection you'll see how you can use this technique to solve quadratic equations. Completing the square is also useful for other purposes, as you'll see later in the module.

Completing the square in a quadratic expression means rearranging it in a particular way. For example, the completed-square form of the quadratic $2x^2 - 12x + 25$ is

$$2(x - 3)^2 + 7.$$

You can check that this expression is equivalent to the original quadratic by multiplying out the brackets and simplifying:

$$\begin{aligned}
2(x - 3)^2 + 7 &= 2(x^2 - 6x + 9) + 7 \\
&= 2x^2 - 12x + 18 + 7 \\
&= 2x^2 - 12x + 25.
\end{aligned}$$

In general, to **complete the square** in a quadratic $ax^2 + bx + c$, you have to rearrange it into the form

$$a(x + r)^2 + s,$$

where a, r and s are constants. The constant a is the same as the constant a in the original expression, and r and s are new constants, each of which can be positive, negative or zero. The rearranged form of the quadratic is called its **completed-square form**.

The key to completing the square in any quadratic is to first learn how to do it for quadratics of the form $x^2 + bx$. Some examples of quadratics of this form are $x^2 + 6x$, $x^2 - 10x$ and $x^2 + x$.

Let's start by considering the quadratic $x^2 + 6x$. To see how to write it in completed-square form, consider what happens when you multiply out the expression $(x + 3)^2$. The '+3' here is obtained by halving the coefficient of x in the original quadratic, which is +6. You obtain

$$(x + 3)^2 = x^2 + 3x + 3x + 9$$
$$= x^2 + 6x + 9.$$

So expanding $(x + 3)^2$ gives the original quadratic $x^2 + 6x$, with an extra term, namely 9, added on. So if you subtract 9 from $(x + 3)^2$, then you'll have an expression that's equivalent to $x^2 + 6x$. That is,

$$x^2 + 6x = (x + 3)^2 - 9.$$

The expression on the right of this equation is the completed-square form of $x^2 + 6x$.

The method can be summarised as follows.

> **Strategy:**
> **To complete the square in a quadratic of the form $x^2 + bx$**
>
> 1. Write down $(x \quad)^2$, filling the gap with the number that's half of b, the coefficient of x (including its + or − sign, of course).
> 2. Subtract the square of the number that you wrote in the gap.

The first step of the strategy ensures that you have squared brackets that, when expanded, give the quadratic $x^2 + bx$ together with an extra term, which is the square of the number written in the gap. In the second step of the strategy you subtract this extra term to obtain a final completed-square form that's equivalent to $x^2 + bx$. Here's an example.

Example 11   *Completing the square in a quadratic of the form* $x^2 + bx$

Write the quadratic expression $x^2 - 10x$ in completed-square form.

Solution

$$x^2 - 10x = (x - 5)^2 - 25$$

Halve this coefficient and write it here.

Square the constant term in brackets and subtract it.

Remember that once you've found the completed-square form of a quadratic, you can always check that it's correct by multiplying it out.

Here are some examples of completing the square for you to try. In this activity, try checking your answers by multiplying them out – this will help you understand how the method works.

Activity 21   *Completing the square in quadratics of the form $x^2 + bx$*

Write the following quadratics in completed-square form.

(a) $x^2 + 8x$ (b) $x^2 - 4x$ (c) $x^2 + x$ (d) $t^2 - 3t$

Once you know how to complete the square in any quadratic of the form $x^2 + bx$, you can also complete the square in any quadratic of the form $x^2 + bx + c$.

Strategy:
To complete the square in a quadratic of the form $x^2 + bx + c$

1. Use the earlier strategy to complete the square in the subexpression $x^2 + bx$.

2. Collect the constant terms.

Example 12   *Completing the square in a quadratic of the form $x^2 + bx + c$*

Write the quadratic $x^2 - 8x + 2$ in completed-square form.

Solution

Complete the square in the subexpression $x^2 - 8x$, leaving the $+2$ unchanged.

$$x^2 - 8x + 2 = (x - 4)^2 - 16 + 2$$

Collect the constant terms.

$$= (x - 4)^2 - 14.$$

Here are some examples for you to try.

> **Activity 22**   *Completing the square in quadratics of the form*
> $x^2 + bx + c$
>
> Write the following quadratics in completed-square form.
>
> (a) $x^2 + 2x + 2$ (b) $x^2 + 3x - 1$ (c) $y^2 + \frac{1}{2}y - \frac{1}{4}$

In fact you can use the method that you've seen for completing the square in quadratics of the form $x^2 + bx$ to allow you to complete the square in any quadratic at all. To complete the square in a quadratic of the form $ax^2 + bx + c$, where $a \neq 1$, you begin by factorising the coefficient a out of the subexpression formed by the terms in x^2 and x. For example, if the quadratic is $2x^2 - 12x + 20$, then you begin by writing

$$2x^2 - 12x + 20 = 2(x^2 - 6x) + 20.$$

It doesn't matter if the coefficient of x^2 in the quadratic isn't a factor of the coefficient of x. For example, for the quadratic $-2x^2 + x + 1$, you begin by writing

$$-2x^2 + x + 1 = -2(x^2 - \tfrac{1}{2}x) + 1.$$

Once you've carried out this initial step, the quadratic in the brackets will be of the form $x^2 + bx$. You can then complete the square in this quadratic, and finally simplify the results to obtain the completed-square form of the original quadratic. Here's an example.

> **Example 13**   *Completing the square in a quadratic of the form*
> $ax^2 + bx + c$
>
> Express $2x^2 - 12x + 20$ in completed-square form.
>
> **Solution**
>
> 🔍 Factorise the coefficient of x^2 out of the subexpression formed by the terms in x^2 and x. 💬
>
> $$2x^2 - 12x + 20 = 2\left(x^2 - 6x\right) + 20$$
>
> 🔍 Now the brackets contain a quadratic of the form $x^2 + bx$. Complete the square in it, keeping it enclosed within its brackets. 💬
>
> $$= 2\left((x - 3)^2 - 9\right) + 20$$
>
> 🔍 Multiply out the *outer* brackets. Don't multiply out the inner brackets, because you want the square $(x - 3)^2$ to appear in the final expression. 💬
>
> $$= 2(x - 3)^2 - 18 + 20$$
>
> 🔍 Collect the constant terms. 💬
>
> $$= 2(x - 3)^2 + 2$$

Here's a summary of the method demonstrated in Example 13.

Strategy:
To complete the square in a quadratic of the form
$ax^2 + bx + c$, **where** $a \neq 1$

1. Rewrite the quadratic with the coefficient a taken out of the expression $ax^2 + bx$ as a factor. This generates a pair of brackets.

2. Use the earlier strategy to complete the square in the simple quadratic inside the brackets. This generates a second pair of brackets, inside the first pair.

3. Multiply out the *outer* brackets.

4. Collect the constant terms.

Activity 23   *Completing the square in quadratics of the form* $ax^2 + bx + c$

Write the following quadratics in completed-square form.

(a) $3x^2 + 6x + 5$ (b) $2y^2 - 5y + 4$ (c) $-x^2 + x - \frac{1}{2}$

4.5 Solving quadratic equations by completing the square

The example below demonstrates how you can use the technique of completing the square to solve a quadratic equation. You can use this method to solve any quadratic equation that has solutions, including those that can't be solved by factorisation using integers.

Example 14   *Solving a quadratic equation by completing the square*

Solve the quadratic equation $2x^2 - 8x + 5 = 0$ by completing the square.

Solution

Check whether the equation can be simplified (see the box on page 163). Here there's no simplification to be done. Next, complete the square on the left-hand side.

$$2(x^2 - 4x) + 5 = 0$$
$$2\left((x - 2)^2 - 4\right) + 5 = 0$$
$$2(x - 2)^2 - 8 + 5 = 0$$
$$2(x - 2)^2 - 3 = 0$$

🔍 Rearrange the equation so that the left-hand side is of the form $(x \quad)^2$. 💬

$$(x-2)^2 = \frac{3}{2}$$

🔍 Take square roots of both sides, remembering that a positive number has both a positive and a negative square root. 💬

$$x - 2 = \sqrt{\frac{3}{2}} \quad \text{or} \quad x - 2 = -\sqrt{\frac{3}{2}}$$

🔍 Get x by itself on the left of each equation. 💬

$$x = 2 + \sqrt{\frac{3}{2}} \quad \text{or} \quad x = 2 - \sqrt{\frac{3}{2}}$$

So the solutions are $x = 2 + \sqrt{3/2}$ and $x = 2 - \sqrt{3/2}$.

Here are some examples for you to try.

Activity 24   *Solving quadratic equations by completing the square*

Solve the following quadratic equations by completing the square.

(a) $x^2 + 4x + 1 = 0$ (b) $3t^2 - 12t + 11 = 0$ (c) $2x^2 + 3x - 3 = 0$

In practice, if you can't solve a particular quadratic equation by factorisation, then instead of solving it by completing the square, you may prefer to use the *quadratic formula*, which is given in the next subsection. This formula is obtained by completing the square in the general quadratic expression $ax^2 + bx + c$.

4.6   The quadratic formula

The formula below expresses the solutions of a general quadratic equation in terms of its coefficients.

The quadratic formula

The solutions of the quadratic equation $ax^2 + bx + c = 0$ are

$$x = \frac{-b \pm \sqrt{b^2 - 4ac}}{2a}.$$

Recall from Unit 1 that the symbol ± means 'plus or minus'.

Later in this subsection you'll see how the quadratic formula is obtained by completing the square – for now you should concentrate on how to use it.

Remember that before you solve a quadratic equation you should always simplify it as much as possible, following the guidelines on page 163.

Example 15   *Using the quadratic formula*

Use the quadratic formula to solve the equation $2x^2 - 6x - 5 = 0$.

Solution

🔍 Check that the equation is in the form $ax^2 + bx + c = 0$, and find the values of a, b and c. 💭

Here $a = 2$, $b = -6$ and $c = -5$.

🔍 Substitute these values into the quadratic formula. 💭

$$x = \frac{-b \pm \sqrt{b^2 - 4ac}}{2a}$$

$$= \frac{-(-6) \pm \sqrt{(-6)^2 - 4 \times 2 \times (-5)}}{2 \times 2}$$

$$= \frac{6 \pm \sqrt{36 + 40}}{4}$$

$$= \frac{6 \pm \sqrt{76}}{4}$$

🔍 Simplify this pair of surds. 💭

$$= \frac{6 \pm \sqrt{4 \times 19}}{4}$$

$$= \frac{6 \pm 2\sqrt{19}}{4}$$

$$= \frac{3 \pm \sqrt{19}}{2}$$

$$= \tfrac{1}{2}(3 \pm \sqrt{19})$$

So the solutions are $x = \tfrac{1}{2}(3 + \sqrt{19})$ and $x = \tfrac{1}{2}(3 - \sqrt{19})$.

As you can see from Example 15, the calculations that you have to do when you use the quadratic formula can be quite complicated, and it's easy to make mistakes. Before you solve a quadratic equation using the quadratic formula, it's always worth checking whether you can solve it more easily by factorisation instead.

When you use the quadratic formula, the solutions that you obtain are often surds. In fact, if you don't obtain surds, then it means that the quadratic equation could have been solved by factorisation instead. If you obtain surds, then you should leave them as surds, expressing them in their simplest form, unless you've been asked for a decimal approximation, or the solutions to the quadratic equation are the answers to a practical problem.

You can practise using the quadratic formula in the next activity. Remember to simplify the equations before you apply the formula, where possible.

Activity 25   *Using the quadratic formula*

Solve the following quadratic equations by using the quadratic formula. In each case where the solutions are not surds, try solving the quadratic equation by factorisation as well.

(a) $x^2 - 6x - 1 = 0$ (b) $9x^2 + 15x - 6 = 0$ (c) $9x^2 + 6x = 11$

(d) $t^2 + \frac{5}{2}t + \frac{3}{2} = 0$ (e) $u^2 = 4u - 4$

To end this subsection, here's an explanation of where the quadratic formula comes from. Given the general quadratic equation,

$$ax^2 + bx + c = 0,$$

where $a \neq 0$, the first step is to complete the square:

$$a\left(x^2 + \frac{b}{a}x\right) + c = 0$$

$$a\left(\left(x + \frac{b}{2a}\right)^2 - \left(\frac{b}{2a}\right)^2\right) + c = 0$$

$$a\left(x + \frac{b}{2a}\right)^2 - a\left(\frac{b}{2a}\right)^2 + c = 0$$

$$a\left(x + \frac{b}{2a}\right)^2 - \frac{b^2}{4a} + c = 0.$$

Next rearrange the equation so that you get the constant terms on the right, and combine them into a single fraction:

$$\left(x + \frac{b}{2a}\right)^2 = \frac{b^2}{4a^2} - \frac{c}{a}$$

$$= \frac{b^2}{4a^2} - \frac{4ac}{4a^2}$$

$$= \frac{b^2 - 4ac}{4a^2}.$$

Now take square roots of both sides:

$$x + \frac{b}{2a} = \pm\sqrt{\frac{b^2 - 4ac}{4a^2}}$$

$$= \pm\frac{\sqrt{b^2 - 4ac}}{2a}.$$

The last step is to get x by itself on the left-hand side:

$$x = -\frac{b}{2a} \pm \frac{\sqrt{b^2 - 4ac}}{2a}$$

$$= \frac{-b \pm \sqrt{b^2 - 4ac}}{2a}.$$

This is the quadratic formula!

4.7 The number of solutions of a quadratic equation

Earlier in this unit, you saw that the graph of an equation of the form $y = ax^2 + bx + c$, where a, b and c are constants with $a \neq 0$, can have two, one or no x-intercepts. Since the x-intercepts of the graph of $y = ax^2 + bx + c$ are the solutions of the quadratic equation $ax^2 + bx + c = 0$, this means that a quadratic equation can have two, one or zero solutions that are real numbers.

In fact every quadratic equation has at least one solution if we allow solutions that are *complex numbers* – these numbers were mentioned in Unit 1, and they include all the real numbers and also many 'imaginary' numbers, such as the square root of -1. You'll see more about this in Unit 12, but until then you only need to consider the solutions of quadratic equations that are real numbers, which are known as their *real solutions*.

When you use the quadratic formula to solve a quadratic equation, the number of real solutions of the equation quickly becomes clear. For example, consider the equation

$$x^2 + 2x + 3 = 0.$$

Here $a = 1$, $b = 2$ and $c = 3$. Substituting these values into the quadratic formula, we obtain

$$x = \frac{-b \pm \sqrt{b^2 - 4ac}}{2a} = \frac{-2 \pm \sqrt{2^2 - 4 \times 1 \times 3}}{2 \times 1}$$

$$= \frac{-2 \pm \sqrt{4 - 12}}{2}$$

$$= \frac{-2 \pm \sqrt{-8}}{2}.$$

This expression involves $\sqrt{-8}$, but there is no such number in the set of real numbers. So this equation has no real solutions. This is confirmed by the graph of $y = x^2 + 2x + 3$ in Figure 24, which does not cross or touch the x-axis and so has no x-intercepts.

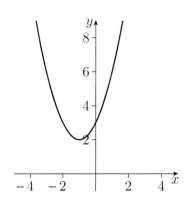

Figure 24   The graph of $y = x^2 + 2x + 3$

Similarly, consider the equation

$$x^2 + 2x + 1 = 0.$$

Here $a = 1$, $b = 2$ and $c = 1$. Substituting these values into the quadratic formula, we obtain

$$x = \frac{-b \pm \sqrt{b^2 - 4ac}}{2a} = \frac{-2 \pm \sqrt{2^2 - 4 \times 1 \times 1}}{2 \times 1}$$

$$= \frac{-2 \pm \sqrt{4 - 4}}{2}$$

$$= \frac{-2 \pm \sqrt{0}}{2}$$

$$= -1.$$

In this calculation the number under the square root sign turns out to be zero, and this leads to just one solution of the equation. This is confirmed by the graph of $y = x^2 + 2x + 1$ in Figure 25, which touches the x-axis but does not cross it. From these examples you can see that it's the value of the expression $b^2 - 4ac$, which appears under the square root sign in the quadratic formula, that determines how many solutions a quadratic equation has. The different possibilities are set out in the box below. The value $b^2 - 4ac$ is called the **discriminant** of the quadratic expression $ax^2 + bx + c$.

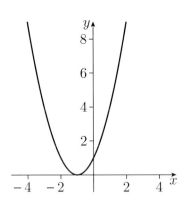

Figure 25 The graph of $y = x^2 + 2x + 1$

The number of real solutions of a quadratic equation

The quadratic equation $ax^2 + bx + c = 0$ has:

- two real solutions if $b^2 - 4ac > 0$ (the discriminant is positive)
- one real solution if $b^2 - 4ac = 0$ (the discriminant is zero)
- no real solutions if $b^2 - 4ac < 0$ (the discriminant is negative).

Activity 26 *Predicting the number of real solutions of a quadratic equation*

Use the discriminant to determine whether each of the following quadratic equations has two, one or no real solutions. Find any real solutions.

(a) $4x^2 - 20x + 25 = 0$ (b) $2x^2 + 6x + 5 = 0$ (c) $4x^2 = 4x + 5$

The discriminant of a quadratic also tells you whether the quadratic can be factorised using integers. You can see that if the discriminant of a quadratic with integer coefficients is a *perfect square*, then you won't get surds when you use the quadratic formula to solve the corresponding quadratic equation. This tells you that the expression can be factorised using integers.

4.8 Solving equations related to quadratic equations

In this section you'll see how to use the techniques for solving quadratic equations to solve some equations that don't look like quadratic equations at first sight, and to solve some equations that are not quadratic.

First, remember that in Unit 1 you saw how to solve some equations containing algebraic fractions. Usually the first step is to clear the fractions, by multiplying through by a suitable expression. All the equations containing algebraic fractions in Unit 1 turned out to be linear equations, but it's also possible for an equation containing algebraic fractions to turn out to be a quadratic equation. Here's an example.

Example 16   *Solving an equation involving algebraic fractions*

Solve the equation

$$\frac{4}{x+2} + x = 3.$$

Solution

🔍 There is a fraction with denominator $x + 2$, so multiply through by $x + 2$ to clear it. For this to be guaranteed to give an equivalent equation, you have to assume that $x + 2 \neq 0$; that is, $x \neq -2$. 💭

Assume that $x \neq -2$.

$$4 + x(x + 2) = 3(x + 2)$$

🔍 Multiply out the brackets. 💭

$$4 + x^2 + 2x = 3x + 6$$

🔍 Get all the non-zero terms on the left-hand side. 💭

$$x^2 - x - 2 = 0$$

🔍 This is a quadratic equation. Solve it by factorising. 💭

$$(x + 1)(x - 2) = 0$$

So $x + 1 = 0$ or $x - 2 = 0$; that is, $x = -1$ or $x = 2$.

These values satisfy the assumption $x \neq -2$, so the solutions of the original equation are $x = -1$ and $x = 2$.

You can sometimes use the methods for solving quadratic equations to solve an equation containing a power of x greater than 2, if you start by factorising the equation. This is illustrated in the next example.

Example 17   *Factorising to reveal a quadratic*

Solve the equation $3x^3 - 12x^2 + 3x = 0$.

Solution

Simplify the equation by dividing through by 3.

$$x^3 - 4x^2 + x = 0$$

There is a common factor, x. Take it out.

$$x(x^2 - 4x + 1) = 0$$

This gives two expressions whose product is zero, so at least one of the expressions is zero.

$$x = 0 \quad \text{or} \quad x^2 - 4x + 1 = 0$$

Now solve the quadratic equation. It cannot be factorised using integers, so use the quadratic formula, with $a = 1$, $b = -4$, $c = 1$.

The solutions of the quadratic equation are

$$
\begin{aligned}
x &= \frac{-b \pm \sqrt{b^2 - 4ac}}{2a} \\
&= \frac{4 \pm \sqrt{16 - 4}}{2} \\
&= \frac{4 \pm \sqrt{12}}{2} \\
&= \frac{4 \pm 2\sqrt{3}}{2} \\
&= 2 \pm \sqrt{3}.
\end{aligned}
$$

So the solutions of the original equation are $x = 0$, $x = 2 + \sqrt{3}$ and $x = 2 - \sqrt{3}$.

The equation in Example 17 is an example of a *cubic* equation. A **cubic equation** is an equation of the form $ax^3 + bx^2 + cx + d = 0$, where a, b, c and d are constants, with $a \neq 0$. You'll see in Unit 3 that every cubic equation has at most three solutions.

In the next example an equation is transformed into a quadratic equation by making a substitution.

Example 18   *Substituting to reveal a quadratic*

Solve the equation $x^4 - 5x^2 + 4 = 0$.

Solution

🔍 Substitute another letter, say X, for x^2. 💬

Let $X = x^2$. The equation becomes

$$X^2 - 5X + 4 = 0$$

🔍 This is a quadratic equation in X. It can be solved by factorisation. 💬

$$(X - 1)(X - 4) = 0$$
$$X = 1 \quad \text{or} \quad X = 4$$

🔍 Use the fact that $X = x^2$. 💬

$$x^2 = 1 \quad \text{or} \quad x^2 = 4$$

🔍 Take square roots of both sides of each equation. 💬

$$x = \pm 1 \quad \text{or} \quad x = \pm 2.$$

So the solutions of the original equation are $x = 1$, $x = -1$, $x = 2$ and $x = -2$.

The method in Example 18 can be used to solve any equation of the form

$$ax^4 + bx^2 + c = 0,$$

where a, b and c are constants, with $a \neq 0$.

Activity 27   *Solving equations related to quadratic equations*

Solve the following equations.

(a) $\dfrac{4}{x} = \dfrac{3x}{x + 1}$ (b) $\dfrac{1}{x - 2} = 1 + 4x$ (c) $2x^3 - 2x^2 - 12x = 0$

(d) $x^4 - 2x^2 - 8 = 0$ (e) $u^4 - 4 = 0$

(f) $s^5 - 9s^3 = 0$ (g) $(t^2 - 3)(t^2 - 3t + 2) = 0$

4.9 Sketching quadratic graphs

In Subsection 4.1 you saw how the graph of the equation $y = ax^2 + bx + c$ changes when you change the values of a, b and c. In this subsection you'll revise how to sketch the graph of any equation of this form. Note that a **sketch** of a graph is a diagram that gives an impression of its shape, with key points marked and positioned approximately correctly relative to a pair of coordinate axes. It's different from a **plot** of a graph, which is a more accurate diagram obtained by precisely plotting a reasonably large number of points on the graph. For example, you were asked to plot a graph in Activity 2 on page 123.

Although a sketch of a graph is not an accurate representation of the graph, it should be sufficiently correct to convey the main properties. The axis scales need not be marked, but there should be some indication of scale – for example, the key points can be labelled with their coordinates. In the case of a parabola, the key points are the points where it crosses the axes, and the vertex. When you're sketching a quadratic graph, it's helpful to remember the properties summarised below. You met these properties in Subsection 4.1.

Sketching a parabola?

> **Properties of the graph of** $y = ax^2 + bx + c$**, where** $a \neq 0$
>
> 1. The graph is a parabola with a vertical axis of symmetry.
> 2. If a is positive it is u-shaped; if a is negative it is n-shaped.
> 3. It has two, one or no x-intercepts.
> 4. It has one y-intercept.

Here's a strategy for sketching a quadratic graph. It's illustrated in the next example.

> **Strategy:**
> **To sketch the graph of** $y = ax^2 + bx + c$**, where** $a \neq 0$
>
> 1. Find whether the parabola is u-shaped or n-shaped.
> 2. Find its intercepts, axis of symmetry and vertex.
> 3. Plot the features found, and hence sketch the parabola.
> 4. Label the parabola with its equation, intercepts and the coordinates of the vertex.

It's fine to label a parabola with the coordinates of the points where it crosses the axis, rather than with its intercepts. For example, the parabola in Example 19 is labelled with $(0, 5)$ rather than with 5. Also, you can choose whether or not to draw the axis of symmetry. If you do include it, you should draw it as a dashed line.

Example 19   *Sketching a quadratic graph*

Sketch the graph of $y = -x^2 - 4x + 5$.

Solution

🔍 Find whether the parabola is u-shaped or n-shaped. 💭

The coefficient of x^2 is negative, so the graph is n-shaped.

🔍 Find the y-intercept. 💭

Putting $x = 0$ gives $y = 5$, so the y-intercept is 5.

🔍 Find any x-intercepts. 💭

Putting $y = 0$ gives

$$-x^2 - 4x + 5 = 0$$
$$x^2 + 4x - 5 = 0$$
$$(x - 1)(x + 5) = 0$$
$$x - 1 = 0 \quad \text{or} \quad x + 5 = 0$$
$$x = 1 \quad \text{or} \quad x = -5.$$

So the x-intercepts are 1 and -5.

🔍 The axis of symmetry lies halfway between the x-intercepts. The number halfway between any two numbers p and q is their mean, $(p + q)/2$. 💭

The value of x halfway between -5 and 1 is $(-5 + 1)/2 = -4/2 = -2$. So the axis of symmetry is the line $x = -2$.

🔍 The vertex lies on the axis of symmetry. 💭

The point with x-coordinate -2 on the graph has y-coordinate $y = -(-2)^2 - 4 \times (-2) + 5 = 9$. So the vertex is $(-2, 9)$.

🔍 Plot the features found. Hence sketch the parabola as a smooth curve, and label it with its equation, intercepts and vertex. 💭

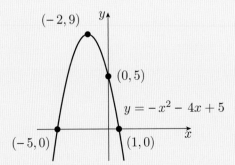

You can use the method demonstrated in Example 19 to sketch the graph of any equation of the form $y = ax^2 + bx + c$, where $a \neq 0$, provided that there are two x-intercepts or one x-intercept. If there is just one x-intercept, then the vertex of the parabola is at this x-intercept. The graphs of both equations in the activity below have one or two x-intercepts.

Activity 28   *Sketching quadratic graphs*

Sketch the graphs of the following equations.

(a) $y = -2x^2 + 3x - 1$ (b) $y = 2x^2 + 8x + 8$

To sketch the graph of an equation of the form $y = ax^2 + bx + c$ when there are no x-intercepts, you need a different method for finding the equation of the axis of symmetry. One method is to first find any two points on the parabola that have the same y-coordinate, and use the fact that the axis of symmetry lies halfway between them.

The next example demonstrates a neat way to find two such points.

Example 20   *Sketching a quadratic graph with no x-intercepts*

Sketch the graph of $y = 2x^2 - 12x + 20$.

Solution

🔍 Find whether the parabola is u-shaped or n-shaped. 💬

The coefficient of x^2 is positive, so the graph is u-shaped.

🔍 Find the y-intercept. 💬

Putting $x = 0$ gives $y = 20$, so the y-intercept is 20.

🔍 Find any x-intercepts. 💬

Putting $y = 0$ gives

$$2x^2 - 12x + 20 = 0$$
$$x^2 - 6x + 10 = 0$$

The discriminant of $x^2 - 6x + 10$ is

$$b^2 - 4ac = (-6)^2 - 4 \times 1 \times 10 = -4.$$

The discriminant is negative, so the quadratic equation above has no solutions, and hence the graph has no x-intercepts.

🔎 To find the axis of symmetry, start by taking out the common factor x from the terms in x^2 and x in the equation whose graph you're trying to sketch. It's convenient to take out any numerical common factors too. 💬

The equation $y = 2x^2 - 12x + 20$ can be rearranged as

$$y = 2x(x - 6) + 20.$$

🔎 From this form of the equation you can see that the points with x-coordinates 0 and 6 have the same y-coordinate, namely 20. The axis of symmetry lies halfway between these two points. 💬

The points $(0, 20)$ and $(6, 20)$ lie on the graph. The number halfway between 0 and 6 is 3, so the axis of symmetry is the line $x = 3$.

🔎 The vertex lies on the axis of symmetry. 💬

The point on the graph with x-coordinate 3 has y-coordinate $y = 2 \times 3^2 - 12 \times 3 + 20 = 2$, so the vertex is $(3, 2)$.

🔎 Plot the features found. Hence sketch the parabola as a smooth curve, and label it with its equation, intercepts and vertex. 💬

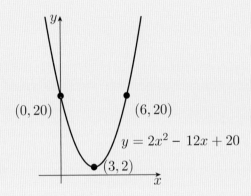

An alternative way to find the vertex of the graph of an equation of the form $y = ax^2 + bx + c$, where $a \neq 0$, is to complete the square in the quadratic expression. For example, consider again the equation in Example 20:

$$y = 2x^2 - 12x + 20.$$

Completing the square in the right-hand side (which was done for this particular expression in Example 13) gives

$$y = 2(x - 3)^2 + 2.$$

Think about what this form of the equation tells you. Since $(x - 3)^2$ is a square, it can never be negative, no matter what the value of x is. The least value that it can take is 0, and it takes this value when $x = 3$. So the least value that y can take is $y = 2 \times 0 + 2 = 2$, and y takes this value when $x = 3$. This tells you that the vertex is $(3, 2)$.

In general, when you want to sketch a graph, there is no single correct approach. You can use any appropriate means to find the information that you need.

Activity 29   *Sketching a quadratic graph with no x-intercepts*

Sketch the graph of $y = x^2 - 2x + 4$.

4.10   Applications of quadratics

Quadratic equations occur frequently when you model real-life problems involving objects that are falling vertically under the influence of gravity, or have been thrown, particularly when the effects of air resistance are small enough to be ignored. Here's an example.

Example 21   *Solving a quadratic equation in a real-life problem*

A boy standing on a vertical cliff $150\,\text{m}$ above sea level kicks a ball into the sea. Let x be the horizontal displacement (in metres) of the ball from the base of the cliff, and y be the vertical displacement (in metres) of the ball measured upwards from sea level. Then the curve followed by the ball can be modelled by the equation

$$y = 150 + x - \frac{x^2}{40}.$$

Find the horizontal distance from the cliff at which the ball hits the sea.

Solution

The ball hits the sea when the vertical displacement y is 0. The corresponding horizontal displacement x satisfies the equation

$$0 = 150 + x - \frac{x^2}{40}.$$

🔍 Clear the fraction and simplify the equation. 💬

Rearranging gives

$$0 = 6000 + 40x - x^2$$
$$x^2 - 40x - 6000 = 0$$

🔍 Factorise. 💬

$$(x - 100)(x + 60) = 0$$
$$x - 100 = 0 \quad \text{or} \quad x + 60 = 0$$
$$x = 100 \quad \text{or} \quad x = -60.$$

The negative answer is meaningless in the context of the question. So the ball hits the sea $100\,\text{m}$ from the cliff.

Activity 30   *Using quadratics*

A ball is thrown vertically upwards. Its vertical displacement s (in metres, measured upwards from the point of release) is modelled by the equation

$$s = 12t - 5t^2,$$

where t is the time in seconds since the moment of release.

(a) How high will the ball be after 2 seconds?

(b) At what times after the ball is thrown will it be at a height of $5\,\text{m}$ above its starting position?

(c) After what time will the ball return to its starting position?

(d) By completing the square in the expression for s, find the maximum height that the ball will reach above its starting position.

The techniques that you need to create models like the ones in Example 21 and Activity 30 are taught in the module MST125.

5 Using the computer for graphs and equations

The following activity completes your study of Unit 2.

Activity 31   *Using the computer algebra system*

Work through Sections 2 and 3 of the MST124 *Computer algebra guide*, where you will learn how to use the computer to manipulate algebraic expressions, solve equations and plot lines and curves.

You will need to use your computer while you work through these sections.

Learning outcomes

After studying this unit, you should be able to:

- plot the graph of an equation by constructing a table of values and plotting points
- find the gradient and intercepts of a straight line from its equation
- interpret the gradient and intercepts of a straight line in real-life situations, where possible
- find the equation of a straight line from its gradient and y-intercept, from its gradient and a point on the line, or from two points on the line
- use the equation of a straight line to draw the line
- find the gradient of a line perpendicular to another line whose gradient you know
- solve simultaneous linear equations, and hence find the point of intersection of two straight lines
- factorise a quadratic expression using integers, where possible
- complete the square in a quadratic expression
- solve quadratic equations by factorising, by completing the square and by using the quadratic formula
- sketch the graph of an equation of the form $y = ax^2 + bx + c$
- use the module computer algebra system to manipulate mathematical expressions and plot lines and curves.

Solutions to activities

Solution to Activity 1

(a) When $x = 6$ and $y = 20$,

$$\text{LHS} = y - 2 = 20 - 2 = 18$$
$$\text{and RHS} = 3x = 3 \times 6 = 18.$$

So the point $(6, 20)$ satisfies the equation.

(b) When $x = -2$ and $y = 8$,

$$\text{LHS} = y - 2 = 8 - 2 = 6$$
$$\text{and RHS} = 3x = 3 \times (-2) = -6.$$

So the point $(-2, 8)$ does not satisfy the equation.

Solution to Activity 2

A table of values for the equation $y = x^2 + 2x + 2$ is as follows.

x	-2	-1	0	1	2
y	2	1	2	5	10

Drawing a smooth curve through these points gives the graph below.

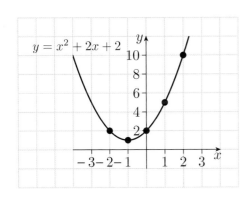

Solution to Activity 3

(a) For every unit moved to the right, the pen tip moves up 3 units, so the gradient is 3.

(b) For every unit moved to the right, the pen tip moves up $\frac{1}{2}$ unit, so the gradient is $\frac{1}{2}$.

(c) For every unit moved to the right, the pen tip moves down 4 units, so the gradient is -4.

(d) For every unit moved to the right, the pen tip moves down $\frac{1}{3}$ unit, so the gradient is $-\frac{1}{3}$.

(e) For every unit moved to the right, the pen tip moves up 1 unit, so the gradient is 1.

(f) For every unit moved to the right, the pen tip moves down 1 unit, so the gradient is -1.

Solution to Activity 4

(a) A is $(-4, 5)$; B is $(1, 3)$; C is $(-1, -2)$; D is $(-6, 0)$.

(b) (i) For the gradient of the line through A and B, take A to be the first point and B the second:
$$\frac{y_2 - y_1}{x_2 - x_1} = \frac{3 - 5}{1 - (-4)} = \frac{-2}{5} = -\frac{2}{5}.$$

(ii) For the gradient of the line through A and D, take A to be the first point and D the second:
$$\frac{y_2 - y_1}{x_2 - x_1} = \frac{0 - 5}{-6 - (-4)} = \frac{-5}{-2} = \frac{5}{2}.$$

(iii) For the gradient of the line through B and C, take B to be the first point and C the second:
$$\frac{y_2 - y_1}{x_2 - x_1} = \frac{-2 - 3}{-1 - 1} = \frac{-5}{-2} = \frac{5}{2}.$$

Solution to Activity 5

(a) The coefficient of x is -4, so the gradient is -4. The constant term is 3, so the y-intercept is 3.

To find the x-intercept, put $y = 0$, which gives
$$0 = -4x + 3.$$
Solving this equation gives $4x = 3$, so $x = \frac{3}{4}$. Hence the x-intercept is $\frac{3}{4}$.

(b) Rearranging the equation in the form $y = mx + c$ gives $y = \frac{1}{3}x - \frac{2}{3}$. The coefficient of x is $\frac{1}{3}$, so the gradient is $\frac{1}{3}$.

The constant term is $-\frac{2}{3}$, so the y-intercept is $-\frac{2}{3}$.

To find the x-intercept, put $y = 0$, which gives
$$0 = \frac{1}{3}x - \frac{2}{3}.$$
Solving this equation gives $\frac{1}{3}x = \frac{2}{3}$, so $x = 2$. Hence the x-intercept is 2.

Solution to Activity 6

(a) Putting $x = 0$ gives $y = \frac{1}{3} \times 0 + 2 = 2$, so $(0, 2)$ lies on the line. (You might also notice that this point lies on the line since the y-intercept is 2.)

Putting $x = 3$ gives $y = \frac{1}{3} \times 3 + 2 = 1 + 2 = 3$, so $(3, 3)$ lies on the line.

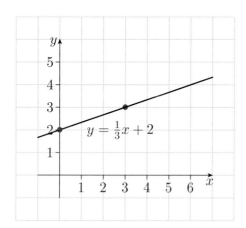

(b) Putting $x = 0$ gives $y = -2 \times 0 + 4 = 4$, so $(0, 4)$ lies on the line.

Putting $x = 4$ gives
$y = -2 \times 4 + 4 = -8 + 4 = -4$, so $(4, -4)$ lies on the line.

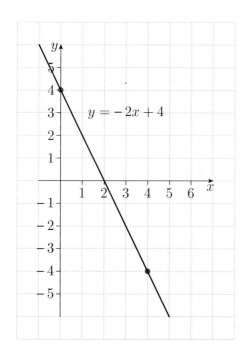

(c) This is a horizontal line, with y-intercept $\frac{7}{2}$.

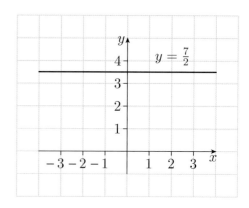

(d) This is a vertical line, with x-intercept -3.

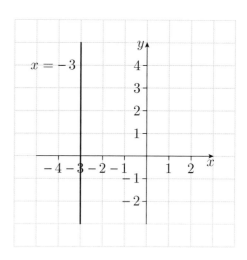

Solution to Activity 7

(a) Using the equation $y - y_1 = m(x - x_1)$ with $m = 3$, $x_1 = 2$ and $y_1 = 1$ gives
$$y - 1 = 3(x - 2).$$
Expanding the brackets and rearranging gives the equation of the line as
$$y = 3x - 5.$$

(b) The gradient of the line is given by
$$\frac{5 - 3}{4 - 2} = \frac{2}{2} = 1.$$
Using the equation $y - y_1 = m(x - x_1)$ with $m = 1$, $x_1 = 2$ and $y_1 = 3$ gives
$$y - 3 = x - 2.$$

So the equation of the line is
$$y = x + 1.$$

(c) Using the equation $y = mx + c$ with $m = 2$ and $c = 3$ gives the equation of the line as
$$y = 2x + 3.$$

(d) The point at which the line crosses the x-axis is $(2, 0)$. Using the equation $y - y_1 = m(x - x_1)$ with $m = -3$, $x_1 = 2$ and $y_1 = 0$ gives
$$y - 0 = -3(x - 2).$$
So the equation of the line is
$$y = -3x + 6.$$

(e) Each point on a vertical line has the same x-coordinate, so the equation of the line is
$$x = 1.$$

(f) The y-coordinates of the two points are the same, so the line is horizontal with equation
$$y = 3.$$

Solution to Activity 8

(a) The gradient of the line $y = 3x + 5$ is 3, so the gradient of a line perpendicular to this line is $-\frac{1}{3}$.

(b) The gradient of the required line is $-\frac{1}{3}$ and it passes through the point $(2, 1)$. Using the equation $y - y_1 = m(x - x_1)$ gives
$$y - 1 = -\tfrac{1}{3}(x - 2)$$
$$y - 1 = -\tfrac{1}{3}x + \tfrac{2}{3}.$$
So the required line is
$$y = -\tfrac{1}{3}x + \tfrac{5}{3}.$$

Solution to Activity 9

(a) The line passes through the points $(0, 200)$ and $(40, 500)$, so its gradient is
$$\frac{500 - 200}{40 - 0} = \frac{300}{40} = 7.5 \, \text{£/person}.$$

The gradient is the rate of increase of the cost of the room with respect to the number of people attending the meeting. Each additional person attending raises the cost by £7.50.

(b) The line passes through the points $(200, 0.07)$ and $(1000, 0.04)$, so its gradient is
$$\frac{0.04 - 0.07}{1000 - 200} = \frac{-0.03}{800} = -\frac{3}{80\,000} \, \frac{\text{£/kg}}{\text{kg}}.$$

The units can be simplified:
$$\frac{\text{£/kg}}{\text{kg}} = \frac{\text{£}}{\text{kg}} \div \text{kg} = \frac{\text{£}}{\text{kg}} \times \frac{1}{\text{kg}} = \frac{\text{£}}{\text{kg}^2} = \text{£/kg}^2.$$

So the gradient is $-\frac{3}{80\,000} \, \text{£/kg}^2$. The gradient is the rate of change of the price (in £/kg) with respect to the quantity (in kg). For each extra kg of sand, the price (per kg) decreases by approximately 3×10^{-5} £/kg.

Solution to Activity 10

The vertical intercept is £200. This represents the basic cost of the meeting room without the additional cost for each person attending.

Solution to Activity 11

(a) The gradient of the graph of the cost of the meeting room is 7.5 £/person. From the graph, the vertical intercept is £200. So the equation of the graph is
$$C = 7.5n + 200,$$
where C represents the cost (in £) of the meeting room and n represents the number of people attending. The gradient of the building sand graph is $-\frac{3}{80\,000} \, \text{£/kg}^2$. The graph passes through the point $(200, 0.07)$, so its equation is given by
$$p - 0.07 = -\frac{3}{80\,000}(q - 200);$$
that is,
$$p = -\frac{3}{80\,000}q + \frac{600}{80\,000} + 0.07$$
$$p = -\frac{3}{80\,000}q + \frac{31}{400}.$$

(b) (i) Using $C = 7.5n + 200$ with $C = 560$ gives
$$560 = 7.5n + 200$$
$$7.5n = 360$$
$$n = \frac{360}{7.5} = 48.$$
So the maximum number of people that can be accommodated is 48.

(ii) Using $p = -\frac{3}{80\,000}q + \frac{31}{400}$ with $q = 500$ gives
$$p = -\frac{3}{80\,000} \times 500 + \frac{31}{400} = \frac{47}{800},$$
so the price per kilogram is approximately £0.059.

Solution to Activity 12

(a) The displacement is 3 km.

(b) The woman remains at the bench for 10 minutes.

(c) On the way to the bench her velocity is the gradient of the first line segment of the graph:
$$\frac{3-0}{30-0} = 0.1 \,\text{km/min}.$$

(d) On the way back her velocity is the gradient of the third line segment of the graph:
$$\frac{0-3}{90-40} = -\frac{3}{50} = -0.06 \,\text{km/min}.$$

(e) On the way to the bench her speed is $0.1 \,\text{km/min}$. On the way back her speed is $0.06 \,\text{km/min}$.

(f) Let s be the displacement in kilometres and t be the time in minutes. The equation of the line segment representing the first part of her walk is $s = 0.1t$.

(g) Her displacement after 50 minutes if she hadn't stopped would be $s = 0.1 \times 50 = 5 \,\text{km}$.

Solution to Activity 13

(a) The equations are
$$s - 5t = -3, \tag{20}$$
$$s + 3t = 13. \tag{21}$$
Making s the subject of equation (20) gives
$$s = 5t - 3. \tag{22}$$
Substituting for s in equation (21) gives
$$5t - 3 + 3t = 13$$
$$8t = 16$$
$$t = 2.$$
Substituting this value for t in equation (22) gives
$$s = 5 \times 2 - 3 = 7.$$
So the solution is $s = 7$, $t = 2$.

(b) The equations are
$$x + 4y = 2, \tag{23}$$
$$2x + 5y = 3. \tag{24}$$
Making x the subject of equation (23) gives
$$x = 2 - 4y. \tag{25}$$

Substituting for x in equation (24) gives
$$2(2 - 4y) + 5y = 3$$
$$4 - 8y + 5y = 3$$
$$-3y = -1$$
$$y = \tfrac{1}{3}.$$
Substituting this value for y in equation (25) gives
$$x = 2 - 4 \times \tfrac{1}{3} = \tfrac{2}{3}.$$
So the solution is $x = \tfrac{2}{3}$, $y = \tfrac{1}{3}$.

Solution to Activity 14

(a) The equations are
$$s + 6t = 20, \tag{26}$$
$$2s + 7t = 35. \tag{27}$$
Multiplying equation (26) by 2 (to make the coefficients of s the same) gives
$$2s + 12t = 40, \tag{28}$$
$$2s + 7t = 35. \tag{29}$$
Subtracting equation (29) from equation (28) gives
$$12t - 7t = 40 - 35$$
$$5t = 5$$
$$t = 1.$$
Substituting this value for t in equation (26) gives
$$s + 6 \times 1 = 20$$
$$s + 6 = 20$$
$$s = 14.$$
So the solution is $s = 14$, $t = 1$.

(b) The equations are
$$2x + 3y = -5, \tag{30}$$
$$3x - 2y = 12. \tag{31}$$
Multiplying equation (30) by 3 and equation (31) by 2 (to make the coefficients of x the same) gives
$$6x + 9y = -15, \tag{32}$$
$$6x - 4y = 24. \tag{33}$$
Subtracting equation (33) from equation (32) gives
$$9y - (-4y) = -15 - 24$$
$$13y = -39$$
$$y = -3.$$

Substituting this value for y in equation (30) gives

$$2x + 3 \times (-3) = -5$$
$$2x - 9 = -5$$
$$2x = 4$$
$$x = 2.$$

So the solution is $x = 2$, $y = -3$.

(c) The equations are

$$3u - v = -\frac{5}{2}, \tag{34}$$
$$2u + 5v = 21. \tag{35}$$

Multiplying equation (34) by 5 (to make the coefficients of v have the same magnitude) gives

$$15u - 5v = -\frac{25}{2}. \tag{36}$$

Adding equation (36) and equation (35) gives

$$17u = \frac{17}{2}$$
$$u = \tfrac{1}{2}.$$

Substituting this value for u in equation (34) gives

$$3 \times \frac{1}{2} - v = -\frac{5}{2}$$
$$-v = -\frac{5}{2} - \frac{3}{2} = -4$$
$$v = 4.$$

So the solution is $u = \tfrac{1}{2}$, $v = 4$.

Solution to Activity 15

(a) The equations are

$$y - 3x = -2,$$
$$2y + x = 10,$$

which can be rearranged as

$$y = 3x - 2, \tag{37}$$
$$y = -\tfrac{1}{2}x + 5. \tag{38}$$

So the gradient of the line in equation (37) is 3 and the gradient of the line in equation (38) is $-\tfrac{1}{2}$. Since the gradients are different, the lines must intersect and there is exactly one solution.

The equations can be solved by eliminating y from equations (37) and (38) to give

$$3x - 2 = -\tfrac{1}{2}x + 5$$
$$\tfrac{7}{2}x = 7$$
$$x = 2.$$

Substituting this value for x in equation (37) gives

$$y = 3 \times 2 - 2$$
$$y = 4.$$

So the solution is $x = 2$, $y = 4$.

(b) The equations are

$$y = 4x - 5,$$
$$2y - 8x = 10.$$

Writing the equations with both unknowns on the LHS, and dividing the second equation by the common factor 2 gives

$$y - 4x = -5$$
$$y - 4x = 5.$$

Since $y - 4x = -5$ and $y - 4x = 5$ cannot both be true, the equations have no solutions.

(c) The equations are

$$4y = 2x + 6,$$
$$2y - x = 3.$$

Writing the equations with both unknowns on the LHS, and dividing the first equation by the common factor 2 gives

$$2y - x = 3,$$
$$2y - x = 3.$$

The two equations are identical, so their graphs are identical. So all values of x and y that satisfy the first equation also satisfy the second equation, and hence there are infinitely many solutions.

Solution to Activity 16

(The effects that you should have seen are described in the text that follows this activity.)

Unit 2 Graphs and equations

Solution to Activity 17

(a) $x^2 + 5x + 6 = (x+2)(x+3)$

(b) $x^2 - 8x + 15 = (x-3)(x-5)$

(c) $x^2 + 4x - 5 = (x-1)(x+5)$

(d) $x^2 - 2x - 35 = (x+5)(x-7)$

(e) $x^2 - 6x + 9 = (x-3)(x-3) = (x-3)^2$

(f) $x^2 - 6x + 8 = (x-2)(x-4)$

(g) $y^2 - 7y - 18 = (y+2)(y-9)$

(h) $u^2 + 4u + 4 = (u+2)(u+2) = (u+2)^2$

(i) $p^2 - 4p - 12 = (p+2)(p-6)$

(j) $s^2 + s - 30 = (s-5)(s+6)$

(k) $v^2 + 5v - 50 = (v-5)(v+10)$

(l) $r^2 - 10r + 16 = (r-2)(r-8)$

Solution to Activity 18

(a) $5x^2 + 13x - 6 = (5x-2)(x+3)$

(b) $3x^2 + 16x + 5 = (3x+1)(x+5)$

(c) $6x^2 - 11x + 3 = (2x-3)(3x-1)$

(d) $5x^2 - 8x - 21 = (5x+7)(x-3)$

(e) $18x^2 + 9x - 2 = (6x-1)(3x+2)$

(f) $4x^2 - 8x + 3 = (2x-3)(2x-1)$

(g) $4p^2 - 19p - 5 = (4p+1)(p-5)$

(h) $6u^2 + 11u - 35 = (2u+7)(3u-5)$

(i) $4t^2 + 4t + 1 = (2t+1)(2t+1) = (2t+1)^2$

(j) $9v^2 - 12v + 4 = (3v-2)(3v-2) = (3v-2)^2$

(k) $\quad -4s^2 + 4s + 3 = -(4s^2 - 4s - 3)$
$$= -(2s+1)(2s-3)$$

(l) $\quad 12y^2 - 10y - 2 = 2(6y^2 - 5y - 1)$
$$= 2(6y+1)(y-1)$$

(In part (l), if you forget to take the common factor 2 out of the quadratic, then you obtain
$$12y^2 - 10y - 2 = (12y+2)(y-1)$$
or
$$12y^2 - 10y - 2 = (6y+1)(2y-2).$$
These answers are fine, though they can be factorised further by taking the common factor 2 out of one of the brackets, which gives the answer above. It's better to take the common factor out at the beginning, as this makes it easier to factorise.)

Solution to Activity 19

(a) $x^2 - 4 = x^2 - 2^2 = (x+2)(x-2)$

(b) $x^2 - 4x = x(x-4)$

(c) $2x^2 + 5x = x(2x+5)$

(d) $x^2 - 25 = x^2 - 5^2 = (x+5)(x-5)$

(e) $9y^2 - 4 = (3y)^2 - 2^2 = (3y+2)(3y-2)$

(f) $25t^2 - 1 = (5t)^2 - 1^2 = (5t+1)(5t-1)$

(g) $9u^2 - u = u(9u-1)$

(h) $p^2 + p = p(p+1)$

Solution to Activity 20

(a) $\quad x^2 + 4x - 21 = 0$
$$(x-3)(x+7) = 0$$
$$x - 3 = 0 \quad \text{or} \quad x + 7 = 0$$
$$x = 3 \quad \text{or} \quad x = -7$$

(b) $\quad 3x^2 - 18x + 24 = 0$
$$x^2 - 6x + 8 = 0$$
$$(x-2)(x-4) = 0$$
$$x - 2 = 0 \quad \text{or} \quad x - 4 = 0$$
$$x = 2 \quad \text{or} \quad x = 4$$

(c) $\quad -t^2 - 6t - 9 = 0$
$$t^2 + 6t + 9 = 0$$
$$(t+3)(t+3) = 0$$
$$t + 3 = 0 \quad \text{or} \quad t + 3 = 0$$
$$t = -3$$

(d) $\quad 8x + 4x^2 - 5 = 0$
$$4x^2 + 8x - 5 = 0$$
$$(2x-1)(2x+5) = 0$$
$$2x - 1 = 0 \quad \text{or} \quad 2x + 5 = 0$$
$$x = \tfrac{1}{2} \quad \text{or} \quad x = -\tfrac{5}{2}$$

(e) $\quad 3x^2 - x = 0$
$$x(3x-1) = 0$$
$$x = 0 \quad \text{or} \quad 3x - 1 = 0$$
$$x = 0 \quad \text{or} \quad x = \tfrac{1}{3}$$

(f) $\quad x^2 - 16 = 0$
$$(x-4)(x+4) = 0$$
$$x - 4 = 0 \quad \text{or} \quad x + 4 = 0$$
$$x = 4 \quad \text{or} \quad x = -4$$

(Because the quadratic equation in this part has no term in x, there's an even simpler way of solving it:

$$x^2 - 16 = 0$$
$$x^2 = 16$$
$$x = 4 \quad \text{or} \quad x = -4.)$$

(g) $\quad \frac{3}{2}u^2 + u - \frac{1}{2} = 0$
$$3u^2 + 2u - 1 = 0$$
$$(3u - 1)(u + 1) = 0$$
$$3u - 1 = 0 \quad \text{or} \quad u + 1 = 0$$
$$u = \frac{1}{3} \quad \text{or} \quad u = -1$$

(h) $\quad x^2 + \frac{9}{4}x + \frac{1}{2} = 0$
$$4x^2 + 9x + 2 = 0$$
$$(4x + 1)(x + 2) = 0$$
$$4x + 1 = 0 \quad \text{or} \quad x + 2 = 0$$
$$x = -\frac{1}{4} \quad \text{or} \quad x = -2$$

(i) $\quad 10(x^2 + 1) = 29x$
$$10x^2 + 10 = 29x$$
$$10x^2 - 29x + 10 = 0$$
$$(5x - 2)(2x - 5) = 0$$
$$5x - 2 = 0 \quad \text{or} \quad 2x - 5 = 0$$
$$x = \frac{2}{5} \quad \text{or} \quad x = \frac{5}{2}$$

Solution to Activity 21

(a) $\quad x^2 + 8x = (x + 4)^2 - 4^2$
$$= (x + 4)^2 - 16$$

(b) $\quad x^2 - 4x = (x - 2)^2 - (-2)^2$
$$= (x - 2)^2 - 4$$

(c) $\quad x^2 + x = \left(x + \frac{1}{2}\right)^2 - \left(\frac{1}{2}\right)^2$
$$= \left(x + \frac{1}{2}\right)^2 - \frac{1}{4}$$

(d) $\quad t^2 - 3t = \left(t - \frac{3}{2}\right)^2 - \left(-\frac{3}{2}\right)^2$
$$= \left(t - \frac{3}{2}\right)^2 - \frac{9}{4}$$

Solution to Activity 22

(a) $\quad x^2 + 2x + 2 = (x + 1)^2 - 1 + 2$
$$= (x + 1)^2 + 1$$

(b) $\quad x^2 + 3x - 1 = (x + \frac{3}{2})^2 - \frac{9}{4} - 1$
$$= (x + \frac{3}{2})^2 - \frac{13}{4}$$

(c) $\quad y^2 + \frac{1}{2}y - \frac{1}{4} = (y + \frac{1}{4})^2 - \frac{1}{16} - \frac{1}{4}$
$$= (y + \frac{1}{4})^2 - \frac{5}{16}$$

Solution to Activity 23

(a) $\quad 3x^2 + 6x + 5 = 3(x^2 + 2x) + 5$
$$= 3\left((x + 1)^2 - 1\right) + 5$$
$$= 3(x + 1)^2 - 3 + 5$$
$$= 3(x + 1)^2 + 2$$

(b) $\quad 2y^2 - 5y + 4 = 2\left(y^2 - \frac{5}{2}y\right) + 4$
$$= 2\left(\left(y - \frac{5}{4}\right)^2 - \frac{25}{16}\right) + 4$$
$$= 2\left(y - \frac{5}{4}\right)^2 - \frac{25}{8} + 4$$
$$= 2\left(y - \frac{5}{4}\right)^2 + \frac{7}{8}$$

(c) $\quad -x^2 + x - \frac{1}{2} = -(x^2 - x) - \frac{1}{2}$
$$= -\left((x - \frac{1}{2})^2 - \frac{1}{4}\right) - \frac{1}{2}$$
$$= -(x - \frac{1}{2})^2 + \frac{1}{4} - \frac{1}{2}$$
$$= -(x - \frac{1}{2})^2 - \frac{1}{4}$$

Solution to Activity 24

(a) First complete the square on the left-hand side.
$$x^2 + 4x + 1 = 0$$
$$(x + 2)^2 - 4 + 1 = 0$$
$$(x + 2)^2 - 3 = 0$$
Now solve this equation.
$$(x + 2)^2 = 3$$
$$x + 2 = \sqrt{3} \quad \text{or} \quad x + 2 = -\sqrt{3}$$
$$x = \sqrt{3} - 2 \quad \text{or} \quad x = -\sqrt{3} - 2$$
So the solutions are $x = \sqrt{3} - 2$ and $x = -\sqrt{3} - 2$.

(b) First complete the square on the left-hand side.
$$3t^2 - 12t + 11 = 0$$
$$3(t^2 - 4t) + 11 = 0$$
$$3((t - 2)^2 - 4) + 11 = 0$$
$$3(t - 2)^2 - 1 = 0$$
Now solve this equation.
$$(t - 2)^2 = \frac{1}{3}$$
$$t - 2 = \frac{1}{\sqrt{3}} \quad \text{or} \quad t - 2 = -\frac{1}{\sqrt{3}}$$
$$t = \frac{1}{\sqrt{3}} + 2 \quad \text{or} \quad t = -\frac{1}{\sqrt{3}} + 2$$
So the solutions are $t = 1/\sqrt{3} + 2$ and $t = -1/\sqrt{3} + 2$.

(c) First complete the square on the left-hand side.

$$2x^2 + 3x - 3 = 0$$

$$2\left(x^2 + \frac{3}{2}x\right) - 3 = 0$$

$$2\left(\left(x + \frac{3}{4}\right)^2 - \frac{9}{16}\right) - 3 = 0$$

$$2\left(x + \frac{3}{4}\right)^2 - \frac{9}{8} - 3 = 0$$

$$2\left(x + \frac{3}{4}\right)^2 - \frac{33}{8} = 0$$

Now solve this equation.

$$\left(x + \frac{3}{4}\right)^2 = \frac{33}{16}$$

$$x + \frac{3}{4} = \frac{\sqrt{33}}{4} \quad \text{or} \quad x + \frac{3}{4} = -\frac{\sqrt{33}}{4}$$

$$x = \frac{\sqrt{33}}{4} - \frac{3}{4} \quad \text{or} \quad x = -\frac{\sqrt{33}}{4} - \frac{3}{4}$$

So the solutions are

$$x = \frac{\sqrt{33} - 3}{4} \quad \text{and} \quad x = -\frac{\sqrt{33} + 3}{4}.$$

Solution to Activity 25

(a) The equation is

$$x^2 - 6x - 1 = 0,$$

so $a = 1$, $b = -6$ and $c = -1$.

The quadratic formula gives

$$x = \frac{-b \pm \sqrt{b^2 - 4ac}}{2a}$$

$$= \frac{-(-6) \pm \sqrt{(-6)^2 - 4 \times 1 \times (-1)}}{2 \times 1}$$

$$= \frac{6 \pm \sqrt{36 + 4}}{2}$$

$$= \frac{6 \pm \sqrt{40}}{2}$$

$$= \frac{6 \pm 2\sqrt{10}}{2}$$

$$= 3 \pm \sqrt{10}.$$

The solutions are $x = 3 + \sqrt{10}$ and $x = 3 - \sqrt{10}$.

(b) The equation is

$$9x^2 + 15x - 6 = 0,$$

which can be simplified to

$$3x^2 + 5x - 2 = 0.$$

So $a = 3$, $b = 5$ and $c = -2$.

The quadratic formula gives

$$x = \frac{-b \pm \sqrt{b^2 - 4ac}}{2a}$$

$$= \frac{-5 \pm \sqrt{5^2 - 4 \times 3 \times (-2)}}{2 \times 3}$$

$$= \frac{-5 \pm \sqrt{25 + 24}}{6}$$

$$= \frac{-5 \pm \sqrt{49}}{6}$$

$$= \frac{-5 \pm 7}{6}$$

$$= \frac{-5 + 7}{6} \quad \text{or} \quad \frac{-5 - 7}{6}$$

$$= \frac{2}{6} \quad \text{or} \quad \frac{-12}{6}$$

$$= \frac{1}{3} \quad \text{or} \quad -2.$$

Alternatively, factorisation gives

$$3x^2 + 5x - 2 = 0$$

$$(3x - 1)(x + 2) = 0$$

$$3x - 1 = 0 \quad \text{or} \quad x + 2 = 0$$

$$x = \frac{1}{3} \quad \text{or} \quad x = -2.$$

The solutions are $x = \frac{1}{3}$ and $x = -2$.

(c) The equation is

$$9x^2 + 6x = 11,$$

which can be rearranged as

$$9x^2 + 6x - 11 = 0.$$

So $a = 9$, $b = 6$ and $c = -11$.

The quadratic formula gives

$$x = \frac{-b \pm \sqrt{b^2 - 4ac}}{2a}$$

$$= \frac{-6 \pm \sqrt{6^2 - 4 \times 9 \times (-11)}}{2 \times 9}$$

$$= \frac{-6 \pm \sqrt{36 + 396}}{18}$$

$$= \frac{-6 \pm \sqrt{432}}{18}$$

$$= \frac{-6 \pm 12\sqrt{3}}{18}$$

$$= \frac{-1 \pm 2\sqrt{3}}{3}.$$

The solutions are $x = \frac{1}{3}(-1 + 2\sqrt{3})$ and $x = \frac{1}{3}(-1 - 2\sqrt{3})$.

(d) The equation is

$$t^2 + \tfrac{5}{2}t + \tfrac{3}{2} = 0,$$

which can be simplified as

$$2t^2 + 5t + 3 = 0.$$

So $a = 2$, $b = 5$ and $c = 3$.

The quadratic formula gives

$$t = \frac{-b \pm \sqrt{b^2 - 4ac}}{2a}$$

$$= \frac{-5 \pm \sqrt{5^2 - 4 \times 2 \times 3}}{2 \times 2}$$

$$= \frac{-5 \pm \sqrt{25 - 24}}{4}$$

$$= \frac{-5 \pm 1}{4}$$

$$= \frac{-5 + 1}{4} \quad \text{or} \quad \frac{-5 - 1}{4}$$

$$= \frac{-4}{4} \quad \text{or} \quad \frac{-6}{4}$$

$$= -1 \quad \text{or} \quad -\frac{3}{2}.$$

Alternatively, factorisation gives

$$2t^2 + 5t + 3 = 0$$

$$(t + 1)(2t + 3) = 0$$

$$t + 1 = 0 \quad \text{or} \quad 2t + 3 = 0$$

$$t = -1 \quad \text{or} \quad t = -\frac{3}{2}.$$

The solutions are $t = -1$ and $t = -\frac{3}{2}$.

(e) The equation is $u^2 = 4u - 4$, which can be rearranged as $u^2 - 4u + 4 = 0$. So $a = 1$, $b = -4$ and $c = 4$.

The quadratic formula gives

$$u = \frac{-b \pm \sqrt{b^2 - 4ac}}{2a}$$

$$= \frac{-(-4) \pm \sqrt{(-4)^2 - 4 \times 1 \times 4}}{2 \times 1}$$

$$= \frac{4 \pm \sqrt{16 - 16}}{2}$$

$$= \frac{4 \pm \sqrt{0}}{2}$$

$$= 2.$$

Alternatively, factorisation gives

$$u^2 - 4u + 4 = 0$$

$$(u - 2)(u - 2) = 0$$

$$u - 2 = 0 \quad \text{or} \quad u - 2 = 0$$

$$u = 2.$$

The only solution is $u = 2$.

Solution to Activity 26

(a) The equation is

$$4x^2 - 20x + 25 = 0,$$

so $a = 4$, $b = -20$ and $c = 25$.

The discriminant is

$$b^2 - 4ac = (-20)^2 - 4 \times 4 \times 25$$

$$= 400 - 400$$

$$= 0.$$

Since the discriminant is 0, there is one solution.

The equation can be solved by factorising, as follows. Since there is only one solution, the two linear expressions in the factorisation must be the same (or one linear expression must be the other multiplied through by some number).

$$4x^2 - 20x + 25 = 0$$

$$(2x - 5)(2x - 5) = 0$$

$$(2x - 5)^2 = 0$$

$$2x - 5 = 0$$

$$x = \frac{5}{2}$$

The only solution is $x = \frac{5}{2}$.

(b) The equation is
$$2x^2 + 6x + 5 = 0,$$
so $a = 2$, $b = 6$ and $c = 5$.

The discriminant is
$$b^2 - 4ac = 6^2 - 4 \times 2 \times 5 = 36 - 40 = -4.$$

Since the discriminant is negative, there are no real solutions.

(c) The equation can be rearranged as follows:
$$4x^2 = 4x + 5$$
$$4x^2 - 4x - 5 = 0.$$
So $a = 4$, $b = -4$ and $c = -5$.

The discriminant is
$$b^2 - 4ac = (-4)^2 - 4 \times 4 \times (-5)$$
$$= 16 + 80$$
$$= 96.$$

Since the discriminant is positive, there are two real solutions.

The equation cannot be factorised using integers, so we solve it by using the quadratic formula. This gives
$$x = \frac{-b \pm \sqrt{b^2 - 4ac}}{2a} = \frac{-(-4) \pm \sqrt{96}}{2 \times 4}$$
$$= \frac{4 \pm 4\sqrt{6}}{8}$$
$$= \tfrac{1}{2}(1 \pm \sqrt{6}).$$

The solutions are $x = \tfrac{1}{2}(1 + \sqrt{6})$ and $x = \tfrac{1}{2}(1 - \sqrt{6})$.

(The value of $b^2 - 4ac$ was already worked out before the quadratic formula was used, so this value was substituted in, instead of working it out again.)

Solution to Activity 27

(a) The equation is $\dfrac{4}{x} = \dfrac{3x}{x+1}$.

Assume that $x \neq 0$ and $x \neq -1$.

Multiply through by $x(x+1)$ to clear the fractions.
$$4(x + 1) = 3x \times x$$

Rearrange this equation.
$$4x + 4 = 3x^2$$
$$3x^2 - 4x - 4 = 0$$
$$(3x + 2)(x - 2) = 0$$
$$3x + 2 = 0 \quad \text{or} \quad x - 2 = 0$$
$$x = -\frac{2}{3} \quad \text{or} \quad x = 2$$

Neither value is 0 or -1, so the solutions of the original equation are $x = -\frac{2}{3}$ and $x = 2$.

(b) The equation is $\dfrac{1}{x-2} = 1 + 4x$.

Assume that $x \neq 2$.

Multiply through by $x - 2$ to clear the fraction.
$$1 = (1 + 4x)(x - 2)$$

Rearrange this equation.
$$1 = 4x^2 - 7x - 2$$
$$4x^2 - 7x - 3 = 0$$

This quadratic cannot be factorised, so use the quadratic formula with $a = 4$, $b = -7$, $c = -3$.
$$x = \frac{-b \pm \sqrt{b^2 - 4ac}}{2a}$$
$$= \frac{-(-7) \pm \sqrt{(-7)^2 - 4 \times 4 \times (-3)}}{2 \times 4}$$
$$= \frac{7 \pm \sqrt{49 + 48}}{8}$$
$$= \frac{7 \pm \sqrt{97}}{8}$$

Neither value is 2, so the solutions of the original equation are $x = \frac{1}{8}(7 + \sqrt{97})$ and $x = \frac{1}{8}(7 - \sqrt{97})$.

(c) The equation is $2x^3 - 2x^2 - 12x = 0$.

Take out the common factor $2x$.
$$2x(x^2 - x - 6) = 0$$
So $2x = 0$ or $x^2 - x - 6 = 0$.

The equation $2x = 0$ gives $x = 0$.

Factorise the quadratic $x^2 - x - 6$.
$$(x - 3)(x + 2) = 0$$
So $x - 3 = 0$ or $x + 2 = 0$, giving $x = 3$ or $x = -2$.

So the solutions of $2x^3 - 2x^2 - 12x = 0$ are $x = 0$, $x = 3$ and $x = -2$.

(d) The equation is $x^4 - 2x^2 - 8 = 0$.

It includes only even powers of x, so let $X = x^2$. The equation becomes
$$X^2 - 2X - 8 = 0.$$
Factorise the quadratic.
$$(X - 4)(X + 2) = 0$$
So $X - 4 = 0$ or $X + 2 = 0$, giving $X = 4$ or $X = -2$.

Now $X = x^2$, so x satisfies $x^2 = 4$ or $x^2 = -2$.

The equation $x^2 = -2$ has no real solutions. The equation $x^2 = 4$ gives $x = \pm 2$.

So the solutions are $x = -2$ and $x = 2$.

(e) The equation is $u^4 - 4 = 0$, which can be rearranged as $u^4 = 4$. Taking the square root of both sides gives $u^2 = \pm 2$.

There are no real solutions satisfying $u^2 = -2$. The equation $u^2 = 2$ gives two solutions, $u = \sqrt{2}$ and $u = -\sqrt{2}$.

(f) The equation is $s^5 - 9s^3 = 0$.

Taking out the common factor s^3 gives
$$s^3(s^2 - 9) = 0.$$
So $s^3 = 0$ or $s^2 - 9 = 0$. The first equation has just one solution, $s = 0$. The second equation has two solutions, $s = \pm 3$.

So the solutions are $s = 0$, $s = 3$ and $s = -3$.

(g) The equation is $(t^2 - 3)(t^2 - 3t + 2) = 0$.

So $t^2 - 3 = 0$ or $t^2 - 3t + 2 = 0$.

If $t^2 - 3 = 0$, then $t^2 = 3$, giving $t = \pm\sqrt{3}$.

If $t^2 - 3t + 2 = 0$, then $(t - 1)(t - 2) = 0$, giving $t = 1$ or $t = 2$.

So the solutions are $t = 1$, $t = 2$, $t = \sqrt{3}$ and $t = -\sqrt{3}$.

Solution to Activity 28

(a) The equation is $y = -2x^2 + 3x - 1$.

Since the coefficient of x^2 is negative, the graph is n-shaped.

Putting $x = 0$ gives $y = -2 \times 0^2 + 3 \times 0 - 1 = -1$, so the y-intercept is -1.

To find the x-intercepts (if any), solve
$$0 = -2x^2 + 3x - 1.$$

Simplify by multiplying through by -1:
$$2x^2 - 3x + 1 = 0.$$
Factorising gives
$$(2x - 1)(x - 1) = 0.$$
So $2x - 1 = 0$ or $x - 1 = 0$, giving $x = \frac{1}{2}$ or $x = 1$. The x-intercepts are $\frac{1}{2}$ and 1.

The axis of symmetry lies halfway between the points $(\frac{1}{2}, 0)$ and $(1, 0)$, so its equation is
$$x = \frac{1/2 + 1}{2} = \frac{3}{4}.$$
The vertex lies on the axis of symmetry, so it has y-coordinate
$$y = -2\left(\frac{3}{4}\right)^2 + 3 \times \frac{3}{4} - 1 = \frac{1}{8}.$$
So the vertex is $(\frac{3}{4}, \frac{1}{8})$.

This is shown in the following graph.

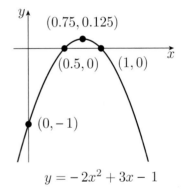

$$y = -2x^2 + 3x - 1$$

(b) The equation is $y = 2x^2 + 8x + 8$.

Since the coefficient of x^2 is positive, the graph is u-shaped.

Putting $x = 0$ gives $y = 2 \times 0^2 + 8 \times 0 + 8 = 8$, so the y-intercept is 8.

To find the x-intercepts (if any), solve
$$0 = 2x^2 + 8x + 8.$$
Simplify by factoring out the common factor 2:
$$x^2 + 4x + 4 = 0.$$
Factorising gives
$$(x + 2)(x + 2) = 0.$$
So $x + 2 = 0$, giving $x = -2$ as the only x-intercept. Hence $(-2, 0)$ is the only point of the curve on the x-axis, so this is the vertex.

The graph is shown below.

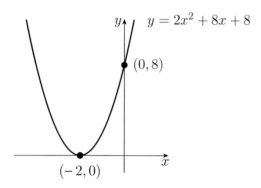

Solution to Activity 29

The equation is $y = x^2 - 2x + 4$.

Since the coefficient of x^2 is positive, the graph is u-shaped.

Putting $x = 0$ gives $y = 0^2 - 2 \times 0 + 4 = 4$, so the y-intercept is 4 and the point $(0, 4)$ lies on the curve.

To find the x-intercepts (if any), solve

$$0 = x^2 - 2x + 4.$$

The discriminant of this quadratic is

$$b^2 - 4ac = (-2)^2 - 4 \times 1 \times 4 = 4 - 16 = -12,$$

which is negative. So the quadratic equation above has no real solutions and there are no x-intercepts.

Rearrange the equation $y = x^2 - 2x + 4$ as

$$y = x(x - 2) + 4.$$

It follows that $x = 0$ and $x = 2$ have the same y-coordinate 4, so the points $(0, 4)$ and $(2, 4)$ lie on the graph.

The axis of symmetry lies halfway between the points $(0, 4)$ and $(2, 4)$, so its equation is

$$x = \frac{1}{2}(0 + 2) = 1.$$

The vertex lies on the axis of symmetry, so it has y-coordinate $y = 1^2 - 2 \times 1 + 4 = 3$.

So the vertex is $(1, 3)$.

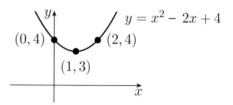

Solution to Activity 30

(a) Substitute $t = 2$ into $s = 12t - 5t^2$ to give

$$s = 12 \times 2 - 5 \times 2^2 = 24 - 20 = 4.$$

So the ball will be at height 4 m after 2 seconds.

(b) To find when the ball is at height 5 m, solve

$$5 = 12t - 5t^2.$$

Rearranging gives

$$5t^2 - 12t + 5 = 0.$$

Use the quadratic formula with $a = 5$, $b = -12$ and $c = 5$ to give

$$\begin{aligned}
t &= \frac{-b \pm \sqrt{b^2 - 4ac}}{2a} \\
&= \frac{-(-12) \pm \sqrt{(-12)^2 - 4 \times 5 \times 5}}{2 \times 5} \\
&= \frac{12 \pm \sqrt{44}}{10} \\
&= \frac{12 \pm 2\sqrt{11}}{10} \\
&= 0.54 \quad \text{or} \quad 1.86 \text{ (to 2 d.p.).}
\end{aligned}$$

So the ball is at height 5 m on two occasions, namely 0.54 s and 1.86 s after it was thrown (once on the way up and once on the way down).

(c) The ball returns to its starting position when its vertical displacement is zero, that is, when $s = 0$. Substituting $s = 0$ in $s = 12t - 5t^2$ gives

$$0 = 12t - 5t^2.$$

Factorising gives

$$t(12 - 5t) = 0.$$

So $t = 0$ or $12 - 5t = 0$, giving $t = 0$ or $t = \frac{12}{5} = 2.4$.

The solution $t = 0$ corresponds to the time when the ball is at its starting position, at the beginning of its motion, so the ball returns to this position 2.4 s later.

(d) Completing the square in the quadratic expression for s gives

$$s = -5\left(t^2 - \frac{12}{5}t\right)$$
$$= -5\left(\left(t - \frac{6}{5}\right)^2 - \frac{36}{25}\right)$$
$$= -5\left(t - \frac{6}{5}\right)^2 + \frac{36}{5}.$$

The maximum value of s occurs when $5\left(t - \frac{6}{5}\right)^2$ is zero, that is, when $t = \frac{6}{5} = 1.2$. So the maximum height that a ball will reach above its starting position is 1.2 m.

When $t = \frac{6}{5}$ the value of s is $\frac{36}{5} = 7.2$, so the maximum height of the ball is 7.2 m.

Acknowledgements

Grateful acknowledgement is made to the following sources:

Page 147: Taken from:
www.metoffice.gov.uk/media/image/4/1/forecast_chart.jpg

Page 156: Credit: Jodrell Bank Centre for Astrophysics, University of Manchester

Page 156: Michael Mags.
http://en.wikipedia.org/wiki/File:Bouncing_ball_strobe_edit.jpg

Every effort has been made to contact copyright holders. If any have been inadvertently overlooked the publishers will be pleased to make the necessary arrangements at the first opportunity.

Unit 3

Functions

Introduction

In mathematics you often work with situations in which one quantity depends on another. For example:

- The distance walked by a woman at a particular speed depends on the time that she's been walking.

- The height of a gondola on a Ferris wheel depends on the angle through which the wheel has rotated since the gondola was in its lowest position.

- The number of 5-litre tins of a particular type of paint needed by a decorator depends on the area that he intends to paint.

Whenever one quantity depends on another, we say that the first quantity is a **function** of the second quantity. The idea of a function is fundamental in mathematics, and in particular it forms the foundation for *calculus*, which you'll begin to study in Unit 6.

A Ferris wheel

In this unit you'll be introduced to the terminology and notation that are used for functions. You'll learn about some standard, frequently-arising types of functions, and how to use graphs to visualise properties of functions. You'll also learn how you can use your knowledge about a few standard functions to help you understand and work with a wide range of related functions. Later in the unit you'll revise *exponential functions* and *logarithms*, and practise working with them. In the final section you'll revise *inequalities*, and see how working with functions and their graphs can help you understand and solve some quite complicated inequalities.

This is a long unit. The study calendar allows extra time for you to study it.

1 Functions and their graphs

This section introduces you to the idea of a function and its graph, and shows you some standard functions. You'll start by learning about *sets*, which are needed when you work with functions and also in many other areas of mathematics.

1.1 Sets of real numbers

In mathematics a **set** is a collection of objects. The objects could be anything at all: they could be numbers, points in the plane, equations or anything else. For example, each of the following collections of objects forms a set:

- all the prime numbers less than 100
- all the points on any particular line in the plane
- all the equations that represent vertical lines
- the solutions of any particular quadratic equation.

A set can contain any number of objects. It could contain one object, two objects, twenty objects, infinitely many objects, or even no objects at all.

Each object in a set is called an **element** or **member** of the set, and we say that the elements of the set **belong to** or are **in** the set.

There are many ways to specify a set. If there are just a few elements, then you can list them, enclosing them in curly brackets. For example, you can specify a set S as follows:

$$S = \{3, 7, 9, 42\}.$$

Another simple way to specify a set is to describe it. For example, you can say 'let T be the set of all even integers' or 'let U be the set of all real numbers greater than 5'. We usually denote sets by capital letters.

The set that contains no elements at all is called the **empty set**, and is denoted by the symbol $\varnothing$.

It's often useful to state that a particular object is or is not a member of a particular set. You can do this concisely using the symbols $\in$ and $\notin$, which mean 'is in' and 'is not in', respectively. For example, if S is the set specified above, then the following statements are true:

$$7 \in S \quad \text{and} \quad 10 \notin S.$$

Activity 1   *Understanding set notation*

Let $X = \{1, 2, 3, 4\}$ and let Y be the set of all odd integers. Which of the following statements are true?

(a) $1 \in X$ (b) $1 \in Y$ (c) $2 \notin X$ (d) $2 \notin Y$

It's often useful to construct 'new sets out of old sets'. For example, if A and B are any two sets, then you can form a new set whose members are all the objects that belong to *both* A and B. This set is called the **intersection** of A and B, and is denoted by $A \cap B$. For instance, if

$$A = \{1, 2, 3, 4\} \quad \text{and} \quad B = \{3, 4, 5\},$$

then

$A \cap B = \{3, 4\}.$

Similarly, if A and B are any two sets, then you can form a new set whose members are all the objects that belong to *either* A or B (or both). This set is called the **union** of A and B, and is denoted by $A \cup B$. For example, if A and B are as specified above, then

$A \cup B = \{1, 2, 3, 4, 5\}.$

You might find it helpful to visualise intersections and unions of sets by using diagrams like those in Figure 1, which are known as **Venn diagrams**. The Venn diagrams in the figure show the intersection and union of the particular sets A and B above.

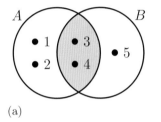 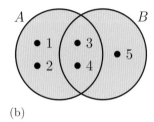

(a)　　　　　　(b)

Figure 1   (a) The intersection (shaded) and (b) the union (shaded) of two sets

Venn diagrams are named after the logician John Venn, who used them in publications starting in 1880. However, the idea of using diagrams in this way did not originate with Venn. The prolific Swiss mathematician Leonhard Euler (pronounced 'oiler') used them in his *Letters to a German Princess* (1760–62). Venn acknowledged Euler's influence by calling his own diagrams 'Eulerian circles'. He extended Euler's idea, using the diagrams to analyse more complex logical problems. As well as working on logic at Cambridge University, Venn was for some time a priest and later a historian. There is more about Euler on page 214.

John Venn (1834–1923)

You can form intersections and unions of more than two sets in a similar way. In general, the **intersection** of two or more sets is the set of all objects that belong to *all* of the original sets, and the **union** of two or more sets is the set of all objects that belong to *any* of the original sets. For example, if A and B are as specified above and

$C = \{20, 21\},$

then

$A \cap B \cap C = \varnothing \quad \text{and} \quad A \cup B \cup C = \{1, 2, 3, 4, 5, 20, 21\}.$

Let $P = \{1, 2, 3, 4, 5, 6\}$, let $Q = \{2, 4, 6, 8, 10, 12\}$ and let R be the set of all integers divisible by 3. Specify each of the following sets.

(a) $P \cap Q$ (b) $Q \cap R$ (c) $P \cap Q \cap R$ (d) $P \cup Q$

The set membership symbol $\in$ is a stylised version of the Greek letter ε (epsilon). The Italian mathematician Giuseppe Peano (1858–1932), the founder of symbolic logic, used ε to indicate set membership in a text published in 1889. He stated that it was an abbreviation for the Latin word 'est', which means 'is'. The symbol was then adopted by the logician Bertrand Russell (1872–1970) in a text published in 1903, but it was typeset in a form that looks like the modern symbol $\in$, and this form has remained in use to the present day. Peano also introduced the symbols $\cap$ and $\cup$ for intersection and union.

The empty set symbol $\varnothing$ was introduced in 1939 by the influential French mathematician André Weil (1906–1998). It was inspired by the letter ø in the Norwegian alphabet.

Sometimes every element of a set A is also an element of a set B. In this case we say that A is a **subset** of B, and we write $A \subseteq B$. For example:

- $\{1, 3\}$ is a subset of $\{1, 2, 3\}$ (as shown in Figure 2)
- the set of integers is a subset of the set of real numbers.

Every set is a subset of itself, and the empty set is a subset of every set.

In this module, and particularly in this unit, you'll mostly be working with sets whose elements are real numbers. In the rest of this subsection, you'll meet some useful ways to visualise and represent sets of this type.

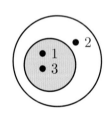

Figure 2 A subset of a set (shaded)

The set of *all* real numbers is denoted by $\mathbb{R}$. You can handwrite this as:

$\mathbb{R}$.

You saw in Unit 1 that you can visualise the real numbers as points on an infinitely long straight line, called the **number line** or the **real line**. Part of the number line is shown in Figure 3. Although only the integers are marked in the diagram, every point on the line represents a real number.

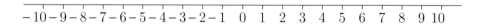

Figure 3 The number line

You can use the number line to visualise sets of real numbers. For example:

- Figure 4(a) shows the set $\{-1, 0, 1\}$.
- Figure 4(b) shows the set of real numbers that are greater than or equal to 2 and also less than or equal to 6.
- Figure 4(c) shows the set of real numbers that are greater than -5.
- Figure 4(d) shows the set of real numbers that are less than $\frac{1}{2}$ or greater than or equal to 3.

In these kinds of diagrams, a solid dot indicates a number that's included in the set, and a hollow dot indicates a number that isn't included. A heavy line that continues to the left or right end of the diagram indicates that the set extends indefinitely in that direction.

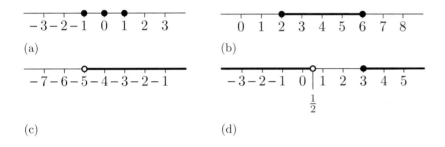

(a)

(b)

(c)

(d)

Figure 4 Sets of real numbers

The sets in Figure 4(b) and (c) are examples of a special type of set of real numbers, called an *interval*. An **interval** is a set of real numbers that corresponds to a part of the number line that you can draw 'without lifting your pen from the paper'. The sets in Figure 4(a) and (d) aren't intervals, as they have 'gaps' in them. In fact, the set in Figure 4(a) is the union of three intervals (each containing a single number), and the set in Figure 4(d) is the union of two intervals.

A number that lies at an end of an interval is called an **endpoint** of the interval. For example, the interval in Figure 4(b) has two endpoints, namely 2 and 6, and the interval in Figure 4(c) has one endpoint, namely -5. The whole set of real numbers, $\mathbb{R}$, is an interval with no endpoints.

An interval that includes all of its endpoints is said to be **closed**, and one that doesn't include any of its endpoints is said to be **open**. For example, the interval in Figure 4(b) is closed (since it includes both its endpoints), and the one in Figure 4(c) is open (since it excludes its single endpoint). An interval that includes one endpoint and excludes another, such as the interval in Figure 5, is said to be **half-open** (or **half-closed**). Since the interval $\mathbb{R}$ has no endpoints, it's both open and closed! This fact may seem strange at the moment, but it will make more sense if you go on to study pure mathematics at higher levels.

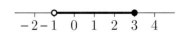

Figure 5 A half-open (or half-closed) interval

Activity 3   *Recognising intervals*

State whether each of the sets below is an interval. For each set that is an interval, state whether it's open, closed or half-open.

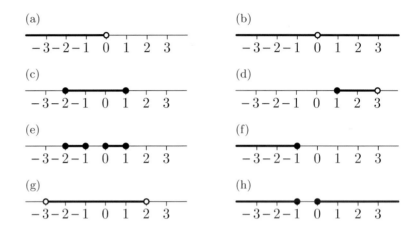

(a)

(b)

(c)

(d)

(e)

(f)

(g)

(h)

A convenient way to describe most intervals is to use **inequality signs**. These are listed below, with their meanings. (Note that some texts use slightly different inequality signs: $\leqslant$ and $\geqslant$ instead of $\leq$ and $\geq$.)

Inequality signs

$<$ is less than

$\leq$ is less than or equal to

$>$ is greater than

$\geq$ is greater than or equal to

For example, the interval in Figure 6(a) is the set of real numbers x such that $x > 2$ (that is, such that x is greater than 2).

Similarly, the interval in Figure 6(b) is the set of real numbers x such that $x > 1$ and $x \leq 4$ (that is, such that x is greater than 1 and x is less than or equal to 4). We usually write this description slightly more concisely, as follows: the interval is the set of real numbers x such that $1 < x \leq 4$ (that is, such that 1 is less than x, which is less than or equal to 4).

Figure 6   Intervals

It might help you to remember the meanings of the inequality signs if you notice that when you use either of the signs $<$ or $>$, the lesser quantity is on the smaller, pointed side of the sign. The same is true for the signs $\leq$ and $\geq$, except that one quantity is less than or equal to the other, rather than definitely less than it.

The statement '$x > 2$' is called an *inequality*. In general, an **inequality** is a mathematical statement that consists of two expressions with an inequality sign between them. A statement such as '$1 < x \leq 4$' is called a **double inequality**. The two inequality signs in a double inequality always point in the same direction as each other.

Activity 4   *Using inequality signs to describe intervals*

(a) Draw diagrams similar to those in Figure 6 to illustrate the intervals described by the following inequalities and double inequalities.

   (i) $0 < x < 1$ (ii) $-3 \leq x < 2$ (iii) $x \leq 5$ (iv) $x > 4$

(b) For each of the following diagrams, write down an inequality or double inequality that describes the interval illustrated.

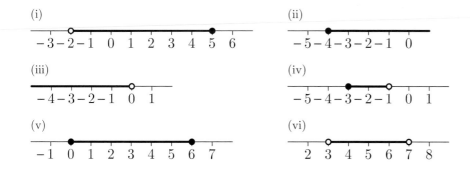

Another useful way to describe intervals is to use **interval notation**. For example, the interval described by the double inequality $4 \leq x < 7$ is denoted in interval notation by $[4, 7)$. The square bracket indicates an included endpoint, and the round bracket indicates an excluded one. An interval that extends indefinitely is denoted by using the symbol ∞ (which is read as 'infinity'), or its 'negative', $-\infty$ (which is read as 'minus infinity'), in place of an endpoint. For example, the interval described by the inequality $x \geq 5$ is denoted by $[5, \infty)$, and the interval described by the inequality $x < 6$ is denoted by $(-\infty, 6)$. We always use a round bracket next to ∞ or $-\infty$ in interval notation. Here's a summary of the notation.

Interval notation

Open intervals

(a, b)	(a, ∞)	$(-\infty, b)$	$(-\infty, \infty)$
$a < x < b$	$x > a$	$x < b$	$\mathbb{R}$

Closed intervals

$[a, b]$	$[a, \infty)$	$(-\infty, b]$	$(-\infty, \infty)$	$\{a\}$
$a \le x \le b$	$x \ge a$	$x \le b$	$\mathbb{R}$	$x = a$

Half-open (or half-closed) intervals

$[a, b)$	$(a, b]$
$a \le x < b$	$a < x \le b$

Notice that you've now seen two different meanings for the notation (a, b), where a and b are real numbers. It can mean either an open interval, or a point in the coordinate plane. The meaning is usually clear from the context.

Activity 5   *Using interval notation*

Write each of the intervals below in interval notation.

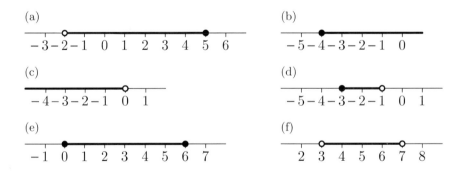

Sometimes you need to work with sets of real numbers that are *unions* of intervals, like those in Figure 7.

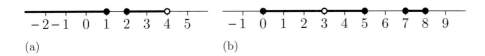

(a)   (b)

Figure 7   Two unions of intervals

You can denote a union of intervals in interval notation by using the usual notation for intervals together with the union symbol ∪. For example, the sets in Figure 7 can be written as

$$(-\infty, 1] \cup [2, 4) \quad \text{and} \quad [0, 3) \cup (3, 5] \cup [7, 8],$$

respectively.

Activity 6   *Denoting unions of intervals*

For each of the following diagrams, write the set illustrated in interval notation.

(a)

(b)   (c)

It's often useful to state that a particular number lies in, or doesn't lie in, a particular interval or union of intervals. You can do this concisely using the symbols ∈ and ∉ in the usual way. For example, as illustrated in Figure 8,

$$1 \in [0, 4] \quad \text{and} \quad -1 \notin [0, 4].$$

In the next subsection you'll begin your study of *functions*.

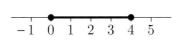

Figure 8   The interval $[0, 4]$

1.2   What is a function?

As mentioned in the introduction to this unit, whenever one quantity depends on another, we say that the first quantity is a **function** of the second quantity. Here are some more examples.

- If a car is driving along a straight road, then its displacement s (in km) from some reference point depends on the time t (in hours) that has elapsed since the start of its journey. So s is a function of t.

- The formula

$$C = 2\pi r$$

  expresses the circumference C of a circle in terms of its radius r (with both C and r measured in the same units). So the value of C depends on the value of r, and hence C is a function of r.

- The electrical voltage between two points on a person's skin either side of his or her heart (which can be measured using electrodes) changes rhythmically with every heartbeat. So the voltage V (in volts, say) depends on the time t (in seconds, say) that has elapsed since some point in time, and hence V is a function of t. There's no simple formula for the relationship between t and V, but it's often displayed as an *electrocardiogram* (ECG), like the one in Figure 9.

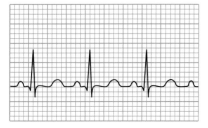

Figure 9
An electrocardiogram (each high peak in voltage corresponds to a heartbeat)

In each of these examples, there's a rule that converts each value of one variable (such as t, in the car example) to a value of the other variable (such as s, in the car example). You can think of the rule as a kind of processor that takes input values and produces output values, as illustrated in Figure 10.

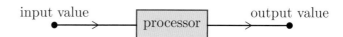

Figure 10 A processor that takes input values and produces output values

For instance, in the car example, an input value of 1.2 (a time, in hours) might be converted by the processor to an output value of 60 (a displacement, in kilometres). Similarly, in the circle example, an input value of 3 (a radius, in centimetres) would be converted by the processor to an output value of $2\pi \times 3 = 6\pi$ (a circumference, in centimetres). Sometimes the rule associated with a function can be expressed using a formula, and sometimes it can't.

In each of the three examples in the list above, there's also a set of allowed input values, and a set of values within which every output value lies. For instance, with the car example, if the journey lasts three hours, then the allowed input values are the real numbers between 0 and 3 inclusive (the possible elapsed times, in hours), and the output values lie in the set $\mathbb{R}$ of real numbers (they are displacements of the car from the reference point, in kilometres).

A *function* is a mathematical object that describes a situation like those listed above. It's defined as follows.

A **function** consists of:

- a set of allowed input values, called the **domain** of the function

- a set of values in which every output value lies, called the **codomain** of the function

- a process, called the **rule** of the function, for converting each input value into *exactly one* output value.

It's often useful to denote a function by a letter. If a function is denoted by f, say, then for any input value x, the corresponding output value is denoted by $f(x)$, which is read as 'f of x'.

For example, suppose that we denote the function associated with the car example by f. If the rule of this function converts the input value 1.2 to the output value 60, then we write

$$f(1.2) = 60.$$

Similarly, suppose that we denote the function associated with the circle example by g. The rule of this function converts the input value 3 to the output value 6π, so we write

$$g(3) = 6\pi.$$

This type of notation is known as **function notation**.

One use of function notation is for specifying the rule of a function, when this can be done using a formula. For example, suppose that h is the function whose domain and codomain each consist of all the real numbers, and whose rule is 'square the input number'. Then, for example,

$$h(2) = 4, \quad h(5) = 25 \quad \text{and} \quad h(-1) = 1,$$

and the rule of h can be written as

$$h(x) = x^2.$$

Similarly, the rule of the function associated with the circle example can be written as $g(r) = 2\pi r$.

When you write down the rule of a function, it doesn't matter what letter you use to represent the input value. So the rule of the function h above could also be written as, for example,

$$h(t) = t^2 \quad \text{or} \quad h(u) = u^2.$$

The variable used to denote the input value of a function is sometimes called the **input variable**.

It's traditional to use the letters f, g and h for functions, and the letters x, t and u for input variables. Although you can use any letters, these ones are often used in general discussions about functions. The most standard letters are f for a function and x for an input variable.

> **Activity 7**   *Understanding function notation*
>
> (a) Suppose that f is the function whose domain and codomain each consist of all the real numbers, and whose rule is $f(t) = 4t$. Write down the values of $f(5)$ and $f(-3)$.
>
> (b) Suppose that g is the function whose domain and codomain each consist of all the real numbers, and whose rule can be written in words as 'multiply the input number by 2 and then subtract 1'. Write down the rule of g using the notation $g(x)$.

It's important to appreciate that *every* value in the domain of a function must have a corresponding output value, given by the rule of the function. So, for example, a function f that has the rule

$$f(x) = \sqrt{x}$$

can't have any negative numbers in its domain, because if x is negative, then $\sqrt{x}$ isn't defined.

As another example, if a function f describes how the displacement in kilometres of a car from a particular point depends on the time in hours since it started a 3-hour journey, then we'd normally take the domain of f to be the interval $[0, 3]$.

In contrast, not every value in the codomain of a function actually has to occur as an output value. For instance, with the car example, we'd normally take the codomain to be the whole set of real numbers, $\mathbb{R}$. It's good enough that this set contains every possible output value: it doesn't matter that it also contains many values that couldn't be output values.

The set of values in the codomain of a function that *do* occur as output values is called the **image set** of the function. For example, if f is the function whose domain and codomain are each the whole set of real numbers, $\mathbb{R}$, and whose rule is $f(x) = x^2$, then the image set of f is the interval $[0, \infty)$.

Here's another fact about functions that it's important to appreciate. Not only must every value in the domain of a function have a corresponding output value, given by the rule of the function, but it must have *exactly one* output value. For example, a function f can't have the rule $f(x) = \pm\sqrt{x}$, because this rule assigns *two* output values to every input value (except zero).

You can visualise the facts about functions described above by using a type of diagram known as a **mapping diagram**, which is based on Venn diagrams. (The word **mapping** is another name for *function*.) For example, the mapping diagram in Figure 11 illustrates the function f that has domain $\{1, 2, 3\}$, codomain $\{2, 4, 6, 8, 10\}$ and rule $f(x) = 2x$. The arrows indicate which input value goes to which output value. Notice that *exactly one* arrow comes out of each input value. This corresponds to the fact that each input value has exactly one output value. Notice also that the image set consists of all the values that have arrows going in to them, and that (for this particular function f) the codomain contains other values too.

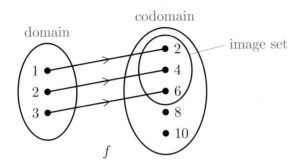

Figure 11   A function f illustrated by a mapping diagram

Here's some more terminology associated with functions. If f is a function, and x is any value in its domain, then the value $f(x)$ is called the **image of x under f**, or the **value of f at x**. This is illustrated in Figure 12. We also say that f **maps** x to $f(x)$.

For example, $f(2) = 4$ for the function f in Figure 11 above, so we can say that the image of 2 under f is 4, or f takes the value 4 at 2, or f maps 2 to 4.

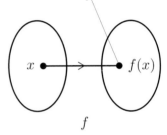

Figure 12   The image of a value x under a function f

> **Activity 8**   *Understanding function terminology*
>
> Suppose that f is the function whose domain and codomain each consist of all the real numbers, and whose rule is $f(t) = 4t$. Write down the following numbers.
>
> (a) The image of 2 under f
>
> (b) The image of -1 under f
>
> (c) The value of f at 0.5
>
> (d) The value of f at -0.2
>
> (e) The number whose image under f is 44
>
> (f) The number whose image under f is 1
>
> (g) The number to which f maps 4
>
> (h) The number that is mapped by f to -8

In this module you'll be working only with functions whose domains and codomains are sets of real numbers. Such functions are called **real functions**. You can also have other types of functions, such as a function whose domain and/or codomain is a set of another type of numbers (complex numbers, for instance), or a set of points in the plane. You'll meet many more types of functions if you go on to study mathematics beyond this module.

Since we'll be working only with real functions in this module, we'll make some simplifying assumptions.

> In this module:
>
> - we use the word 'function' to mean 'real function'
> - we take the codomain of every function to be the whole set of real numbers, since this set contains every possible output value.

These assumptions allow you to specify any function by stating its domain and its rule. It's important to remember that to specify a function, *a domain must be stated*, as well as a rule. Two functions with the same rule but different domains are different functions.

> The concept of a function was first formally defined by the Swiss mathematician Johann Bernoulli (1667–1748) in 1718. But the mathematician who gave prominence to the concept, and who was responsible for the notation $f(x)$, was Bernoulli's compatriot Leonhard Euler. Euler was one of the most talented and productive mathematicians of all time. He became blind in the early 1770s but his output, rather than stopping, actually increased. His work covers almost every area of mathematics, and his collected works run to over 70 volumes, with further volumes still to appear.

Leonhard Euler (1707–83)

1.3 Specifying functions

You've seen that to specify a function you have to state its domain and its rule. There are various ways to state the domain and rule of a function. Here's the format that we'll usually use in this module. For example, to specify the function f whose rule is $f(x) = x^2 + 1$ and whose domain is the interval consisting of the real numbers between 0 and 6, inclusive, we'll write either

$$f(x) = x^2 + 1 \quad (0 \le x \le 6)$$

or

$$f(x) = x^2 + 1 \quad (x \in [0, 6]).$$

We'll be even more concise when we want to specify a function whose domain is the largest possible set of real numbers for which its rule is applicable. For example, the function

$$g(x) = \sqrt{x} \quad (x \in [0, \infty))$$

is such a function: its domain is as large as it can be, because $\sqrt{x}$ is defined only for non-negative values of x. We'll usually specify a function like this by stating just its rule. This is because of the following convention, which is widely used in mathematics.

Domain convention

When a function is specified by *just a rule*, it's understood that the domain of the function is the largest possible set of real numbers for which the rule is applicable.

For example, if you read 'the function $h(x) = 1/x$', and no domain is stated, then you can assume that the domain of h is the set of all real numbers except 0.

Notice that we say, for example, 'the function $h(x) = 1/x$', when we really mean 'the function h with rule $h(x) = 1/x$'. This is another convenient convention, which is used throughout this module and throughout mathematics in general.

Activity 9   *Using the domain convention*

Describe the domain of each of the following functions, both in words and using interval notation.

(a) $f(x) = \dfrac{1}{x-4}$ (b) $g(x) = \dfrac{1}{(x-2)(x+3)}$ (c) $h(x) = \sqrt{x-1}$

Another situation where we sometimes specify a function by giving just a rule, rather than a rule and a domain, is where the domain is clear from the context. For example, if the function f is such that $f(t)$ is the displacement in kilometres of a car at time t (in hours) after it began a 3-hour journey, then we assume that the domain of f is the interval $[0,3]$, since in this context these are the values that t can take.

Functions specified by equations for one variable in terms of another

Functions don't have to be specified using function notation. Sometimes it's convenient to express a function using an equation that expresses one variable in terms of another variable. For example, as mentioned earlier, the circumference C of a circle is given in terms of its radius r by the formula

$$C = 2\pi r. \tag{1}$$

Here C is a function of r, and, as you've seen, we can write this function as

$$g(r) = 2\pi r \quad (r > 0).$$

215

But there's no need to use function notation: equation (1) is a perfectly good specification of the rule of the function.

In general, any equation that expresses one variable in terms of another variable specifies the rule of a function. If we wish to specify a domain that's not the largest possible set of real numbers for which the equation is applicable, then we can do so in the usual way. For example, we can write

$$C = 2\pi r \quad (r > 0).$$

When a function is specified using an equation that expresses one variable in terms of another variable, the output variable is called the **dependent variable**, because its value depends on the value of the input variable. The input variable is called the **independent variable**. For example, for the function discussed above whose rule is $C = 2\pi r$, the dependent variable is C and the independent variable is r.

We often refer to an equation that specifies a function *as* a function. For example, we might say 'the function $y = x^2 + 1$', when we really mean 'the function specified by the rule $y = x^2 + 1$'. This is another convenient convention.

Both types of notation for functions – function notation and equations relating input and output variables – are used throughout this module.

Piecewise-defined functions

Sometimes it's useful to specify the rule of a function by using different formulas for different parts of its domain. For example, you can specify a function f as follows:

$$f(x) = \begin{cases} x^2 & (x \geq 0) \\ x + 5 & (x < 0). \end{cases}$$

To find the image of a number x under this function f, you use the rule $f(x) = x^2$ if x is greater than or equal to zero, and the rule $f(x) = x + 5$ if x is less than zero. For example,

$$f(2) = 2^2 = 4 \quad \text{and} \quad f(-2) = -2 + 5 = 3.$$

A function defined in this way is called a **piecewise-defined function**.

Such piecewise-defined functions can be used to construct curves with a great variety of shapes, so they are used extensively in the design of objects such as car bodies and roads.

1.4 Graphs of functions

A convenient way to visualise many of the properties of a function is to draw or plot its *graph*. The **graph** of a function f is the graph of the equation $y = f(x)$, for all the values of x that are in the domain of f. In other words, it's the set of points (x, y) in the coordinate plane such that x is in the domain of f and $y = f(x)$.

For example, the graph of the function $f(x) = x^2 + 1$ is the graph of the equation $y = x^2 + 1$, which is shown in Figure 13(a).

Similarly, the graph of the function $g(x) = x^2 + 1 \ (0 < x \leq 2)$ is the graph of the equation $y = x^2 + 1$ for values of x in the interval $(0, 2]$, which is shown in Figure 13(b).

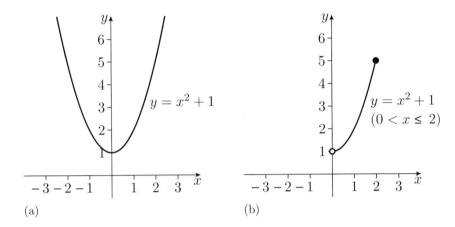

(a)

(b)

Figure 13   The graphs of (a) $f(x) = x^2 + 1$ (b) $f(x) = x^2 + 1 \ (x \in (0, 2])$

Notice that when we draw graphs we use similar conventions to those that we use for illustrations of sets on the number line. For example, we use solid and hollow dots to indicate whether points at the 'ends' of a graph do or don't lie on the graph. In Figure 13(b) the graph is labelled with its rule and also with its domain, but we often omit the latter.

A function whose rule you can't express using a formula still has a graph. For example, Figure 14(a) shows the graph of a function f that describes the displacement of a car along a road from its starting point during a 3-hour journey. Similarly, the electrocardiogram that you saw earlier, which is repeated in Figure 14(b), is the graph of a function (with the axes omitted). This graph represents the changing voltage between two points on a person's skin over a time period of about two seconds.

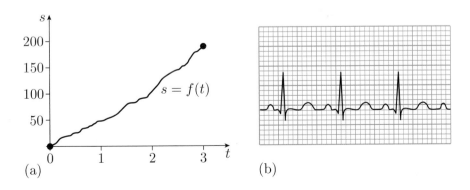

(a)

(b)

Figure 14   (a) The graph of $s = f(t)$, where $f(t)$ is the displacement of a car in kilometres at time t (in hours) (b) an electrocardiogram

The graph of a function is normally drawn with the input numbers on the horizontal axis and the output numbers on the vertical axis. (So, if the axes are labelled with variables, then the variable on the horizontal axis is the independent variable, and the variable on the vertical axis is the dependent variable.) In this module we'll assume that graphs of functions are always drawn like this.

You can 'read off' the output number corresponding to any particular input number by drawing a vertical line from the input number on the horizontal axis to the graph and then a horizontal line across to the vertical axis. For example, for the function f whose graph is shown in Figure 15, the value of $f(3)$ is about 5.

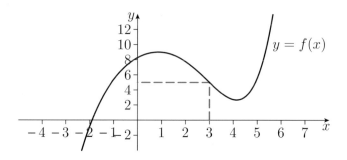

Figure 15   The graph of a function f

One way to produce a graph of a function is to use a table of values, in the way that you saw in Unit 2. You're asked to do this in the next activity.

Activity 10   *Plotting the graph of a function using a table of values*

Consider the function $f(x) = x^3$.

(a) Use your calculator to complete the following table of values for this function.

x	-2	-1.5	-1	-0.5	0	0.5	1	1.5	2
x^3									

(b) Plot the points given by your completed table on a pair of axes.

(c) Draw a smooth curve through the points.

If you use a table of values to plot the graph of a function whose domain isn't the whole set of real numbers, remember to choose input values that lie in the domain, and to make sure that you don't extend the graph beyond the endpoints of the domain. Where appropriate, you should mark the ends of the graph with solid or hollow dots.

A quicker way to obtain a graph of a function is to use a computer. You can learn how to do that in the next activity.

Activity 11   *Plotting graphs of functions on the computer*

Work through Section 4 of the *Computer algebra guide*.

As mentioned in Unit 2, one disadvantage of using a table of values to plot a graph is that you can't be entirely sure about the shape of the graph between the values in the table, or to the right or left of them. A graph produced by a computer has similar disadvantages, as in essence it's plotted using a large table of values. In general, it's useful to become familiar with the shapes of the graphs of a variety of functions and function types, and to learn how to sketch such graphs. You'll have opportunities to do that throughout this module.

You saw in Unit 2 how to sketch the graphs of equations of the form $y = ax + b$ and $y = ax^2 + bx + c$, where a, b and c are constants. So you already know how to sketch the graphs of functions of the form $f(x) = ax + b$ and $f(x) = ax^2 + bx + c$. The next example illustrates how to adapt the methods in Unit 2 in order to sketch the graph of a function whose rule has one of these forms, but whose domain isn't the largest possible set of real numbers for which the rule is applicable.

Example 1   *Sketching the graph of a function whose domain is not the largest set of numbers for which its rule is applicable*

Sketch the graph of the function
$$f(x) = \tfrac{1}{4}x^2 - 2x + 6 \quad (5 \le x < 7).$$

Solution

First sketch the graph of $y = \tfrac{1}{4}x^2 - 2x + 6$, by using any of the methods from Unit 2. Also include on the sketch the points corresponding to the endpoints of the domain of f, plotted as solid or hollow dots as appropriate, and labelled with their coordinates.

The required graph is part of the graph of $y = \tfrac{1}{4}x^2 - 2x + 6$, which is a u-shaped parabola. Completing the square gives
$$\begin{aligned}
f(x) &= \tfrac{1}{4}x^2 - 2x + 6 \\
&= \tfrac{1}{4}(x^2 - 8x) + 6 \\
&= \tfrac{1}{4}((x - 4)^2 - 16) + 6 \\
&= \tfrac{1}{4}(x - 4)^2 - 4 + 6 \\
&= \tfrac{1}{4}(x - 4)^2 + 2.
\end{aligned}$$

The least value taken by $(x - 4)^2$ is 0, so the least value taken by $(x - 4)^2 + 2$ is 2. This occurs when $x - 4 = 0$, that is, when $x = 4$.

So the parabola has vertex $(4, 2)$. Also, since the expression $\frac{1}{4}(x-4)^2 + 2$ is always positive, the parabola has no x-intercepts. Its y-intercept is 6.

The endpoints of the domain of f are 5 and 7. We have

$$f(5) = \tfrac{1}{4} \times 5^2 - 2 \times 5 + 6 = \tfrac{9}{4} \quad \text{and}$$
$$f(7) = \tfrac{1}{4} \times 7^2 - 2 \times 7 + 6 = \tfrac{17}{4}.$$

So the points $(5, \frac{9}{4})$ and $(7, \frac{17}{4})$ lie on the graph of $y = \frac{1}{4}x^2 - 2x + 6$.

These features give the following graph.

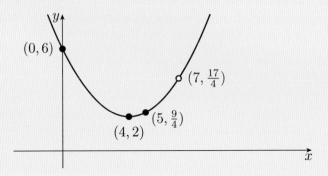

🔍 Erase the parts of the graph that don't lie between the points $(5, \frac{9}{4})$ and $(7, \frac{17}{4})$ (or draw a new graph). 💭

So the graph of f is as follows.

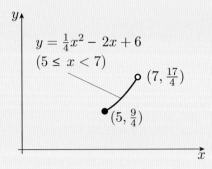

With a little practice, you should be able to sketch the graph of a function like the one in Example 1 without having to sketch a larger graph first. It's straightforward to do this for a simple graph, such as a straight line.

Activity 12   *Sketching the graphs of functions whose domains are not the largest sets of numbers for which their rules are applicable*

Sketch the graphs of the following functions.

(a) $f(x) = 3 - 2x$ $(-1 < x < 4)$

(b) $f(x) = -\frac{1}{2}x^2 - 2x - 5$ $(x \geq -5)$

You can use the graph of a function to visualise its domain on the horizontal axis. The domain consists of all the possible input numbers of the function, that is, all points on the horizontal axis that lie directly below or above a point on the graph, as illustrated in Figure 16.

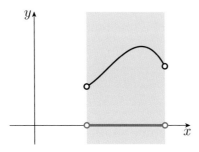

Figure 16   The domain of a function marked on the horizontal axis

Activity 13   *Identifying the domains of functions*

Write down the domains of the functions whose graphs are shown below, using interval notation. All the endpoints of the intervals involved are integers, and in part (b) the graph continues indefinitely to the left and right.

(a)

(b)

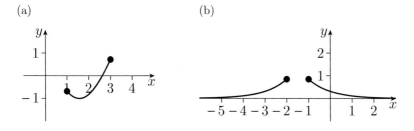

As you've seen, a function has exactly one output number for every input number. So if you draw the vertical line through any number in the domain of a function on the horizontal axis, then it will cross the graph of the function *exactly once*, as illustrated in Figure 17(a). If you can draw a vertical line that crosses a curve more than once, then the curve isn't the graph of a function. For example, the curve in Figure 17(b) isn't the graph of a function.

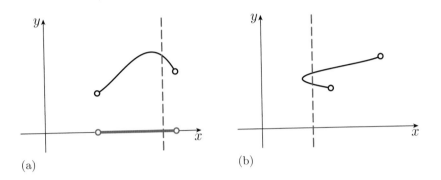

(a)   (b)

Figure 17   (a) The graph of a function (b) a curve that isn't the graph of a function

Activity 14   *Identifying graphs of functions*

Which of the following diagrams are the graphs of functions?

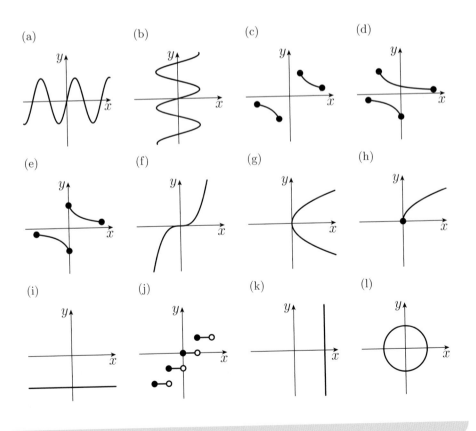

Increasing and decreasing functions

Figure 18 shows the graph of a function with domain $[-1, 9]$. As x increases, the graph first slopes up, then slopes down, then slopes up again. It changes from sloping up to sloping down when $x = 2$, and it changes from sloping down to sloping up again when $x = 6$.

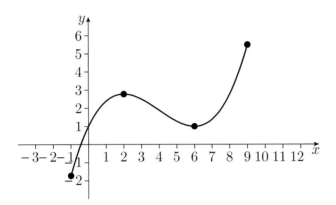

Figure 18   The graph of a function

To express these facts about the function f, we say that f is *increasing on the interval* $[-1, 2]$, *decreasing on the interval* $[2, 6]$, and increasing again on the interval $[6, 9]$. Here are the formal definitions of these terms. The definitions are illustrated in Figure 19.

> ### Functions increasing or decreasing on an interval
>
> A function f is **increasing on the interval** I if for all values x_1 and x_2 in I such that $x_1 < x_2$,
>
> $$f(x_1) < f(x_2).$$
>
> A function f is **decreasing on the interval** I if for all values x_1 and x_2 in I such that $x_1 < x_2$,
>
> $$f(x_1) > f(x_2).$$
>
> (The interval I must be part of the domain of f.)

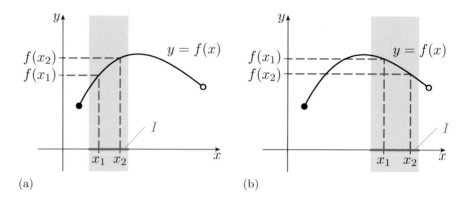

(a)   (b)

Figure 19   (a) A function increasing on an interval I (b) a function decreasing on an interval I

For example, the function $f(x) = x^2$, whose graph is shown in Figure 20, is decreasing on the interval $(-\infty, 0]$ and increasing on the interval $[0, \infty)$.

Figure 20   The graph of the function $f(x) = x^2$

Activity 15   *Identifying increasing functions*

Which of the following graphs show functions that are increasing on their whole domains?

(a)   (b)   (c)   (d)

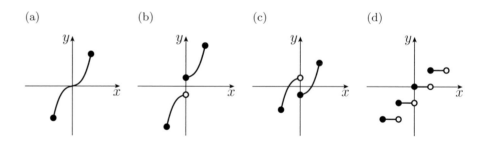

1.5 Image sets of functions

Remember that the *image set* of a function is the set consisting of all the values in its codomain that occur as output numbers. For example, the image set of the function $f(x) = x^2$ is the interval $[0, \infty)$, because all non-negative numbers occur as output numbers of this function, but no negative numbers do. You saw in the last subsection that if you have a graph of a function, then you can visualise the *domain* of the function on the horizontal axis, as illustrated in Figure 21(a). In the same way, you can visualise the *image set* of the function on the vertical axis.

The image set consists of all the possible output numbers, that is, all the points on the vertical axis that lie directly to the right or left of a point on the graph, as illustrated in Figure 21(b).

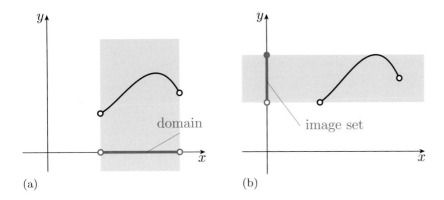

(a)   (b)

Figure 21 (a) The domain of a function marked on the horizontal axis (b) the image set marked on the vertical axis

So you can use the graph of a function to help you find its image set, as demonstrated in the next example. Remember that a 'play button' icon in the margin next to a worked example indicates that a tutorial clip is available for the example.

Example 2 *Finding the image set of a function*

Find the image set of the function

$$f(x) = x^2 + 6x + 14 \quad (-6 < x < 2).$$

Solution

 Obtain a sketch, plot or computer plot of the graph of the function. Remember to 'stop' the graph at the endpoints of its domain, and to mark the resulting ends of the graph with solid or hollow dots, as appropriate. There's no need to find the intercept(s).

The parabola is u-shaped. Completing the square gives

$$f(x) = x^2 + 6x + 14$$
$$= (x+3)^2 - 9 + 14$$
$$= (x+3)^2 + 5.$$

The least value taken by $(x+3)^2$ is 0, so the least value taken by $(x+3)^2 + 5$ is 5. This occurs when $x + 3 = 0$, that is, when $x = -3$.

So the vertex is $(-3, 5)$.

Also

$$f(-6) = (-6)^2 + 6 \times (-6) + 14 = 14 \quad \text{and}$$
$$f(2) = 2^2 + 6 \times 2 + 14 = 30.$$

So the graph stops at the points $(-6, 14)$ and $(2, 30)$, both of which are excluded.

These features give the following graph.

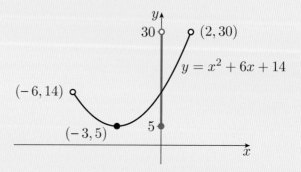

The graph shows that the smallest value in the image set is the y-coordinate of the vertex, and that the image set contains all the values larger than this number, up to but not including $f(2)$.

The graph shows that the image set of f is $[5, 30)$.

You might have expected that if the domain of a function f is the interval $(-6, 2)$, then its image set is the interval $(f(-6), f(2))$. Example 2 shows that this isn't necessarily true.

Activity 16   *Finding image sets of functions*

Find the image sets of the following functions.

(a) $f(x) = -x^2 + 10x - 24$ $(3 \le x < 6)$

(b) $f(x) = 2 - 2x$ $(-2 < x < 0)$

(c) $f(x) = x^2 - 1$

(d) $f(x) = 1/x^2$

Hint for part (d): try to work out the answer by thinking about what output numbers are possible for this function. If you're still not sure, try plotting the graph of the function on a computer.

1.6 Some standard types of functions

As mentioned earlier, it's useful to become familiar with some standard types of functions and their graphs. You'll meet some types of functions in this subsection, and further types later in the unit and in Unit 4. If you study mathematics beyond this module, then you'll meet many more types of functions.

Linear functions

First consider any function whose rule is of the form

$$f(x) = mx + c,$$

where m and c are constants. Its graph is the graph of the equation $y = mx + c$, which, as you saw in Unit 2, is the straight line with gradient m and y-intercept c. For this reason, any function of the form above is called a **linear function**.

Figure 22 shows the graphs of some linear functions.

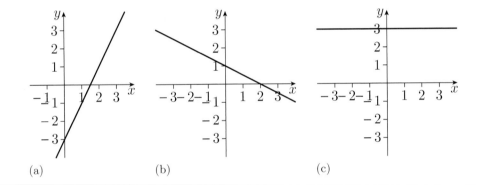

(a)   (b)   (c)

Figure 22   The graphs of the linear functions (a) $f(x) = 2x - 3$ (b) $f(x) = -\frac{1}{2}x + 1$ (c) $f(x) = 3$

A linear function whose rule is of the form

$$f(x) = c,$$

where c is a constant, is called a **constant function**. Its graph is a horizontal line. For example, the function $f(x) = 3$, whose graph is shown in Figure 22(c), is a constant function.

Quadratic functions

From what you saw in Unit 2, you also know that the graph of any function of the form

$$f(x) = ax^2 + bx + c, \tag{2}$$

where a, b and c are constants with $a \neq 0$, is a parabola. You saw how to find various features of the parabola, such as its vertex and intercepts, from the values of a, b and c. Any function whose rule is of form (2) is called a **quadratic function**. The graphs of some quadratic functions are shown in Figure 23.

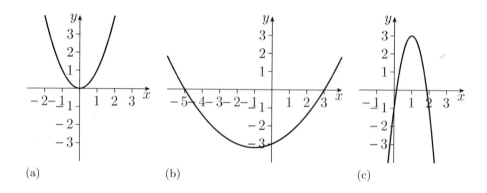

(a) (b) (c)

Figure 23   The graphs of the functions (a) $f(x) = x^2$
(b) $f(x) = \frac{1}{5}x^2 + \frac{2}{5}x - 3$ (c) $f(x) = -4x^2 + 8x - 1$

Polynomial functions

Linear functions and quadratic functions are particular types of *polynomial functions*. Here are some more polynomial functions:

$$f(x) = 2x^4 - 5x^3 + x^2 + 2x - 2$$
$$g(x) = x^3$$
$$h(x) = -\frac{1}{7}x^7 + \frac{1}{3}x^6 + x^5 - \frac{5}{2}x^4 - \frac{4}{3}x^3 + 4x^2 + 1.$$

In general, if an expression is a sum of finitely many terms, each of which is of the form ax^n where a is a number and n is a non-negative integer, then the expression is called a **polynomial expression in** x. If the right-hand side of the rule of a function is a polynomial expression in x, then the function is called a **polynomial function**.

> The word 'polynomial' appears to be a hybrid word meaning 'many names' that is a mixture of Greek and Latin.

Polly, no meal

Note that the terms of a polynomial expression must all have powers that are non-negative integers; for example, $\sqrt{x}$ (which is the same as $x^{1/2}$) is *not* a polynomial expression.

The highest power of the variable x in a polynomial expression or function is called the **degree** of the polynomial expression or function. For example, the highest power of x in the rule of the polynomial function f above is x^4, so the degree of this polynomial function is 4. Similarly, the polynomial functions g and h above have degrees 3 and 7, respectively.

Quadratic functions are polynomial functions of degree 2, since the highest power of x in the rule of a quadratic function is x^2.

Linear functions are polynomial functions of degree 1, 0 or no degree at all. If a linear function is of the form $f(x) = ax + b$ where $a \neq 0$, then the highest power of x is x^1, so the degree is 1. If it is of the form $f(x) = c$ where $c \neq 0$, then the highest power of x is x^0 (since the function can be expressed as $f(x) = cx^0$), so the degree is 0. The particular linear function $f(x) = 0$ is usually regarded as not having a degree at all (or sometimes as having degree $-\infty$), for technical reasons.

Polynomial functions of degrees 3, 4 and 5 are called **cubic**, **quartic** and **quintic functions**, respectively.

Figure 24 shows the graphs of the three polynomial functions above.

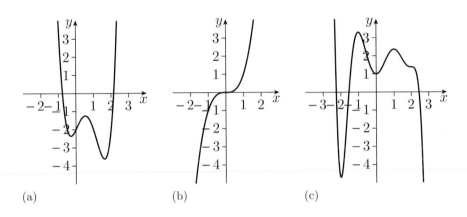

(a)   (b)   (c)

Figure 24   The graphs of the functions
(a) $f(x) = 2x^4 - 5x^3 + x^2 + 2x - 2$ (b) $g(x) = x^3$
(c) $h(x) = -\frac{1}{7}x^7 + \frac{1}{3}x^6 + x^5 - \frac{5}{2}x^4 - \frac{4}{3}x^3 + 4x^2 + 1$

Activity 17   *Investigating graphs of polynomial functions*

Use the module computer algebra system (CAS) to experiment with plotting the graphs of some polynomial functions, to obtain a general idea of the sorts of shapes that they have.

For example, you might like to try plotting the following polynomial functions: $f(x) = -x^3$, $f(x) = x^4$, $f(x) = x^4 - 4x^3$, $f(x) = x^5 - 4x^3$.

In Activity 17 you should have seen evidence of the following. Every polynomial function has a graph that's a smooth, unbroken curve (or a straight line; we normally consider a straight line to be a particular type of curve). The graph often has a 'wiggly' section, but (unless the function is a constant function) if you trace your pen tip along the graph towards the right, then eventually the wiggles stop and your pen either keeps moving 'uphill' or keeps moving 'downhill'. The same happens if you trace your pen tip towards the left.

In fact, the graph of every polynomial function (with domain $\mathbb{R}$) that isn't a constant function **tends to infinity** or **tends to minus infinity** at the left and right. In other words, no matter how large a positive number you choose, as you trace your pen tip along the graph, the y-values of the graph either eventually exceed your chosen number (if the graph tends to infinity) or are eventually less than the negative of your chosen number (if the graph tends to minus infinity).

You can tell whether the graph of a polynomial function tends to infinity or tends to minus infinity at each end by looking at the term in its rule that has the highest power of x. This term is called the **dominant term**, because for large values of x, the value taken by the dominant term 'outweighs' (*dominates*) the sum of the values taken by all the other terms. For example, the dominant term in the rule

$$f(x) = 2x^4 - 5x^3 + x^2 + 2x - 2$$

is $2x^4$. If the dominant term has a plus sign and

- contains an even power of x, then the graph tends to infinity at both ends

- contains an odd power of x, then the graph tends to minus infinity at the left and to infinity at the right.

If the dominant term has a minus sign, then similar facts hold, but with infinity replaced by minus infinity and vice versa.

To see examples of these facts, look at the graphs in Figure 24 above, and at the graphs that you plotted in Activity 17.

The modulus function

All the functions that you've met so far have graphs that are smooth curves. The *modulus function* has a graph that's smooth except at one point, where it turns a corner!

As you saw in Unit 2, the **modulus** of a real number (also known as its **magnitude** or **absolute value**) is its 'distance from zero', or its 'value without its sign'. For example, the modulus of 3 is 3, and the modulus of -3 is also 3. The modulus of a real number x is denoted by $|x|$. So, for example, $|-3| = 3$.

The **modulus function** is

$$f(x) = |x|.$$

It follows from the definition of modulus that

$$|x| = \begin{cases} x, & \text{if } x \geq 0, \\ -x, & \text{if } x < 0. \end{cases}$$

So the graph of the modulus function is the same as the graph of $y = x$ when $x \geq 0$, and the same as the graph of $y = -x$ when $x < 0$. It's shown in Figure 25. It has a corner at the origin, and the image set is $[0, \infty)$.

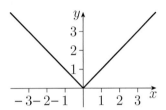

Figure 25   The graph of the modulus function, $f(x) = |x|$

The reciprocal function

Remember that if x is any non-zero number, then the **reciprocal** of x is $1/x$. The **reciprocal function** is the function

$$f(x) = \frac{1}{x}.$$

Its domain consists of all real numbers except 0. That is, its domain is the set $(-\infty, 0) \cup (0, \infty)$. The graph of the reciprocal function is shown in Figure 26.

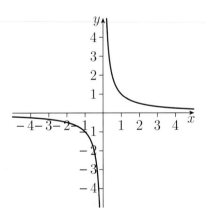

Figure 26   The graph of the reciprocal function, $f(x) = 1/x$

The graph consists of two separate pieces, each of which gets closer and closer to one of the coordinate axes at each end. To see why this is, first think about the piece of the graph to the right of the y-axis, that is, the piece that shows the values of $1/x$ for positive values of x. Its shape can be explained as follows. As x gets larger and larger, the value of $1/x$ gets closer and closer to zero. Similarly, as x gets closer and closer to zero, the value of $1/x$ gets larger and larger. The shape of the piece of the graph to the left of the y-axis, for negative values of x, has a similar explanation: you might like to think it through.

If a curve has the property that, as you trace your pen tip along it further and further from the origin, it gets *arbitrarily close* to a straight line, then that line is called an **asymptote** of the curve. The phrase 'arbitrarily close' here has the following meaning: no matter how small a distance you choose, if you trace your pen tip along the curve far enough, then eventually the curve lies within that distance of the line, and stays within that distance of the line.

So the coordinate axes are asymptotes of the graph of the reciprocal function. Asymptotes are often drawn as dashed lines on graphs, when they don't coincide with the coordinate axes.

> The word 'asymptote' comes from a Greek word meaning 'not coinciding', used to describe a straight line that a curve approaches arbitrarily closely but doesn't meet.

Rational functions

The reciprocal function and all polynomial functions are particular examples of *rational functions*. In general, a **rational function** is a function whose rule is of the form

$$f(x) = \frac{p(x)}{q(x)},$$

where p and q are polynomial functions. If q is a constant function, then f is a polynomial function, and if $p(x) = 1$ and $q(x) = x$, then f is the reciprocal function. Here are some more examples of rational functions:

$$f(x) = \frac{x^2 + 1}{2x + 4}, \quad f(x) = \frac{2x^2 - 6x - 8}{x^2 - x - 6}, \quad f(x) = \frac{7x + 5}{x^2 + 1}.$$

The graphs of these rational functions are shown in Figure 27. The dashed lines are asymptotes. The third graph has the x-axis as an asymptote.

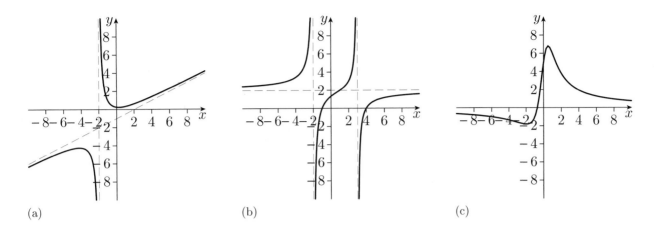

(a)　　　　　　　　　(b)　　　　　　　　　(c)

Figure 27   The graphs of (a) $f(x) = \dfrac{x^2 + 1}{2x + 4}$ (b) $f(x) = \dfrac{2x^2 - 6x - 8}{x^2 - x - 6}$

(c) $f(x) = \dfrac{7x + 5}{x^2 + 1}$

Every rational function has a graph that consists of one or more pieces, each of which is a smooth curve. The graphs of many rational functions have asymptotes, which can be horizontal, vertical or slant. For example, the graph in Figure 27(a) has one vertical asymptote and one slant asymptote.

A detailed study of the graphs of rational functions is beyond the scope of this module, but you can learn more about them in the follow-on module to this one, *Essential mathematics 2* (MST125).

2   New functions from old functions

In this section, you'll learn how to use your knowledge about the graphs of a few functions to deduce facts about the graphs of many more functions. For example, you can use the graph of the function $f(x) = x^2$, which is shown in Figure 28, to deduce the appearance of the graphs of the functions $g(x) = x^2 + 1$ and $h(x) = 3x^2$. The rules of these functions are obtained from the rule for f simply by adding 1 and by multiplying by 3, respectively.

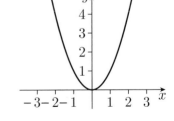

Figure 28   The graph of $f(x) = x^2$

2.1   Translating the graphs of functions

Let's start by considering what happens to the graph of a function when you add a constant to the right-hand side of its rule. You can see some instances of this in the next activity.

Activity 18   *Investigating graphs of equations of the form*
$y = f(x) + c$

Open the *Translating and scaling graphs* applet. Make sure that the
$y = f(x) + c$ option is selected, and that the original function is $f(x) = x^2$.

Change the value of c to display the graph of $y = x^2 + c$ for various values
of c, and observe how the new graphs are related to the original graph. In
particular, notice the effect of positive values of c, and the effect of
negative values of c.

Now change the original function to a different function of your choice, and
repeat the process above.

The effects that you saw in Activity 18 are examples of *translations* of
graphs. **Translating** a shape means sliding it to a different position,
without rotating or reflecting it, or distorting it in any way.

You saw that if you add any constant c to the right-hand side of the rule of
a function, then its graph is translated *vertically*. Specifically, it's
translated up by c units (the translation is down if c is negative). This is
because when you add the constant c, the y-values all increase by c.

There's another fairly simple change that you can make to the rule of a
function, which causes its graph to be translated *horizontally*. To do this,
you replace each occurrence of the input variable x in the right-hand side
of the rule of the function by an expression of the form $x - c$, where c is a
constant. For example, if you start with the function $f(x) = x^2$, then you
can replace x by $x - 3$, say, to obtain the new function $g(x) = (x - 3)^2$.
You're asked to investigate changes of this sort in the next activity.

Activity 19   *Investigating graphs of equations of the form*
$y = f(x - c)$

In the *Translating and scaling graphs* applet, select the $y = f(x - c)$
option, and make sure that the original function is $f(x) = x^2$.

Change the value of c to display the graph of $y = (x - c)^2$ for various
values of c, and observe how the new graphs are related to the original
graph. In particular, notice the effect of positive values of c, and the effect
of negative values of c.

Now change the original function to a different function of your choice, and
repeat the process above.

In Activity 19 you saw that if you replace every occurrence of the input
variable x in the right-hand side of the rule of a function by the expression
$x - c$, where c is a constant, then the graph of the function is translated
horizontally. Specifically it's translated to the right by c units (the

translation is to the left if c is negative). For example, if you replace x by $x - 3$, then the graph is translated to the right by 3 units (here $c = 3$). Similarly, if you replace x by $x + 3$, then the graph is translated to the left by 3 units (here $c = -3$).

To see why this happens, let's think about what happens when you translate the graph of a particular function to the right by c units (where c might be positive, negative or zero).

For example, Figure 29 shows the graph of the equation $y = x^2$ (in black), and the graph that's obtained by translating it to the right by 3 units (in green). Let's try to work out the equation of this second graph. To do this, we have to find a relationship between x and y that holds for every point (x, y) on the second graph. Now, whenever the point (x, y) lies on the second graph, the point $(x - 3, y)$ lies on the original graph, so the second coordinate, y, is the square of the first coordinate, $x - 3$. Hence the following equation holds:

$$y = (x - 3)^2.$$

This equation expresses a relationship between x and y, so it is the equation of the second graph.

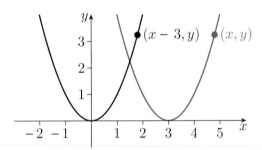

Figure 29   The graph of $y = x^2$, and the graph obtained by translating it by 3 units to the right

More generally, consider any function f, and suppose that you translate its graph to the right by c units, as illustrated in Figure 30 in a case where $c > 0$. Then whenever the point (x, y) lies on the second graph, the point $(x - c, y)$ lies on the original graph, so the following equation holds:

$$y = f(x - c).$$

So this equation is the equation of the second graph.

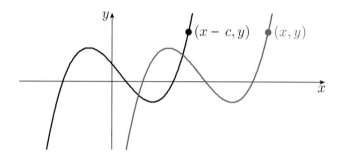

Figure 30   The graph of an equation of the form $y = f(x)$, and the graph obtained by translating it by c units to the right, where $c > 0$

This reasoning explains the effects that you saw in Activity 19.

Here's a summary of what you've seen so far in this subsection.

> ### Translations of graphs
>
> Suppose that f is a function and c is a constant. To obtain the graph of:
>
> - $y = f(x) + c$, translate the graph of $y = f(x)$ up by c units (the translation is down if c is negative)
>
> - $y = f(x - c)$, translate the graph of $y = f(x)$ to the right by c units (the translation is to the left if c is negative).

These effects are illustrated in Figure 31.

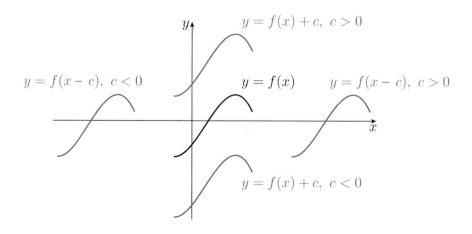

Figure 31   Pieces of graphs of equations of the form $y = f(x) + c$ and $y = f(x - c)$

Activity 20   *Understanding translations of graphs*

You saw the graph of $y = 1/x$ in the previous section, and it's repeated in Figure 32. Using this graph, and without using a computer, match up the equations below with their graphs.

(a) $y = \dfrac{1}{x-2}$ (b) $y = \dfrac{1}{x} - 2$ (c) $y = \dfrac{1}{x} + 2$ (d) $y = \dfrac{1}{x+2}$

Graphs:

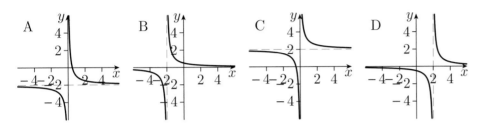

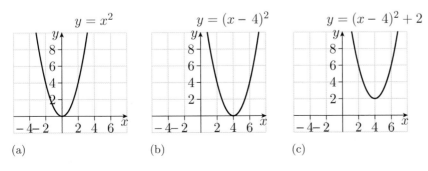

Figure 32   The graph of
$$y = \frac{1}{x}$$

Now suppose that you change the rule of a function in such a way that its graph is translated horizontally, and then you change the rule of the *new* function in such a way that *its* graph is translated vertically. The final result is that the graph of the original function is translated both horizontally and vertically. For example, consider the equation $y = x^2$, whose graph is shown in Figure 33(a). If you replace x by $x - 4$, then you obtain the equation

$$y = (x - 4)^2,$$

and the graph is translated to the right by 4 units, as shown in Figure 33(b). If you now add the constant 2, then you obtain the equation

$$y = (x - 4)^2 + 2,$$

and the original graph is now translated to the right by 4 units and up by 2 units, as shown in Figure 33(c).

(a)   (b)   (c)

Figure 33   The graphs of (a) $y = x^2$ (b) $y = (x - 4)^2$ (c) $y = (x - 4)^2 + 2$

In general, suppose that you start with an equation $y = f(x)$. If you first replace x by $x - c$, where c is a constant, then you obtain the equation $y = f(x - c)$, and the graph is translated to the right by c units. If you then add the constant d to the right-hand side, then you obtain the equation

$$y = f(x - c) + d,$$

and the original graph is translated to the right by c units and up by d units.

In fact, the order in which you make the two changes doesn't matter. One way to see this is to think about the situation geometrically. If you translate a graph to the right by c units and then up by d units, then the overall effect will be the same as if you had translated it up by d units and then to the right by c units. You can also confirm it algebraically, as follows. Suppose that you carry out the two changes to the equation $y = f(x)$ in the opposite order to the order used above. Adding d to the right-hand side of the equation $y = f(x)$ gives the equation $y = f(x) + d$, and then replacing x in this equation by $x - c$ gives the final equation $y = f(x - c) + d$, which is the same as the final equation obtained above.

Activity 21 *Understanding successive horizontal and vertical translations of graphs*

You saw the graph of $y = |x|$ in the previous section, and it's repeated in Figure 34. Using this graph, and without using a computer, match up the equations below with their graphs.

(a) $y = |x - 2| + 1$ (b) $y = |x + 2| + 1$ (c) $y = |x - 2| - 1$

(d) $y = |x + 2| - 1$

Graphs:

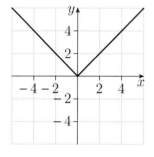

Figure 34   The graph of $y = |x|$

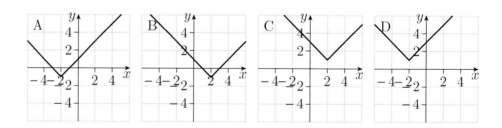

2.2 Scaling the graphs of functions vertically

In this subsection you'll see what happens to the graph of a function when you multiply the right-hand side of its rule by a constant. The new function that you obtain is called a **constant multiple** of the original function. For example, the function $g(x) = 3x^2$ is a constant multiple of the function $f(x) = x^2$.

Activity 22   *Investigating graphs of equations of the form $y = cf(x)$*

In the *Translating and scaling graphs* applet, select the $y = cf(x)$ option, and make sure that the original function is $f(x) = x^2 - 1$.

Change the value of c to display the graph of $y = c(x^2 - 1)$ for various values of c, and observe how the new graphs are related to the original graph. In particular, notice the effect of positive values of c, and the effect of negative values of c. Also notice the effect of values of c such that $|c| < 1$, and the effect of values of c such that $|c| > 1$.

Now change the original function to $y = x^3$, and repeat the process above. If you wish, also try another function of your choice as the original function.

The effects that you saw in Activity 22 are called **vertical scalings**. **Scaling** a graph **vertically** by a **factor** of c means the following.

- If c is positive, then move each point on the graph vertically, in the direction away from the x-axis, until it's c times as far from the x-axis as it was before.

- If c is negative, then move each point on the graph vertically, in the direction away from the x-axis, until it's $|c|$ times as far from the x-axis as it was before, and then reflect it in the x-axis.

- If c is zero, then move each point on the graph vertically until it lies on the x-axis.

(In each of the first two cases, if $|c|$ is less than 1, then each point is actually moved *closer* to the x-axis than it was before.)

Informally, when you scale a graph vertically by a factor of c, you stretch or squash it parallel to the y-axis (depending on whether $|c|$ is greater than or less than 1), and if c is negative, you also reflect it in the x-axis.

In Activity 22 you should have seen evidence of the following.

> **Vertical scalings of graphs**
>
> Suppose that c is a constant. To obtain the graph of $y = cf(x)$,
>
> scale the graph of $y = f(x)$ vertically by a factor of c.

These effects are illustrated in Figure 35. They occur because when you multiply the right-hand side of the rule of a function by the constant c, the y-value corresponding to each x-value is multiplied by c.

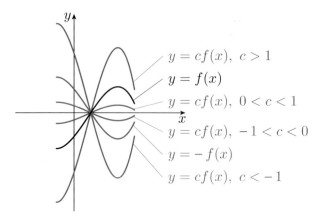

Figure 35   Pieces of graphs of equations of the form $y = cf(x)$

Notice in particular what happens when $c = -1$. For any function f, the graph of $y = -f(x)$ is the same shape as the graph of $y = f(x)$, but reflected in the x-axis. The function that results from multiplying the right-hand side of the rule of a function f by -1 is called the **negative** of the function f.

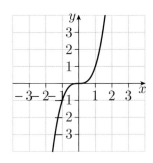

Figure 36   The graph of $y = x^3$

Activity 23   *Understanding vertical scalings of graphs*

You saw the graph of $y = x^3$ in Subsection 1.6, and it's repeated in Figure 36. Using this graph, and without using a computer, match up the equations below with their graphs.

(a) $y = 2x^3$ (b) $y = \frac{1}{2}x^3$ (c) $y = -x^3$ (d) $y = -\frac{1}{2}x^3$

Graphs:

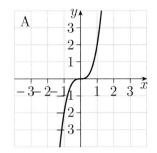
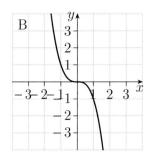
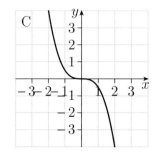
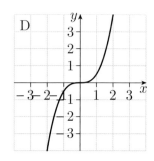

You can combine vertical scalings of graphs with vertical and/or horizontal translations of graphs, in the same way that horizontal and vertical translations of graphs were combined in the previous subsection. For example, suppose that you start with the equation $y = x^3$, whose graph is shown in Figure 37(a). If you multiply the right-hand side of this equation by 4, then you obtain the equation $y = 4x^3$, and the graph is scaled vertically by a factor of 4, as illustrated in Figure 37(b). If you then add the constant 1 to the right-hand side of this new equation, then you obtain the final equation $y = 4x^3 + 1$, and the original graph is first scaled vertically by a factor of 4, then translated up by 1 unit, as illustrated in Figure 37(c).

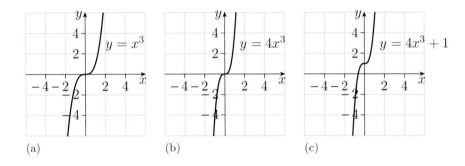

(a)　　　　　(b)　　　　　(c)

Figure 37　The graphs of (a) $y = x^3$ (b) $y = 4x^3$ (c) $y = 4x^3 + 1$

When you combine vertical scalings and translations in this way, the order in which you carry out the changes to the rule of the function *does* often matter. Different orders can give different results. For example, suppose that you start with the equation $y = x^3$, as above, and you make the same two changes as above, but in the opposite order. Adding the constant 1 to the right-hand side of the equation $y = x^3$ gives the intermediate equation $y = x^3 + 1$, and the graph is translated up by 1 unit, as illustrated in Figure 38(b). Then multiplying the right-hand side by 4 gives the final equation $y = 4(x^3 + 1)$, and the original graph is first translated up by 1 unit and then scaled vertically by a factor of 4, as illustrated in Figure 38(c). You can see that the final equation and graph are different from those obtained above.

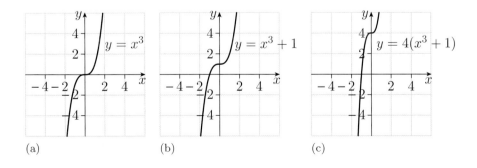

(a)　　　　　(b)　　　　　(c)

Figure 38　The graphs of (a) $y = x^3$ (b) $y = x^3 + 1$ (c) $y = 4(x^3 + 1)$

In general, you can make any number of successive changes to the rule of a function to scale and translate its graph in various ways, but you have to be careful about the order in which you carry out the changes. Sometimes the order matters, and sometimes it doesn't.

If you change the rule of a function to carry out a horizontal translation, a vertical translation and a vertical scaling, then you can make the changes in any order, except that the changes for the vertical translation and vertical scaling must be made in the correct order relative to each other.

Example 3   *Understanding successive scalings and translations of graphs*

For each of the following functions, describe how you could obtain its graph by applying scalings and translations to the graph of the function $f(x) = x^3$.

(a) $g(x) = \frac{1}{2}(x+3)^3$ (b) $h(x) = \frac{1}{2}(x+3)^3 - 2$

Solution

(a) Try to work out how the equation $y = \frac{1}{2}(x+3)^3$ is obtained from the equation $y = x^3$ by making two or more changes of the types that you've seen, one after another.

Consider the equation $y = x^3$. If you multiply the right-hand side by $\frac{1}{2}$, you obtain the equation $y = \frac{1}{2}x^3$. If you then replace x by $x+3$, you obtain the equation $y = \frac{1}{2}(x+3)^3$.

So the graph of the equation $y = \frac{1}{2}(x+3)^3$ is obtained by starting with the graph of $y = x^3$, scaling it vertically by the factor $\frac{1}{2}$, and then translating it to the left by 3 units.

(b) Use the same method as in part (a). Here you can recognise that the given equation is obtained from the equation in part (a) by making a simple change.

The equation $y = \frac{1}{2}(x+3)^3 - 2$ is obtained from the final equation in part (a) by adding -2 to the right-hand side.

So the graph of the equation $y = \frac{1}{2}(x+3)^3 - 2$ is obtained by starting with the graph of $y = x^3$, scaling it vertically by the factor $\frac{1}{2}$, then translating it to the left by 3 units, and finally translating it down by 2 units.

Figure 39 shows the graph of the function $f(x) = x^3$ and the results of applying the scalings and translations in Example 3 to this graph.

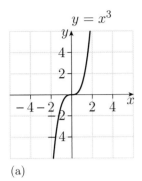

$y = x^3$

(a)

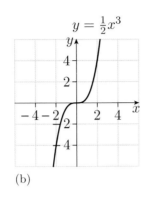

$y = \frac{1}{2}x^3$

(b)

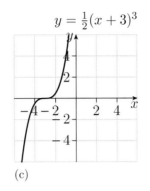

$y = \frac{1}{2}(x + 3)^3$

(c)

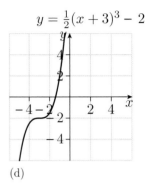

$y = \frac{1}{2}(x + 3)^3 - 2$

(d)

Figure 39   Three graphs obtained by scaling and/or translating the graph of $y = x^3$

Activity 24   *Understanding successive scalings and translations of graphs*

For each of the following functions, describe how you could obtain its graph by applying scalings and translations to the graph of the function $f(x) = |x|$ (which is shown in Figure 40).

(a) $g(x) = 2|x| + 3$ (b) $h(x) = 2|x + 2| + 3$ (c) $j(x) = \frac{1}{2}|x - 3| - 4$

(d) $k(x) = -|x - 1| + 1$

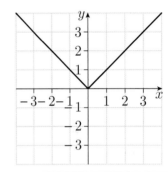

Figure 40   The graph of $y = |x|$

In the final activity of this subsection, you'll see how the new ideas that you've met can give you a deeper understanding of the shapes of the graphs of quadratic functions.

Activity 25   *Understanding the graph of a quadratic function*

Consider the quadratic function $f(x) = 2x^2 + 12x + 19$.

(a) Complete the square in the quadratic expression on the right-hand side.

(b) Hence describe how you could obtain the graph of this function by applying scalings and translations to the graph of the function $f(x) = x^2$ (which is shown in Figure 41).

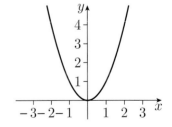

Figure 41   The graph of $y = x^2$

243

You can see that the method that you were asked to use in Activity 25 can be applied to *any* quadratic function. You just need to start by completing the square in the quadratic expression that forms the right-hand side of its rule.

This tells you the following enlightening fact: the graph of any quadratic function is the same basic shape as the graph of $y = x^2$, but scaled vertically, and then translated horizontally and/or vertically.

2.3   Scaling the graphs of functions horizontally

In the first activity of this subsection, you're asked to investigate a change to the rule of a function that results in its graph being scaled *horizontally*. The change is that you replace each occurrence of the input variable x in the right-hand side of the rule of the function by an expression of the form x/c, where c is a constant.

Activity 26   *Investigating graphs of equations of the form $y = f\left(\dfrac{x}{c}\right)$*

In the *Translating and scaling graphs* applet, select the $y = f(x/c)$ option, and make sure that the original function is $y = x^3$.

Change the value of c to display the graph of $y = (x/c)^3$ for various non-zero values of c, and observe how the new graphs are related to the original graph. In particular, notice the effect of positive values of c, and the effect of negative values of c. Also notice the effect of values of c such that $|c| < 1$, and the effect of values of c such that $|c| > 1$.

Now change the original function to $y = x^2$, and repeat the process above. If you wish, also try another function of your choice as the original function.

The effects that you saw in Activity 26 are called **horizontal scalings**. **Scaling** a graph **horizontally** by a **factor** of c means the following.

- If c is positive, then move each point on the graph horizontally, in the direction away from the y-axis, until it's c times as far from the y-axis as it was before.

- If c is negative, then move each point on the graph horizontally, in the direction away from the y-axis, until it's $|c|$ times as far from the y-axis as it was before, and then reflect it in the y-axis.

- If c is zero, then move each point on the graph horizontally until it lies on the y-axis.

(In each of the first two cases, if $|c|$ is less than 1, then each point is actually moved *closer* to the y-axis than it was before.)

Informally, when you scale a graph horizontally by a factor of c, you stretch or squash it parallel to the x-axis (depending on whether $|c|$ is greater than or less than 1), and if c is negative, you also reflect it in the y-axis.

In Activity 26 you should have seen evidence of the following.

> **Horizontal scalings of graphs**
>
> Suppose that c is a non-zero constant. To obtain the graph of
> $$y = f\left(\frac{x}{c}\right),$$
>   scale the graph of $y = f(x)$ horizontally by a factor of c.

These effects are illustrated in Figure 42.

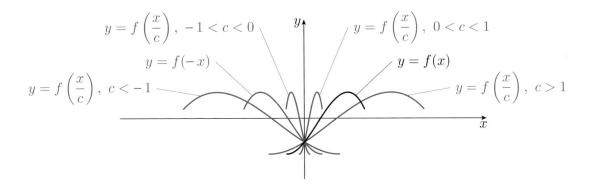

Figure 42   Pieces of graphs of equations of the form $y = f(x/c)$

To see why these effects occur, let's suppose that you scale the graph of a particular function horizontally by a factor of c (where c might be positive or negative), and let's try to work out how this affects the rule of the function.

For example, Figure 43 shows the graph of the equation $y = x^2$ (in black), and the graph that's obtained by scaling it horizontally by a factor of 3 (in green). Let's try to work out the equation of this second graph.

To do this, we have to find a relationship between x and y that holds for every point (x, y) on the second graph. Now whenever the point (x, y) lies on the second graph, the point $(x/3, y)$ lies on the original graph, so the following equation holds:
$$y = \left(\frac{x}{3}\right)^2.$$

This equation expresses a relationship between x and y, so it is the equation of the second graph.

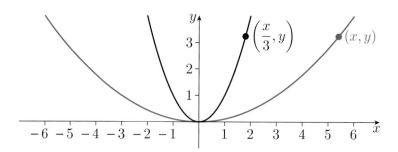

Figure 43   The graph of $y = x^2$, and the graph obtained by scaling it horizontally by a factor of 3

More generally, consider any function f, and suppose that you scale its graph horizontally by a factor of c, as illustrated in Figure 44 in a case where $c > 1$. Then whenever the point (x, y) lies on the second graph, the point $(x/c, y)$ lies on the original graph, so the following equation holds:

$$y = f\left(\frac{x}{c}\right).$$

So this equation is the equation of the second graph.

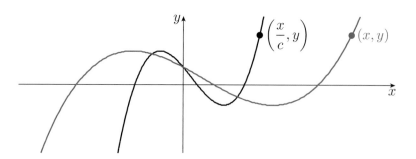

Figure 44   The graph of an equation $y = f(x)$, and the graph obtained by scaling it horizontally by a factor of c, where $c > 1$

Notice in particular what happens when $c = -1$. For any function f, the graph of $y = f(-x)$ is the same shape as the graph of $y = f(x)$, but reflected in the y-axis.

For convenience, the two facts that you've seen (in this subsection and the previous one) about reflections of graphs in the coordinate axes are summarised below, and illustrated in Figure 45.

Reflections of graphs in the coordinate axes

To obtain the graph of $y = -f(x)$, reflect the graph of $y = f(x)$ in the x-axis.

To obtain the graph of $y = f(-x)$, reflect the graph of $y = f(x)$ in the y-axis.

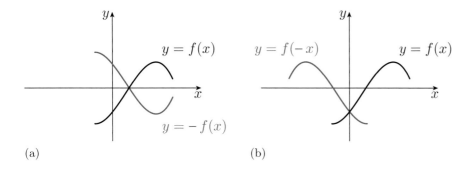

(a)

(b)

Figure 45 Pieces of graphs of equations of the form (a) $y = -f(x)$ and (b) $y = f(-x)$

In the final two activities of this section, you'll need to put together all the facts and skills about the effects of changing the equations of graphs that you've learned in this section.

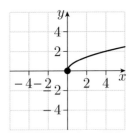

Figure 46   The graph of $y = \sqrt{x}$

Activity 27   *Understanding horizontal and vertical translations and scalings of graphs*

The graph of the function $f(x) = \sqrt{x}$ is shown in Figure 46. Using this graph, and without using a computer, match up the equations below with their graphs.

(a) $y = \sqrt{-x}$ (b) $y = -\sqrt{x}$ (c) $y = 2\sqrt{x-2}$

(d) $y = \frac{1}{2}\sqrt{x} + 2$ (e) $y = -\frac{1}{2}\sqrt{x}$ (f) $y = -\sqrt{x+2}$

(g) $y = -\sqrt{-x}$ (h) $y = \frac{1}{2}\sqrt{x+2}$ (i) $y = -2\sqrt{x} + 2$

Graphs:

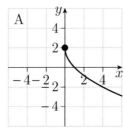
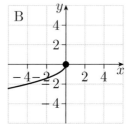
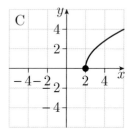

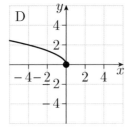
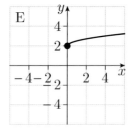
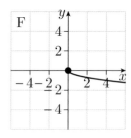

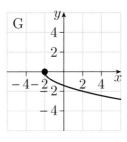
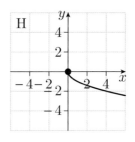
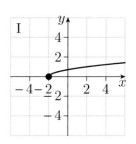

By considering graphs of functions that you met in Subsection 1.6, and without using a computer, draw sketch graphs of the following functions. In particular, mark the values of the intercepts, and in part (c) draw the asymptotes, and label the vertical one with its equation. (You met the idea of an *asymptote* on page 232.)

(a) $f(x) = 2|x| + 1$ (b) $h(x) = (x-1)^3$ (c) $g(x) = \dfrac{1}{x+3}$

Hint: in part (a), think about the graph of $y = |x|$; in part (b), think about the graph of $y = x^3$; in part (c), think about the graph of $y = 1/x$.

3 More new functions from old functions

In this section you'll meet some ways in which you can combine the rules of two or more functions to obtain the rule of a new function. You'll also see that for some functions there's a related function, called the *inverse function* of the original function, which 'reverses' the effect of the original function.

3.1 Sums, differences, products and quotients of functions

In this short subsection you'll see how to combine functions by forming sums, differences, products and quotients of them. These combinations mean just what the names suggest.

Suppose that f and g are functions.   The **sum** of f and g has the rule

$$h(x) = f(x) + g(x).$$

There are two **differences** of f and g, with rules

$$h(x) = f(x) - g(x) \quad \text{and} \quad h(x) = g(x) - f(x).$$

The **product** of f and g has the rule

$$h(x) = f(x)g(x).$$

There are two **quotients** of f and g, with rules

$$h(x) = \frac{f(x)}{g(x)} \quad \text{and} \quad h(x) = \frac{g(x)}{f(x)}.$$

For example, if $f(x) = x^2$ and $g(x) = x$, then the sum of f and g has the rule $h(x) = x^2 + x$. The domain of each of the combined functions above is the intersection of the domain of f and the domain of g, with the additional requirement for the first quotient of f and g that the numbers x such that $g(x) = 0$ are removed, since it's not possible to divide by zero, and a similar additional requirement for the second quotient.

Activity 29   *Understanding sums, differences, products and quotients of functions*

Consider the functions $f(x) = 2x - 1$ and $g(x) = x + 3$. Find the rules of the sum, the two differences, the product and the two quotients of f and g, and state the domain of each of these functions.

You can form sums and products of three or more functions. For example, the sum of the functions $f(x) = x^2$, $g(x) = x$ and $h(x) = 1$ is the function $s(x) = x^2 + x + 1$.

There isn't much more to be said about sums, products, differences and quotients of functions, at this stage. It's usually not easy to deduce the shape of the graph of any one of these functions from the shapes of the graphs of the original functions. These types of combinations of functions will be important later in the module.

3.2 Composite functions

There's another useful way to combine two functions to obtain a new function. This is to apply one function after the other.

For example, suppose that f and g are functions. Consider any value that lies in the domain of f. If you input this value to the function f, then you obtain an output value. If this output value is in the domain of the function g, then you can, in turn, input it to the function g, to obtain a final output value. This process is illustrated in Figure 47.

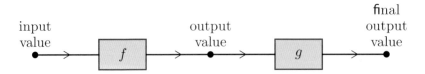

Figure 47   An input value processed by two functions f and g one after the other

The function whose rule is given by this process, and whose domain is the largest set of real numbers to which you can apply the process, is called a **composite function**, or just **composite**, of f and g. It's denoted by $g \circ f$ (the symbol $\circ$ is read as 'circle'). Note that the function that's applied *first* is written *second* in this notation – you'll see why shortly.

The largest set of real numbers for which you can apply the process is the set of all numbers in the domain of f such that $f(x)$ lies in the domain of g. For example, Figure 48 illustrates the process of finding the image of the number 3 under the composite function $g \circ f$, where $f(x) = x^2$ and $g(x) = x + 1$. It shows that $(g \circ f)(3) = 10$.

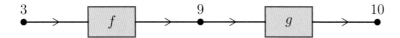

Figure 48   The image of 3 under $g \circ f$, where $f(x) = x^2$ and $g(x) = x + 1$

Activity 30   *Understanding composite functions*

Suppose that $f(x) = x^2$ and $g(x) = x + 1$, as in the paragraph above. Find the image of 5 under the composite function $g \circ f$.

In general, for any two functions f and g, the process of finding the image of an input value x under the composite function $g \circ f$ is as shown in Figure 49.

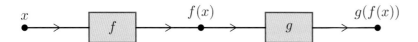

Figure 49   The image of x under $g \circ f$, for any functions f and g

So a composite function can be defined concisely as follows.

Composite functions

Suppose that f and g are functions. The **composite function $g \circ f$** is the function whose rule is

$$(g \circ f)(x) = g(f(x)),$$

and whose domain consists of all the values x in the domain of f such that $f(x)$ is in the domain of g.

It's important to remember that $g \circ f$ means f followed by g, not the other way round, as you might at first expect. To understand why the notation is this way round, consider the equation in the box above:

$$(g \circ f)(x) = g(f(x)).$$

It would be confusing if f and g were in different orders on the two sides of the equation.

The process of forming a composite function from two functions is called **composing** the functions. You can compose two functions f and g in either order, so they have *two* composite functions: $g \circ f$, which means first f and then g, and $f \circ g$, which means first g and then f. These two composite functions are illustrated in Figure 50.

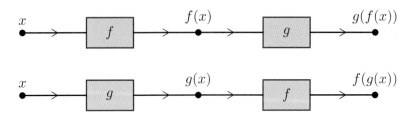

Figure 50   The image of x under $g \circ f$ and $f \circ g$, respectively

The next example shows you how to work out the rules of composite functions.

Example 4   *Composing functions*

Suppose that $f(x) = x^2$ and $g(x) = x + 1$. Find the rules of the composite functions $g \circ f$ and $f \circ g$.

Solution

$$(g \circ f)(x) = g(f(x)) = g(x^2) = x^2 + 1$$

and

$$(f \circ g)(x) = f(g(x)) = f(x + 1) = (x + 1)^2.$$

Figure 51 illustrates the composite functions in Example 4.

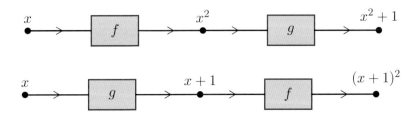

Figure 51   The image of x under particular composite functions $g \circ f$ and $f \circ g$

Notice that the composite functions $g \circ f$ and $f \circ g$ in Example 4 are *different functions*. If f and g are two different functions, then the composite functions $g \circ f$ and $f \circ g$ are usually different from each other.

Activity 31   *Composing functions*

(a) Suppose that $f(x) = x - 3$ and $g(x) = \sqrt{x}$. Find the rules of the following composite functions.

(i) $g \circ f$ (ii) $f \circ g$ (iii) $f \circ f$ (iv) $g \circ g$

(b) Determine the domain of the function $g \circ f$.

You can compose more than two functions. For example, if f, g and h are functions, then you can form a composite function whose rule is given by first applying f, then g, then h. This composite function is denoted by $h \circ g \circ f$, and its rule can be stated as

$$(h \circ g \circ f)(x) = h(g(f(x))).$$

Example 5   *Composing three functions*

Suppose that $f(x) = x + 2$, $g(x) = 1/x$ and $h(x) = \sqrt{x}$. Find the rule of the composite function $h \circ g \circ f$.

Solution

$$
\begin{aligned}
(h \circ g \circ f)(x) &= h(g(f(x))) \\
&= h(g(x + 2)) \\
&= h\left(\frac{1}{x + 2}\right) \\
&= \sqrt{\frac{1}{x + 2}} \\
&= \frac{1}{\sqrt{x + 2}}.
\end{aligned}
$$

Activity 32   *Composing three functions*

Suppose that $f(x) = x + 2$, $g(x) = 1/x$ and $h(x) = \sqrt{x}$, as in Example 5. Find the rules of the following composite functions.

(a) $f \circ g \circ h$ (b) $g \circ h \circ f$ (c) $f \circ h \circ g$ (d) $f \circ g \circ f$

3.3   Inverse functions

In this subsection you'll learn what's meant by the *inverse* of a function. To illustrate the idea, let's consider the function $f(x) = 2x$. The mapping diagram in Figure 52 shows *some* of the inputs and corresponding outputs of this function, linked by arrows.

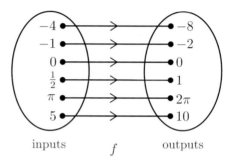

inputs f outputs

Figure 52   Some inputs and outputs of the function $f(x) = 2x$

Imagine a full version of the mapping diagram in Figure 52, which shows *all* the inputs and outputs of the function f. You can't actually draw such a diagram, of course, because f has infinitely many inputs and outputs.

The *inverse function*, or simply *inverse*, of the function f, which is denoted by f^{-1}, is the function whose mapping diagram is obtained by reversing the directions of all the arrows in this full version of the diagram. For example, Figure 53 shows some of the inputs and outputs of f^{-1}.

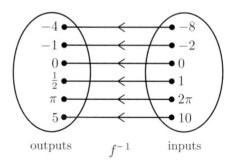

outputs f^{-1} inputs

Figure 53   Some inputs and outputs of the function f^{-1}, where $f(x) = 2x$

This figure shows that, for example,

$$f^{-1}(-8) = -4, \quad f^{-1}(1) = \tfrac{1}{2} \quad \text{and} \quad f^{-1}(10) = 5.$$

You can imagine a full version of the mapping diagram in Figure 53, which shows *all* the inputs and outputs of f^{-1}. You can think of the inverse functions of other functions in the same way. Essentially, the inverse function f^{-1} of a function f is the function that 'has the reverse effect' of f. That is, if inputting a number x to f gives the number y, then inputting the number y to f^{-1} gives the original number x, as illustrated in Figure 54. For example, if f is the function $f(x) = 2x$, as above, then inputting 5 to f gives 10, and inputting 10 to f^{-1} gives 5.

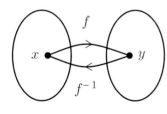

Figure 54   A mapping diagram illustrating a function f and its inverse function f^{-1}

Another way to think of the inverse function f^{-1} of a function f is that f^{-1} 'undoes' the effect of f. For example, if f is the function $f(x) = 2x$, as above, and you input the number 5 to f, then you get 10; and if you then take this output 10 and input it to the inverse function f^{-1}, then you get 5 back again.

You can sometimes write down the rule of an inverse function by thinking about it in this way. For example, consider once more the function $f(x) = 2x$. This function *doubles* numbers, so the function that undoes its effect *halves* numbers. So the rule of the inverse function of this function f is

$$f^{-1}(x) = \tfrac{1}{2}x.$$

In the next activity you're asked to write down the rules of the inverse functions of some other simple functions.

Activity 33   *Finding the rules of inverse functions of simple functions*

(a) Write down the rules of the inverse functions of the following functions.

   (i) $f(x) = x + 1$ (ii) $f(x) = x - 3$ (iii) $f(x) = \tfrac{1}{3}x$

(b) Can you think of a function with an inverse function that has the same rule as the original function? Can you think of another such function?

Some functions don't have inverse functions. For example, consider the function $f(x) = x^2$. Some of the inputs and outputs of this function are shown in Figure 55.

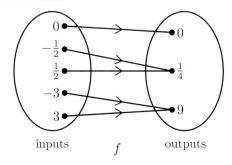

inputs f outputs

Figure 55   Some inputs and outputs of the function $f(x) = x^2$

If you reverse the directions of all the arrows in the full version of this mapping diagram, then the new diagram that you get *isn't the mapping diagram of a function*. That's because, in the new diagram, some of the input numbers have more than one output number, as illustrated in Figure 56. Remember that, for a function, every input number must have *exactly one* output number.

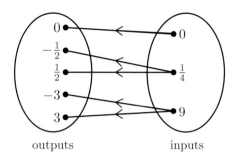

Figure 56   After reversing the directions of the arrows in Figure 55

You can see that this problem will arise whenever, for the original function f, there are two or more different input values that have the same output value. A function for which this *doesn't* happen, and which therefore *does* have an inverse function, is said to be **one-to-one**. In other words, we have the following definition.

> **One-to-one functions**
>
> A function f is **one-to-one** if for all values x_1 and x_2 in its domain such that $x_1 \neq x_2$,
>
> $$f(x_1) \neq f(x_2).$$

For example, the function $f(x) = x^3$ is one-to-one, because no two different numbers have the same cube. On the other hand, the function $f(x) = x^2$ isn't one-to-one, because, for instance,

$$f(3) = 3^2 = 9 \quad \text{and} \quad f(-3) = (-3)^2 = 9,$$

so $f(3) = f(-3)$.

Activity 34   *Recognising whether functions are one-to-one*

Which of the following functions are one-to-one? For each function that isn't one-to-one, state two input numbers that have the same output number.

(a) $f(x) = |x|$ (b) $f(x) = x + 1$ (c) $f(x) = x^4$ (d) $f(x) = x^5$

(e) $f(x) = -x$ (f) $f(x) = 1$

A useful way to recognise whether a function is one-to-one is to look at its graph. You've seen that, for a one-to-one function, every output number is obtained from exactly one input number. So if you draw any horizontal line that crosses the graph of the function, then it crosses it *exactly once*, as illustrated in Figure 57(a). If you can draw a horizontal line that crosses a graph more than once, then the graph isn't the graph of a one-to-one function. For example, the function whose graph is shown in Figure 57(b) isn't one-to-one, since the dashed horizontal line shows that the two input numbers marked as x_1 and x_2 have the same output number.

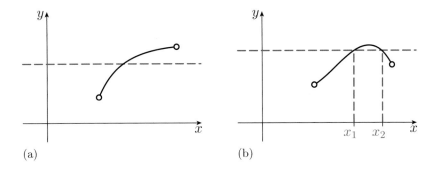

(a)   (b)

Figure 57   The graphs of (a) a one-to-one function and (b) a function that isn't one-to-one

Activity 35   *Recognising the graphs of one-to-one functions*

For each of the following diagrams, state whether it's the graph of a one-to-one function, the graph of a function that isn't one-to-one, or not even the graph of a function.

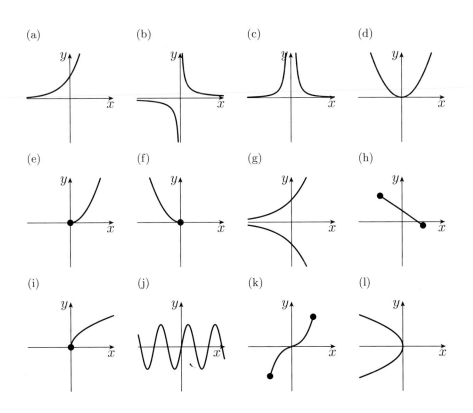

The following important fact summarises the ideas that you've just met.

> Only one-to-one functions have inverse functions.

A function that has an inverse function is said to be **invertible**. So 'invertible function' means the same as 'one-to-one function'.

Now let's consider the domains of inverse functions. If f is any one-to-one function, then the domain of f^{-1} is the image set of the original function f. To see this, think of the mapping diagram for the original function f. Now imagine reversing the directions of all the arrows, to obtain the mapping diagram for the inverse function f^{-1}. The numbers that have arrows starting from them are the numbers in the image set of the original function f. So the domain of f^{-1} is the image set of f.

You can also see, by thinking about these diagrams, that the image set of an inverse function f^{-1} is the domain of the original function f. Here's a concise definition of an inverse function, which summarises what you've seen so far. It's illustrated in Figure 58.

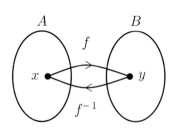

Figure 58   A mapping diagram illustrating a function f and its inverse function f^{-1}. The set B is the *image set* of f, not necessarily its whole codomain.

Inverse functions

Suppose that f is a one-to-one function, with domain A and image set B. Then the **inverse function**, or simply **inverse**, of f, denoted by f^{-1}, is the function with domain B whose rule is given by

$$f^{-1}(y) = x, \quad \text{where} \quad f(x) = y.$$

The image set of f^{-1} is A.

The next example illustrates how you can use this definition to find an inverse function, even when the rule of the original function is more complicated than those that you've seen so far.

Example 6   *Finding an inverse function*

Find the inverse function of the function

$$f(x) = 2x + 1.$$

Solution

🔍 To find the rule of f^{-1}, rearrange the equation $f(x) = y$ to express x in terms of y. 🐟

The equation $f(x) = y$ gives

$$2x + 1 = y$$
$$2x = y - 1$$
$$x = \tfrac{1}{2}(y - 1).$$

Hence the rule of f^{-1} is

$$f^{-1}(y) = \tfrac{1}{2}(y - 1).$$

💬 Usually, change the input variable from y to x, as this is the letter normally used for the input variable of a function. 💬

That is, it is

$$f^{-1}(x) = \tfrac{1}{2}(x - 1).$$

💬 The domain of f^{-1} is the image set of f, which is $\mathbb{R}$. By the domain convention, you don't need to write down this domain. 💬

The domain of f^{-1} is the whole of $\mathbb{R}$, so the rule above completely specifies f^{-1}.

The method used to find the rule of the inverse function in Example 6 is summarised below.

Strategy:
To find the rule of the inverse function of a one-to-one function f

- Write $y = f(x)$ and rearrange this equation to express x in terms of y.

- Use the resulting equation $x = f^{-1}(y)$ to write down the rule of f^{-1}. (Usually, change the input variable from y to x.)

If it's *possible* to rearrange an equation $y = f(x)$ to express x in terms of y (so that each value of y gives exactly one value of x), then this shows that the function f *has* an inverse function, whose rule is given by the rearranged equation. Remember that to fully specify the function f^{-1}, you also have to indicate its domain, which, as you've seen, is the image set of f. (As always, if the domain of f^{-1} is the largest set of real numbers for which its rule is applicable, then there's no need to state its domain explicitly.)

Find the inverse functions of the following functions. (Remember to find the domain of the inverse function in each case.)

(a) $f(x) = 3x - 4$ (b) $f(x) = 2 - \frac{1}{2}x$ (c) $f(x) = 5 + \dfrac{1}{x}$

In cases that are trickier than those in Activity 36, it often helps to obtain a graph of the original function f. For example, this can be useful if the domain of the function f isn't the largest set of real numbers for which its rule is applicable, or if you're not sure whether f is one-to-one. Here's an example.

Example 7   *Finding another inverse function*

Does the function

$$f(x) = x^2 - 4x + 1 \quad (x \in [-1, 1])$$

have an inverse function? If so, find it.

Solution

🔍 Obtain a sketch or computer plot of the graph of f. 💬

The graph of f is shown below.

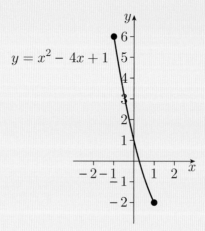

$y = x^2 - 4x + 1$

🔍 Think about whether every horizontal line that crosses the graph of f does so exactly once. 💬

The graph shows that f is one-to-one and therefore has an inverse function.

🔍 Try to find the rule of f^{-1} in the usual way, by rearranging the equation $f(x) = y$. For a quadratic function like f, it helps to begin by completing the square. 💬

The equation $f(x) = y$ gives

$$x^2 - 4x + 1 = y$$
$$(x - 2)^2 - 4 + 1 = y$$
$$(x - 2)^2 - 3 = y$$
$$(x - 2)^2 = y + 3$$
$$x - 2 = \pm\sqrt{y + 3}$$
$$x = 2 \pm \sqrt{y + 3}$$

🔍 Decide whether the + or the − applies. Remember that the final equation above is a rearrangement of the equation $f(x) = y$, so x is an element of the domain of f, which is $[-1, 1]$. Now 2 *plus* the positive square root of something can't be equal to a number in this interval, but 2 *minus* the positive square root of something can, so the correct sign is −. 💬

Since the domain of f is $[-1, 1]$, each input value x of f is less than 2. So

$$x = 2 - \sqrt{y + 3}.$$

Hence the rule of f^{-1} is

$$f^{-1}(y) = 2 - \sqrt{y + 3};$$

that is,

$$f^{-1}(x) = 2 - \sqrt{x + 3}.$$

🔍 To find the domain of f^{-1}, find the image set of f, using the graph to help you. 💬

The domain of f^{-1} is the image set of f. The graph shows that this is

$$[f(1), f(-1)] = [-2, 6].$$

🔍 Finally, specify f^{-1} by stating its domain and rule. 💬

So the inverse function of f is the function

$$f^{-1}(x) = 2 - \sqrt{x + 3} \quad (x \in [-2, 6]).$$

Activity 37   *Finding more inverse functions*

In each of parts (a)–(c), determine whether the function has an inverse function. If it does, then find the inverse function.

(a) $f(x) = x^2 + 2x + 2$ $(x \in (-2, 2))$

(b) $f(x) = x^2 + 2x + 2$ $(x \in (0, 2))$

(c) $f(x) = 1 - x$ $(x \in [-3, 1])$

Here's a useful fact that sometimes gives you a quick way of confirming that a function has an inverse function.

> If a function is either increasing on its whole domain, or decreasing on its whole domain, then it is one-to-one and so has an inverse function.

This fact holds because if a function is either increasing on its whole domain or decreasing on its whole domain, then any horizontal line drawn on its graph will cross the graph at most once, as illustrated in Figure 59.

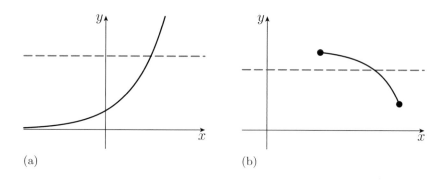

(a)   (b)

Figure 59   (a) A function that's increasing on its whole domain (b) a function that's decreasing on its whole domain

Here's another useful property of inverse functions, which you can understand by thinking about mapping diagrams. If a function f has an inverse function f^{-1}, then f^{-1} also has an inverse function, namely f. In other words, f and f^{-1} are inverses of each other. This is because the mapping diagram for each of these functions is obtained by reversing the directions of the arrows in the mapping diagram for the other function. In particular, each of the functions f and f^{-1} 'undoes' the effect of the other. So if you take any value x in the domain of f, input it to f, and then input the resulting output value to f^{-1}, then you get the value x back again; and similarly if you take any value x in the domain of f^{-1}, input it to f^{-1}, and then input the resulting output value to f, then you get the value x back again. These two facts can be stated concisely as follows, using the notation for composite functions.

For any pair of inverse functions f and f^{-1},
$$(f^{-1} \circ f)(x) = x, \quad \text{for every value } x \text{ in the domain of } f, \text{ and}$$
$$(f \circ f^{-1})(x) = x, \quad \text{for every value } x \text{ in the domain of } f^{-1}.$$

A warning

When you're working with the notation f^{-1}, where f is a function, it's important to appreciate that it *doesn't* mean the function g with rule

$$g(x) = (f(x))^{-1}; \quad \text{that is,} \quad g(x) = \frac{1}{f(x)}.$$

This function g is called the **reciprocal** of the function f, and it's never denoted by f^{-1}. For example, consider the function $f(x) = x + 5$. Its inverse function is

$$f^{-1}(x) = x - 5,$$

whereas its reciprocal is

$$g(x) = \frac{1}{x + 5}.$$

Graphs of inverse functions

There's a useful geometric connection between the graph of a function and the graph of its inverse function. Figure 60(a) shows the graphs of the function $f(x) = x^2 - 1$ ($x \geq 0$) and its inverse function $f^{-1}(x) = \sqrt{x + 1}$ ($x \geq -1$), drawn on axes with equal scales. Similarly, Figure 60(b) shows the graphs of the function $f(x) = 2x + 1$ ($x \in [-2, 1]$) and its inverse function $f^{-1}(x) = \frac{1}{2}(x - 1)$ ($x \in [-3, 3]$), again drawn on axes with equal scales.

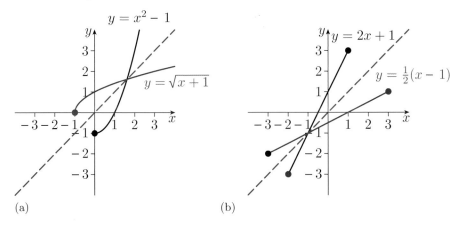

(a)　　　　　　　　　　　(b)

Figure 60　Graphs of pairs of inverse functions

In each case the graphs of f and f^{-1} are the reflections of each other in the line $y = x$, which is shown as a green dashed line.

This happens for every pair of inverse functions, when their graphs are drawn on axes *with equal scales*. To see why, let's start by considering any point on the graph of the function $f(x) = x^2 - 1$ $(x \geq 0)$. For example, the point $(2,3)$ lies on this graph, because inputting 2 to this function f gives the output 3. It follows that inputting 3 to the inverse function f^{-1} gives the output 2, and so the point $(3,2)$ lies on the graph of f^{-1}. You can see that, for any pair of inverse functions f and f^{-1}, if you swap the coordinates of any point on the graph of f, then you'll get the coordinates of a point on the graph of f^{-1}, and vice versa.

Now when you swap the coordinates of a point, the resulting point is the reflection of the original point in the line $y = x$ (provided the axes have equal scales). This is illustrated in Figure 61, for the example discussed above. This reasoning explains the connection between the graphs of a function and its inverse function, which is summarised below.

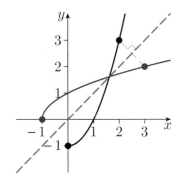

Figure 61   The points $(2,3)$ and $(3,2)$ are reflections of each other in the line $y = x$

Graphs of inverse functions

The graphs of a pair of inverse functions are the reflections of each other in the line $y = x$ (when the coordinate axes have equal scales).

Activity 38   *Sketching graphs of inverse functions*

Each of the following diagrams shows the graph of a function, drawn on axes with equal scales. The line $y = x$ is shown as a green dashed line. The vertical dashed lines in graph (c) are asymptotes.

For each graph, sketch the graph of the inverse function.

(a)

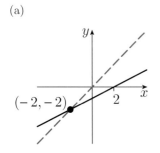

(b)

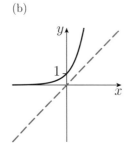

(c)

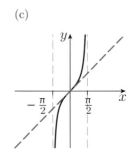

(d)

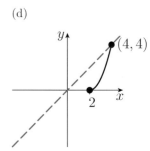

Functions that aren't one-to-one

Finally in this subsection, let's consider functions that don't have inverses, because they're not one-to-one. An example of such a function is $f(x) = x^2$, whose graph is shown in Figure 62.

When you have a function like this, it's sometimes useful to consider 'some sort of inverse' of the function. For example, you'd probably consider the function $h(x) = \sqrt{x}$ to be 'some sort of inverse' of the function $f(x) = x^2$.

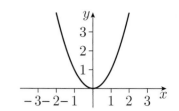

Figure 62   The graph of the function $f(x) = x^2$

Here's the approach that we take in situations like this. Starting with the function f that's not one-to-one, we specify a new function that has the same rule as f, but a smaller domain. We choose the new domain to make sure that the following two conditions are satisfied:

*   the new function is one-to-one and therefore has an inverse

*   the image set of the new function is the same as the image set of the original function.

For example, for the function $f(x) = x^2$, we could take the new function to be the function

$$g(x) = x^2 \quad (x \in [0, \infty)),$$

whose graph is shown in Figure 63(a). This function g is one-to-one, and therefore has an inverse function, namely

$$g^{-1}(x) = \sqrt{x},$$

whose graph is shown in Figure 63(b).

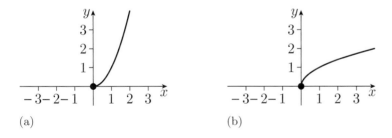

(a)   (b)

Figure 63   The graphs of (a) the function $g(x) = x^2$ $(x \in [0, \infty))$ and (b) its inverse function $g^{-1}(x) = \sqrt{x}$

A function that's obtained from another function f by keeping the rule the same but removing some numbers from the domain is called a **restriction** of the original function f. The process of obtaining such a function is called **restricting** the domain of f, or **restricting** f. So the function g above is a restriction of the function $f(x) = x^2$. The graph of a restriction of a function is obtained by erasing part of the graph of the original function.

When you want to restrict the domain of a function that isn't one-to-one to enable you to find an inverse function, there's always more than one possibility for the new domain. For example, for the function $f(x) = x^2$, you could have chosen the new domain $(-\infty, 0]$ instead of $[0, \infty)$. This would have given you the new function g whose graph is shown in

Figure 64(a). The inverse function of this function is $g^{-1}(x) = -\sqrt{x}$, whose graph is shown in Figure 64(b).

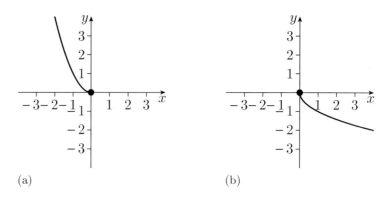

(a)   (b)

Figure 64   The graphs of (a) the function $g(x) = x^2$ $(x \in (-\infty, 0])$ and (b) its inverse function $g^{-1}(x) = -\sqrt{x}$

Usually when we restrict the domain of a function to enable us to find an inverse function, we choose the new domain that seems to be the most convenient.

Activity 39   *Restricting a function to find an inverse function*

Consider the function $f(x) = (x-1)^2$, whose graph is shown in Figure 65. Specify a one-to-one function g that is a restriction of f and has the same image set as f. Find the inverse function g^{-1} of g, and sketch its graph.

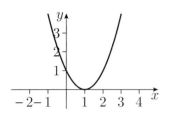

Figure 65   The graph of $y = (x-1)^2$

In Unit 4 you'll see some more examples of this process of restricting the domain of a function to enable you to find an inverse function. It's useful in particular for *trigonometric functions*, which you'll meet in that unit.

4 Exponential functions and logarithms

In this section you'll revise exponential functions and logarithms. In particular, you'll have the opportunity to practise working with logarithms. It's important that you can do this fluently and correctly.

4.1 Exponential functions

An **exponential function** is a function whose rule is of the form

$$f(x) = b^x,$$

where b is a positive constant, not equal to 1. (Note that in some other texts the case $b = 1$ is not excluded.) The number b is called the **base number**, or just **base**, of the exponential function. For example, $f(x) = 2^x$ and $g(x) = \left(\frac{1}{2}\right)^x$ are exponential functions, with base numbers 2 and $\frac{1}{2}$, respectively. The graphs of these two functions are shown in Figure 66. The y-intercept is 1 in each case.

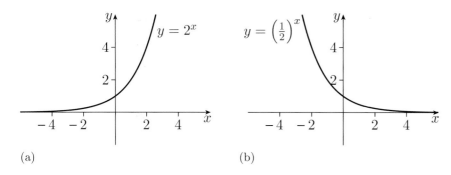

(a)   (b)

Figure 66   The graphs of (a) $y = 2^x$ (b) $y = \left(\frac{1}{2}\right)^x$

To see why these graphs have the shapes that they do, first consider the function $f(x) = 2^x$. Some values of this function are given in Table 1. The corresponding points are shown in Figure 67 (except that the final two points are off the scale).

Table 1   Values of 2^x

x	-4	-3	-2	-1	0	1	2	3	4
2^x	$\frac{1}{16}$	$\frac{1}{8}$	$\frac{1}{4}$	$\frac{1}{2}$	1	2	4	8	16

Notice that $f(0) = 2^0 = 1$, which explains why the y-intercept is 1.

Notice also that each time the value of x increases by 1 unit to the next integer up, the value of $f(x)$ *doubles*. So as x takes values that are further and further along the number line to the right, the value of $f(x) = 2^x$ increases, and increases more and more rapidly. This explains the shape of the graph as x increases.

Similarly, each time the value of x decreases by 1 unit to the next integer down, the value of $f(x)$ *halves*. So, as x takes values that are further and further along the number line to the left, the value of $f(x) = 2^x$ gets closer and closer to zero, but never reaches zero. This gives the shape of the graph as x decreases.

The shape of the graph of the function $g(x) = \left(\frac{1}{2}\right)^x$ can be explained in a similar way, and you might like to think it through for yourself.

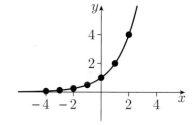

Figure 67   Points on the graph of $y = 2^x$ with integer values of x

Alternatively, you can deduce it from the shape of the graph of the function $f(x) = 2^x$. Notice that, for any number x,

$$\left(\tfrac{1}{2}\right)^x = (2^{-1})^x = 2^{-x}.$$

So the rule of the function $g(x) = \left(\tfrac{1}{2}\right)^x$ can be written as $g(x) = 2^{-x}$, and hence, by what you saw in Subsection 2.3, its graph is the same shape as the graph of $f(x) = 2^x$, but reflected in the y-axis.

In the next activity you're asked to investigate the shapes of the graphs of some more exponential functions.

Activity 40   *Investigating the graphs of exponential functions*

Open the *Exponential functions* applet. Display the graph of $y = b^x$ for various positive values of b, and observe the shapes of the graphs.

In particular, notice how the graphs obtained when $0 < b < 1$ differ from those obtained when $b > 1$.

In Activity 40 you should have observed the following facts, which are illustrated in Figure 68.

Graphs of exponential functions

The graph of the function $f(x) = b^x$, where $b > 0$ and $b \neq 1$, has the following features.

- The graph lies entirely above the x-axis.
- If $b > 1$, then the graph is increasing, and it gets steeper as x increases.
- If $0 < b < 1$, then the graph is decreasing, and it gets less steep as x increases.
- The x-axis is an asymptote.
- The y-intercept is 1.
- The closer the value of b is to 1, the flatter is the graph.

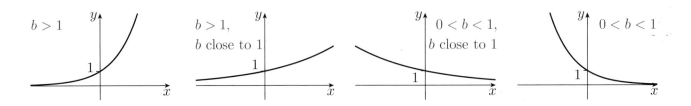

Figure 68   Graphs of equations of the form $y = b^x$

A helpful way to remember the final feature listed in the box above is to notice that when the value of b is *exactly* 1, the function $f(x) = b^x$ is the function $f(x) = 1^x$, that is, $f(x) = 1$, and hence its graph is the horizontal line with y-intercept 1, as shown in Figure 69. Remember, though, that this function f isn't an exponential function – it's a constant function.

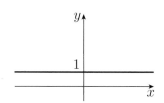

Figure 69   The graph of $y = 1$

The exponential function

There's a particular exponential function that's crucially important in mathematics. You've seen that the graph of every exponential function $f(x) = b^x$ passes through the point $(0, 1)$. The steepness of the graph at this point depends on the value of b, as you can see from the examples in Figure 70.

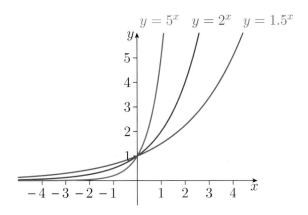

Figure 70   Graphs of exponential functions

In the next activity you're asked to investigate the steepness of the graphs of exponential functions at the point $(0, 1)$.

Activity 41   *Investigating the gradient of the graph of $y = b^x$ at $(0, 1)$*

Use the *Exponential functions* applet to do the following.

(a) Reset the applet and choose the option to show a grid. Zoom in on the point $(0, 1)$ until the graph looks like a straight line. Keep the scales on the axes the same as each other.

(b) Change the value of b until the gradient of the graph at $(0, 1)$ appears to be exactly 1; that is, until the graph goes up by the same distance vertically as it goes along horizontally to the right. What value of b seems to achieve this?

In Activity 41 you should have found that the value of b that gives a gradient of 1 at $(0, 1)$ seems to be about 2.7. In fact, the precise value is a special number, usually denoted by the letter e, whose first few digits are $2.718\,28\ldots$. The number e is irrational, like π, so its digits have no repeating pattern, and it can't be written down exactly as a fraction or a terminating decimal. It occurs frequently in mathematics, and you'll learn more about it, and why it's so important, later in the module.

So the exponential function with the rule $f(x) = e^x$ has the special property that its gradient is exactly 1 at the point $(0, 1)$. Its graph is shown in Figure 71. This function is important both in applications of mathematics and in pure mathematics, and because of its importance it's sometimes referred to as **the** **exponential function**. The expression e^x is sometimes written as $\exp x$, or $\exp(x)$. An approximate value for e is available from your calculator keypad, just as for π, and you can also work out values of e^x by using a function button on your calculator.

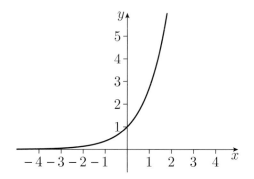

Figure 71   The graph of $y = e^x$

> The use of the letter e for the base of *the* exponential function was introduced by Leonhard Euler (see page 214).

4.2   What is a logarithm?

In this subsection, you'll revise *logarithms*, which are closely related to exponential functions. Logarithms are sometimes called *logs*, for short.

The first thing to remember about logarithms is that whenever you're working with them, you're always using logarithms to a particular *base* (also called *base number*). Let's start by considering *logarithms to base 10*, which are known as **common logarithms**. These are defined as follows. The **logarithm to base** 10 of a number x is the power to which 10 must be raised to give the number x.

For example,

the logarithm to base 10 of 100 is 2, because $100 = 10^2$.

Similarly,

the logarithm to base 10 of 1000 is 3, because $1000 = 10^3$, and
the logarithm to base 10 of $\frac{1}{10}$ is -1, because $\frac{1}{10} = 10^{-1}$.

The logarithm to base 10 of a number x is denoted by $\log_{10} x$, so the three logarithms found above can be written as follows:

$\log_{10} 100 = 2$
$\log_{10} 1000 = 3$
$\log_{10} \left(\frac{1}{10}\right) = -1.$

You can see that if you can easily write a number as a power of 10, then it's straightforward to find its logarithm to base 10. For other numbers, you can use your calculator to find an approximate value. For example, a calculator gives

$\log_{10} 42 = 1.623\,249\,2\ldots,$

which is the same as saying that

$10^{1.623\,249\,2\ldots} = 42.$

The button on a calculator for finding common logarithms is usually labelled 'log'.

Activity 42   *Understanding logarithms to base* 10

(a) Find the following numbers, without using your calculator.

   (i) $\log_{10} 10\,000$ (ii) $\log_{10} \frac{1}{100}$ (iii) $\log_{10} 10$ (iv) $\log_{10} 1$

(b) If the number x is such that $\log_{10} x = \frac{1}{2}$, what is x?

(c) Use your calculator to find the following numbers, to three decimal places.

   (i) $\log_{10} 3700$ (ii) $\log_{10} 370$ (iii) $\log_{10} 37$

   (iv) $\log_{10} 3.7$ (v) $\log_{10} 0.37$ (vi) $\log_{10} 0.037$

Notice that only positive numbers have logarithms to base 10. For example, the negative number -2 has no logarithm to base 10, because there's no power to which 10 can be raised to give -2. Similarly, 0 has no logarithm to base 10, because there's no power to which 10 can be raised to give 0.

However, logarithms themselves can be positive, negative or zero. For example, you've seen that

$\log_{10} 100 = 2, \quad \log_{10} \left(\frac{1}{10}\right) = -1 \quad \text{and} \quad \log_{10} 1 = 0.$

Now let's consider logarithms to other bases. Like the base of an exponential function, the base of a logarithm can be any positive number except 1. Logarithms to other bases work in the same way as logarithms to base 10. Here's a general definition of logarithms, to any base.

> ## Logarithms
>
> The **logarithm to base** b of a number x, denoted by $\log_b x$, is the power to which the base b must be raised to give the number x. So the two equations
>
> $$y = \log_b x \quad \text{and} \quad x = b^y$$
>
> are equivalent.
>
> Remember that:
>
> - the base b must be positive and not equal to 1
> - only positive numbers have logarithms, but logarithms themselves can be any number.

For example, $\log_6 36 = 2$ because $36 = 6^2$.

Activity 43 *Understanding logarithms to any base*

(a) Find the following numbers without using your calculator.

  (i) $\log_3 9$ (ii) $\log_2 8$ (iii) $\log_4 64$ (iv) $\log_5 25$ (v) $\log_4 2$

  (vi) $\log_8 2$ (vii) $\log_2 \frac{1}{2}$ (viii) $\log_2 \frac{1}{8}$ (ix) $\log_3 \frac{1}{27}$

  (x) $\log_8 \frac{1}{8}$ (xi) $\log_3 3$ (xii) $\log_4 \frac{1}{4}$ (xiii) $\log_6 6$

  (xiv) $\log_5 \sqrt{5}$ (xv) $\log_7 \sqrt[3]{7}$ (xvi) $\log_2 1$ (xvii) $\log_{15} 1$

(b) Find the solution of each of the following equations in x.

  (i) $\log_2 x = 5$ (ii) $\log_8 x = \frac{1}{3}$ (iii) $\log_7 x = 1$

You've seen that it's straightforward to write down the logarithm to base b of a number if you can express the number as a power of b. In particular, for any base b, it's straightforward to write down the logarithm to base b of 1, and the logarithm to base b of b itself, because

$$1 = b^0 \quad \text{and} \quad b = b^1.$$

This gives the following useful facts.

Logarithm of the number 1 and logarithm of the base

For any base b,

$$\log_b 1 = 0 \quad \text{and} \quad \log_b b = 1.$$

Logarithms were invented by the Scottish mathematician John Napier for the purpose of easing the labour involved in astronomical and navigational calculations. Napier's rather awkward initial formulation, published in 1614, was greeted enthusiastically by the English mathematician Henry Briggs (1561–1630), who immediately set about trying to improve it. The following year Briggs visited Napier, and together they invented logarithms to base 10, the first publication of which appeared in 1617 shortly after Napier's death.

John Napier (1550–1617)

The most common choices for the base of logarithms are 10, 2 and e. (Remember that e is the important constant whose value is approximately 2.718.) Usually, once you've chosen a base, you use the same base for all the logarithms in your calculations (otherwise, your calculations may be wrong!).

In university-level mathematics, the number most commonly used as the base for logarithms is e. As you'll see later in the module, logarithms to base e turn out to be easier to work with in many ways than logarithms to any other base.

Logarithms to base e are called **natural logarithms**. The notation 'ln' is often used in place of '$\log_e$', and this is the notation that will be used in this module. For example, the natural logarithm of 5 is written as

$$\ln 5 \quad \text{rather than} \quad \log_e 5.$$

(The first symbol in 'ln' is the letter l, not the digit 1.)

There's no consensus about how the notation 'ln' should be pronounced, but some common pronunciations are 'log', 'ell enn', 'linn' and 'lawn'. The box below summarises the definition of a natural logarithm, using this notation.

Natural logarithms

The **natural logarithm** of a number x, denoted by $\ln x$, is the power to which the base e must be raised to give the number x. So the two equations

$$y = \ln x \quad \text{and} \quad x = e^y$$

are equivalent.

Scientific calculators have a button for finding natural logarithms, usually labelled 'ln'.

The properties that $\log_b 1 = 0$ and $\log_b b = 1$ for any base b give the following two useful properties of natural logarithms.

$$\ln 1 = 0 \quad \text{and} \quad \ln e = 1.$$

Here are some calculations involving natural logarithms for you to try.

Activity 44   *Understanding natural logarithms*

(a) Find the following numbers without using your calculator.

  (i) $\ln e^4$ (ii) $\ln e^2$ (iii) $\ln e^{3/5}$ (iv) $\ln \sqrt{e}$

  (v) $\ln\left(\dfrac{1}{e}\right)$ (vi) $\ln\left(\dfrac{1}{e^3}\right)$

(b) If the number x is such that $\ln x = -\frac{1}{2}$, what is x?

(c) Use your calculator to find the following numbers to three decimal places.

  (i) $\ln 5100$ (ii) $\ln 510$ (iii) $\ln 51$

  (iv) $\ln(51e)$ (v) $\ln(51e^2)$

The natural logarithm of a number x is sometimes denoted by $\log x$, rather than by $\ln x$ or $\log_e x$. For example, this notation is used by some computer algebra systems. Confusingly, the same notation, $\log x$, is also sometimes used to denote $\log_{10} x$, the common logarithm of x. For example, as mentioned earlier, the button on a calculator for finding common logarithms is usually labelled 'log'. Even more confusingly, the notation $\log x$ is also sometimes used to denote the logarithm of x with no specific base (but the same base for each use of the notation). So, wherever you see the notation $\log x$ used, it's important to check its meaning. The notation $\log x$ isn't used at all in the main books of this module, but you may have to use it with your calculator or computer.

Logarithms to base e were first described as 'natural' logarithms by the Danish mathematician Nicolaus Mercator (1620–87), in his treatise *Logarithmotechnica* published in 1668. Mercator's treatise was difficult to follow, so later writers tended to refer to the exposition of it given by the English mathematician John Wallis (1616–1703), published in the same year. The first published use of the notation 'ln' for a natural logarithm was in a book written by an American mathematician, Irving Stringham, which was published in 1893. He explained his choice, in a textbook published a little later, as follows: 'In place of ^{e}log we shall henceforth use the shorter symbol ln, made up of the initial letters of *logarithm* and of *natural* or *Napierian*.'

4.3 Logarithmic functions

A **logarithmic function** is a function whose rule is of the form

$$f(x) = \log_b x,$$

where b is a positive constant, not equal to 1. The number b is called the **base** or **base number** of the logarithmic function. For example, $f(x) = \log_2 x$ and $g(x) = \ln x$ are logarithmic functions, with bases 2 and e, respectively.

For any positive constant b not equal to 1, the logarithmic function $f(x) = \log_b x$ is the inverse function of the exponential function $g(x) = b^x$. This is because, as you've seen, the two equations

$$y = \log_b x \quad \text{and} \quad x = b^y$$

are rearrangements of each other.

In particular, the function $f(x) = \ln x$ is the inverse function of the function $g(x) = e^x$, which explains why these two functions usually share the same button on a calculator.

So the graphs of $f(x) = \log_b x$ and $g(x) = b^x$ are reflections of each other in the line $y = x$ (provided that the coordinate axes have equal scales).

For example, Figure 72 shows the graphs of $y = \ln x$ and $y = e^x$.

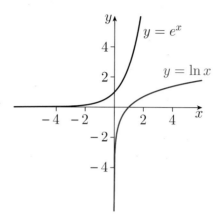

Figure 72   The graphs of $y = \ln x$ and $y = e^x$

You can deduce the following general properties of the graphs of logarithmic functions from the properties of the graphs of exponential functions, using the fact that they're reflections of each other in the line $y = x$. These properties are illustrated in Figure 73.

Graphs of logarithmic functions

The graph of the function $f(x) = \log_b x$, where $b > 0$ and $b \neq 1$, has the following features.

- The graph lies entirely to the right of the y-axis.

- If $b > 1$, then the graph is increasing, and it gets less steep as x increases.

- If $0 < b < 1$, then the graph is decreasing, and it gets less steep as x increases.

- The y-axis is an asymptote.

- The x-intercept is 1.

- The closer the value of b is to 1, the steeper is the graph.

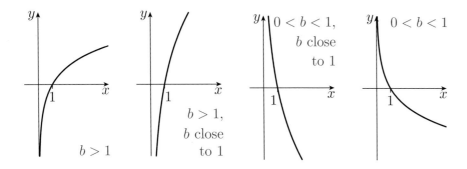

Figure 73   Graphs of equations of the form $y = \log_b x$

The properties in the box below are often useful when you're working with logarithms. They're just the two facts about composing a pair of inverse functions that are stated in the box on page 263, in the particular case when the functions are $f(x) = b^x$ and $f^{-1}(x) = \log_b x$.

> For any base b,
> $$\log_b(b^x) = x \quad \text{and} \quad b^{\log_b x} = x.$$
> In particular,
> $$\ln(e^x) = x \quad \text{and} \quad e^{\ln x} = x.$$

These properties hold for all appropriate values of x.

Activity 45   *Simplifying expressions involving e and $\ln$*

Simplify the following expressions.

(a) $e^{\ln(7x)}$ (b) $\ln(e^{8x})$ (c) $\ln(e^{2x}) + \ln(e^{3x})$ (d) $\ln(e^2) - \ln e$

(e) $\ln(e^{x/2}) + 3\ln 1$ (f) $e^{2\ln c}$ (g) $e^{\ln(3a)} + 4e^0$

(h) $\ln(e^{y+2}) + 2\ln(e^{y-1})$ (i) $e^{3\ln B}$ (j) $e^{2+\ln x}$

Hint: in some parts you may need to use the index laws from Unit 1.

4.4 Logarithm laws

In this subsection you'll revise three laws for logarithms, which are often useful when you're working with logarithms. These laws are really just the same as the following three index laws that were given in Unit 1, rewritten using logarithm notation.

Three index laws from Unit 1

$$b^m b^n = b^{m+n} \qquad \frac{b^m}{b^n} = b^{m-n} \qquad (b^m)^n = b^{mn}$$

Here are the three logarithm laws.

Three logarithm laws

$$\log_b x + \log_b y = \log_b (xy)$$

$$\log_b x - \log_b y = \log_b \left(\frac{x}{y}\right)$$

$$r \log_b x = \log_b (x^r)$$

As with the index laws, these logarithm laws apply to all appropriate numbers. So the base b of the logarithms can be any positive number except 1, the numbers x and y must be positive (since only positive numbers have logarithms), and r can be any number (in particular, it can be fractional and/or negative).

To see how these three logarithm laws are deduced from the three index laws above, let's write $m = \log_b x$ and $n = \log_b y$. This is the same as saying that $x = b^m$ and $y = b^n$.

So,

$$xy = b^m b^n = b^{m+n},$$

from which it follows that

$$\log_b(xy) = m + n = \log_b x + \log_b y.$$

This is the first logarithm law.

Also,

$$\frac{x}{y} = \frac{b^m}{b^n} = b^{m-n},$$

from which it follows that

$$\log_b \left(\frac{x}{y}\right) = m - n = \log_b x - \log_b y.$$

This is the second logarithm law.

Finally,

$$x^r = (b^m)^r = b^{mr},$$

from which it follows that

$$\log_b(x^r) = mr = r\log_b x.$$

This is the third logarithm law.

Example 8   *Using the logarithm laws*

Write the expression $3\ln 6 - 2\ln 2$ as the logarithm of a single number.

Solution

$$3\ln 6 - 2\ln 2 = \ln 6^3 - \ln 2^2 = \ln\left(\frac{6^3}{2^2}\right) = \ln 54$$

Here are some examples for you to try.

Activity 46   *Using the logarithm laws*

(a) Write each of the following expressions as the logarithm of a single number or expression.

  (i) $\ln 5 + \ln 3$ (ii) $\ln 2 - \ln 7$ (iii) $3\ln 2$

  (iv) $\ln 3 + \ln 4 - \ln 6$ (v) $\ln 24 - 2\ln 3$ (vi) $\frac{1}{3}\log_{10} 27$

  (vii) $3\log_2 5 - \log_2 3 + \log_2 6$ (viii) $\frac{1}{2}\ln(9x) - \ln(x+1)$

(b) Simplify the following expressions.

  (i) $\ln c^3 - \ln c$ (ii) $3\ln(p^2)$ (iii) $\ln(y^2) + 2\ln y - \frac{1}{2}\ln(y^3)$

  (iv) $\ln(3u) - \ln(2u)$ (v) $\ln(4x) + 3\ln x - \ln(e^6)$ (vi) $\frac{1}{2}\ln(u^8)$

(c) Can you explain the pattern in the answers to Activity 42(c)? (This activity is on page 271.)

  Hint: notice that each number in Activity 42(c) is of the form $\log_{10}(37 \times 10^n)$, for some integer n.

(d) Suppose that the multiplication button on your scientific calculator doesn't work. Can you use the remaining buttons to find the value of 1567×2786, at least approximately?

  Hint: start by writing $1567 \times 2786 = e^{\ln(1567 \times 2786)}$.

Solving exponential equations

An **exponential equation** is one in which the unknown is in the exponent, such as

$$5^x = 130.$$

Equations like this often arise when you use exponential functions to model real-life situations. You'll see some examples in the next subsection.

You can solve exponential equations by using the third of the three logarithm laws given earlier in this subsection. For this purpose it's best to think of the law with its left and right sides swapped:

$$\log_b(x^r) = r \log_b x. \quad \text{In particular,} \quad \ln(x^r) = r \ln x.$$

Example 9 *Solving an exponential equation*

Solve the equation $2 \times 1.5^{3x} = 45$, giving the solution to three significant figures.

Solution

The equation can be solved as follows.

$$2 \times 1.5^{3x} = 45$$

🔍 Rearrange it into the form $(\text{number})^{(\text{expression in } x)} = \text{number}.$ 💬

$$1.5^{3x} = 22.5$$

🔍 Take the natural logarithm of both sides. 💬

$$\ln(1.5^{3x}) = \ln 22.5$$

🔍 Use the fact that $\ln(x^r) = r \ln x.$ 💬

$$3x \ln 1.5 = \ln 22.5$$

🔍 Divide both sides by the coefficient of the unknown. 💬

$$x = \frac{\ln 22.5}{3 \ln 1.5}$$

🔍 Use your calculator to evaluate the answer. 💬

$$x = 2.56 \text{ (to 3 s.f.)}.$$

The solution is approximately $x = 2.56$.

(Check: when $x = 2.56$,
LHS $= 2 \times 1.5^{3 \times 2.56} = 45.020\,557\ldots \approx 45 = $ RHS.)

The crucial step in the method demonstrated in Example 9 is to 'take logs of both sides' of the exponential equation. Then you can use the property in the box above to turn the exponent into a factor, which makes it straightforward to solve the equation. You don't have to use natural logarithms in this method – you can use logarithms to any base, as long as you're consistent.

In fact, if your calculator has a button for finding logarithms to any base, then you can make the working in Example 9 slightly shorter by proceeding as follows, starting from the second equation in the solution:

$$1.5^{3x} = 22.5$$
$$3x = \log_{1.5} 22.5$$
$$x = \tfrac{1}{3} \log_{1.5} 22.5$$
$$x = 2.56 \text{ (to 3 s.f.)}.$$

Activity 47   *Solving exponential equations*

Solve the following exponential equations, giving your answers to three significant figures.

(a) $5^x = 0.5$ (b) $4e^{7t} = 64$ (c) $5 \times 2^{u/2} + 30 = 600$

(d) $2^{3x-5} = 100$

Remember that you can always check a solution that you've found for an equation by substituting it into the equation.

In the final activity of this subsection you can learn how to use the computer to work with expressions involving exponentials and logarithms.

Activity 48   *Working with exponentials and logarithms on the computer*

Work through Section 5 of the *Computer algebra guide.*

4.5 Alternative form for exponential functions

You've seen that an *exponential function* is one whose rule is of the form

$$f(x) = b^x,$$

where b is a positive constant, not equal to 1.

There's a useful alternative way to express a rule of this form. If you let k be the number such that $e^k = b$ (in other words, if you take $k = \ln b$), then

$$f(x) = b^x = (e^k)^x = e^{kx}.$$

For example, another way to express the rule

$$f(x) = 5^x$$

is, approximately,

$$f(x) = e^{1.609\,438x},$$

because $\ln 5 = 1.609\,437\,912\ldots$.

In general, we have the following fact.

> Any exponential function $f(x) = b^x$, where b is a positive constant not equal to 1, can be written in the alternative form
>
> $$f(x) = e^{kx},$$
>
> where k is a non-zero constant. The constant k is given by $k = \ln b$.

Activity 49   *Understanding the alternative form of an exponential function*

Consider the exponential function $f(x) = 3^x$. Write its rule in the form $f(x) = e^{kx}$, giving the constant k to seven significant figures. Use each form of the rule in turn to work out $f(1.5)$ to three significant figures, and check that you get the same answer.

The fact in the box above gives us the following alternative definition of an exponential function.

An **exponential function** is a function whose rule is of the form

$$f(x) = e^{kx},$$

where k is a non-zero constant. This alternative form is the one that's usually used in university-level mathematics, as it turns out to be easier to work with, for reasons that you'll see later in this module.

The properties of the graphs of exponential functions that you saw in Subsection 4.1 can be stated in terms of this alternative form as in the box below. These properties are illustrated in Figure 74.

> **Graphs of exponential functions**
>
> The graph of the function $f(x) = e^{kx}$, where $k \neq 0$, has the following features.
>
> - The graph lies entirely above the x-axis.
> - If $k > 0$, then the graph is increasing, and it gets steeper as x increases.
> - If $k < 0$, then the graph is decreasing, and it gets less steep as x increases.
> - The x-axis is an asymptote.
> - The y-intercept is 1.
> - The closer the value of k is to 0, the flatter is the graph.

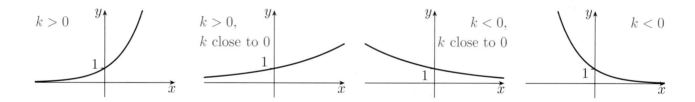

Figure 74 Graphs of equations of the form $y = e^{kx}$

The fact that every exponential function can be written in the form $f(x) = e^{kx}$ also tells you the following enlightening fact.

> The graph of every exponential function is a horizontal scaling of the graph of the exponential function $f(x) = e^x$.

That's because, from what you saw in Subsection 2.3, if f is any function, then the graph of $y = f(kx)$ is a horizontal scaling of the graph of $y = f(x)$ by the factor $c = 1/k$. So the graphs of all exponential functions have the same basic shape, just stretched or squashed horizontally by different amounts, and possibly reflected in the y-axis.

It follows that the graphs of all logarithmic functions are *vertical* scalings of each other, since the graphs of logarithmic functions are reflections of the graphs of exponential functions in the line $y = x$.

4.6 Exponential models

Functions with rules of the form $f(x) = ab^x$, where a is a non-zero number and b is a positive number not equal to 1, are useful for modelling some types of real-life situations. Models of this type are called **exponential models**.

From what you saw in the previous subsection, rules of this form are the same as rules of the form $f(x) = ae^{kx}$, where a and k are non-zero numbers. We'll use this alternative form in this subsection.

From your work in Subsection 2.2, you know that the graph of the function $f(x) = ae^{kx}$ is obtained by vertically scaling the graph of the function $g(x) = e^{kx}$ by a factor of a. Also, as you saw in Subsection 4.5, the graph of the function $g(x) = e^{kx}$ is itself obtained by horizontally scaling the graph of the function $h(x) = e^x$ by a factor of $1/k$. So the graph of any function of the form $f(x) = ae^{kx}$ is obtained by scaling the graph of the function $h(x) = e^x$ both horizontally and vertically. In particular, since the graph of $h(x) = e^x$ has y-intercept 1, the graph of $f(x) = ae^{kx}$ has y-intercept a. Figure 75 shows the graphs of some functions of this form.

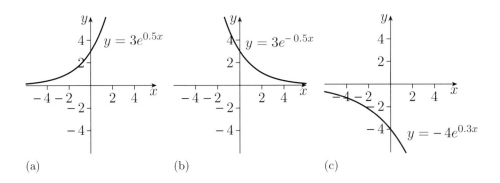

Figure 75 The graphs of three functions of the form $f(x) = ae^{kx}$

A quantity that changes in a way that can be modelled by a function whose rule is of the form $f(x) = ae^{kx}$, where a and k are non-zero constants, is said to **change exponentially**. If a and k are both positive, then the graph of f looks like the graph in Figure 76(a), or a part of it. In this case the quantity is said to **grow exponentially**, the function is called an **exponential growth function**, and the graph is called an **exponential growth curve**.

Similarly, if a is positive as before but k is negative, then the graph of f looks like the graph in Figure 76(b), or a part of it. In this case the quantity is said to **decay exponentially**, the function is called an **exponential decay function**, and the graph is called an **exponential decay curve**.

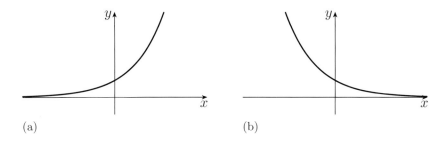

(a)   (b)

Figure 76   (a) An exponential growth curve (b) an exponential decay curve

An example of a real-life situation that can often be modelled by an exponential decay function is the concentration of a prescription drug in a patient's bloodstream. The concentration always peaks shortly after the drug is administered, and then falls, quickly at first but more slowly later, as the drug is metabolised or eliminated from the body. For example, Figure 77 shows such a model. The model covers the period of time after the concentration of the drug peaks. The unit 'μg/ml' is micrograms per millilitre.

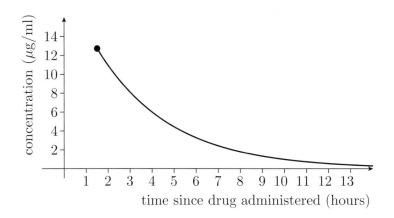

Prescription drugs

Figure 77   An exponential decay curve modelling the concentration of a particular prescription drug in a patient's bloodstream

The next example is about a model of this type. The solution to part (a) of the example involves solving a pair of *simultaneous exponential equations*.

Example 10   *Using an exponential model*

A drug is administered to a patient, and blood tests show that after one and a quarter hours the concentration of the drug in the patient's bloodstream is 105 ng/ml (nanograms per millilitre), and after two and three quarter hours it is 86.0 ng/ml. Assume that the concentration of the drug in the patient's bloodstream can be modelled by an exponential decay function f, where $f(t)$ is the concentration (in ng/ml) at time t (in hours) after the drug was administered, for $t \geq 1$.

(a) Find the function f, giving each of the two constants in it to three significant figures.

(b) What is the predicted concentration of the drug after 10 hours?

Solution

(a) Let $f(t) = ae^{kt}$, where a and k are constants.

🔍 Use the information that you know about f to find the values of a and k. 💬

From the information given in the question, $f(1.25) = 105$ and $f(2.75) = 86.0$, so

$$ae^{1.25k} = 105 \quad \text{and} \quad ae^{2.75k} = 86.0. \tag{3}$$

🔍 These are simultaneous exponential equations in a and k. To solve them, first eliminate a, by dividing one equation by the other. 💬

Hence

$$\frac{ae^{2.75k}}{ae^{1.25k}} = \frac{86}{105},$$

which gives

$$e^{2.75k - 1.25k} = \frac{86}{105}$$

$$e^{1.5k} = \frac{86}{105}$$

$$1.5k = \ln\left(\frac{86}{105}\right)$$

$$k = \frac{\ln(86/105)}{1.5}$$

$$k = -0.133\,075\ldots.$$

🔍 Now find a, by substituting into one of equations (3). 💬

Substituting $k = -0.133\,075\ldots$ into the first of equations (3) gives

$$ae^{1.25\times(-0.133\,075\ldots)} = 105$$

$$a = \frac{105}{e^{1.25\times(-0.133\,075\ldots)}}$$

$$a = 124.002\ldots.$$

So $a = 124$ and $k = -0.133$, both to three significant figures.

Hence the required function f is given, approximately, by

$$f(t) = 124e^{-0.133t} \quad (t \geq 1).$$

(b) The predicted concentration after 10 hours, in ng/ml, is

$$f(10) = (124.002\ldots)e^{(-0.133\,075\ldots)\times 10} = 32.7712\ldots.$$

That is, the concentration is predicted to be about $33\,\text{ng/ml}$.

There are many other types of real-life situations that can be modelled by exponential growth and decay functions. These include the level of radioactivity in a sample of radioactive material, which decreases over time, and, sometimes, the size of a population of organisms, such as bacteria, plants, animals or even human beings, which often increases over a period of time. The next activity is about an exponential model for the growth of a population of bacteria.

Radioactive waste

Activity 50   *Using an exponential model*

The fluid in a test tube was inoculated with a sample of bacteria, which began to divide after 8 hours. Tests after 9 hours and 12 hours showed that the test tube contained about 300 and 4200 bacteria per millilitre, respectively. Assume that the number of bacteria per millilitre can be modelled by an exponential growth function f, where $f(t)$ is the number of bacteria per millilitre at time t (in hours), for $8 \leq t \leq 24$.

(a) Find the function f, giving each of the two constants in it to three significant figures.

(b) What is the predicted number of bacteria per millilitre after 24 hours? Give your answer in scientific notation, to two significant figures.

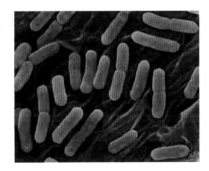

Bacteria dividing

Exponential growth and decay functions have an interesting characteristic property. If f is such a function, and you start with any value of x and *add* a number to it, then the value of $f(x)$ is *multiplied* by a factor. This factor doesn't depend on the value of x that you started with, but only on the number that you added.

For example, if f is such a function, and $f(5)$ happens to be 3 times larger than $f(1)$, then also $f(20)$ will be 3 times larger than $f(16)$ (because you need to add the same number of units, namely 4, to get from 16 to 20 as from 1 to 5). Similarly, $f(154)$ will be 3 times larger than $f(150)$, and $f(2)$ will be 3 times larger than $f(-2)$, and so on.

To see why this happens, consider any exponential growth or decay function $f(x) = ae^{kx}$. When you start with a particular value of x, and add p units, say, the value of $f(x)$ changes from

$$f(x) = ae^{kx} \quad \text{to} \quad f(x+p) = ae^{k(x+p)}.$$

Now,

$$ae^{k(x+p)} = ae^{kx+kp} = ae^{kx}e^{kp} = f(x) \times e^{kp}.$$

So the value of $f(x)$ is multiplied by the factor e^{kp}.

Here's a concise statement of the fact discussed above.

A characteristic property of exponential growth and decay functions

If $f(x) = ae^{kx}$, then whenever p units are added to the value of x, the value of $f(x)$ is multiplied by e^{kp}.

For any exponential function f, the factor by which $f(x)$ is multiplied when a particular amount is added to the value of x is called a **growth factor** or a **decay factor**, according to whether f is an exponential growth or decay function. Growth factors are greater than 1, and decay factors are between 0 and 1, exclusive. The next example illustrates how to find growth or decay factors.

Example 11   *Finding growth factors for exponential growth*

Suppose that the number $f(t)$ of bacteria per millilitre of fluid in a test tube at time t (in hours) after it was inoculated is modelled by the exponential growth function

$$f(t) = 3e^{0.4t} \quad (9 \le t \le 30).$$

By what factor is the number of bacteria predicted to multiply

(a) every hour?   (b) every two and a half hours?

Give your answers to three significant figures.

Solution

🔍 Use the property in the box above. 💭

(a) In every hour, the number of bacteria is predicted to multiply by the factor

$$e^{0.4 \times 1} = e^{0.4} = 1.49 \text{ (to 3 s.f.).}$$

(b) In every period of 2.5 hours, the number of bacteria is predicted to multiply by the factor

$$e^{0.4 \times 2.5} = e^1 = 2.72 \text{ (to 3 s.f.).}$$

Here are some examples of exponential growth and decay for you to analyse.

Activity 51 *Finding growth factors for exponential growth*

Suppose that the number of trees of a particular variety in a region, at time t (in decades) after the variety was introduced, is modelled by the exponential growth function

$$f(t) = 700e^{0.06t} \quad (10 \le t \le 50).$$

By what factor is the size of the tree population predicted to multiply

(a) every decade?   (b) every century?   (c) every five years?

Give your answers to three significant figures.

The phrase 'grown exponentially' is used frequently in the media. However the intended meaning is nearly always that a quantity has grown a lot, or has grown quickly, rather than the true meaning. It's possible for a quantity to grow slowly but exponentially. For example, this is true of the size of the population of trees in Activity 51.

Modelling tree populations is a long-term project

Activity 52 *Finding decay factors for exponential decay*

Suppose that the radioactivity level $r(t)$ (in becquerels) of a sample of radioactive material at time t (in years) after the level was first measured is modelled by the function

$$r(t) = 2800e^{-0.035t} \quad (t \ge 0).$$

By what factor is the radioactivity level predicted to multiply

(a) every year?   (b) every 25 years?   (c) every century?

Give your answers to two significant figures.

The characteristic property of exponential growth and decay functions in the box above gives us a useful way to describe how quickly a particular instance of exponential growth or decay is taking place. For example, consider again the situation in Example 11, where the number $f(t)$ of bacteria per millilitre of fluid in a test tube at time t (in hours) after it was inoculated is modelled by the exponential growth function

$$f(t) = 3e^{0.4t} \quad (9 \le t \le 30).$$

You can see that, by the property in the box, if p is the number such that

$$e^{0.4p} = 2, \tag{4}$$

then whenever you add p to t, the value of $f(t)$ is multiplied by *exactly* 2. This value of p is called the *doubling period* for the function f. Solving equation (4) gives

$$0.4p = \ln 2; \quad \text{that is,} \quad p = (\ln 2)/0.4 = 1.732\,867\ldots.$$

So the number of bacteria per millilitre doubles every 1.7 hours, approximately. In general we make the following definitions.

Doubling and halving periods

Suppose that f is an exponential growth function. Then p is the **doubling period** of f if whenever you add p to x, the value of $f(x)$ doubles.

Similarly, suppose that f is an exponential decay function. Then p is the **halving period** of f if whenever you add p to x, the value of $f(x)$ halves.

Here's a summary of how to find doubling or halving periods.

Strategy:
To find a doubling or halving period

If $f(x) = ae^{kx}$ is an exponential growth function (so $k > 0$), then the doubling period of f is the solution p of the equation $e^{kp} = 2$; that is, $p = (\ln 2)/k$.

Similarly, if $f(x) = ae^{kx}$ is an exponential decay function (so $k < 0$), then the halving period of f is the solution p of the equation $e^{kp} = \frac{1}{2}$; that is, $p = (\ln \frac{1}{2})/k = -(\ln 2)/k$.

In many exponential models, such as the ones in Example 11 and Activities 51 and 52, the input variable represents time. When this is the case, the doubling or halving period is more usually called the **doubling** or **halving time**. In the particular case of radioactive decay, the halving time is usually called the **half-life**.

Activity 53   *Finding doubling and halving periods*

Find the doubling time of the exponential growth in Activity 51, and the half-life of the exponential decay in Activity 52. Give your answers to three significant figures.

Radiocarbon dating is a method of estimating the age of material that originates from a living organism, such as an animal or a plant. A living organism absorbs the radioactive isotope carbon-14 from the atmosphere. When it dies, the amount of carbon-14 in its remains decays exponentially, with a half-life of 5730 years. A measurement of the amount of carbon-14 that's left can be used to estimate when the organism was alive, up to about 60 000 years ago. For example, radiocarbon dating of organic material at Stonehenge was used in 2008 to determine that the monument was built in about 2300 BC.

Radiocarbon dating was developed by Willard Libby at the University of Chicago in 1950. He was awarded the Nobel Prize for Chemistry in 1960.

Willard Libby (1908–80)

Stonehenge, Wiltshire

5   Inequalities

In the module so far you've worked with equations of various types. However, sometimes you need to work not with equations, but with *inequalities*. Whereas an equation expresses the fact that two quantities are equal, an inequality expresses the fact that one quantity is greater than, less than, greater than or equal to, or less than or equal to, another quantity.

5.1 Terminology for inequalities

You saw some examples of inequalities in Section 1 of this unit. Here are a few more:

$$x \geq 5, \quad 3a - 2 > b + 1, \quad p^2 - 5p + 6 \leq 0, \quad 2^t > 10.$$

In general, an **inequality** is the same as an equation, except that instead of an equals sign it contains one of the four inequality signs, $<, \leq, >$ and $\geq$. In other words, an inequality is made up of two expressions, with one of the four inequality signs between them.

> **Inequality signs**
>
> $<$ is less than
> $\leq$ is less than or equal to
> $>$ is greater than
> $\geq$ is greater than or equal to

Much of the terminology that applies to equations also applies to inequalities. For example:

- an inequality **in** x is one that contains the variable x and no other variables (the first inequality above is an example)

- the **solutions** of an inequality are the values of its variables that **satisfy** it – in other words, they are the real numbers for which it is true (for instance, the values $x = 6$ and $t = 4$ are solutions of the first and fourth inequalities above, respectively, and there are many other solutions)

- **solving** an inequality means finding all its solutions

- two inequalities are **equivalent** if they contain the same variables and are satisfied by the same values of those variables

- **rearranging** an inequality means transforming it into an equivalent inequality.

Most inequalities have either infinitely many solutions or no solutions. A useful way to specify all the solutions of an inequality is to state the set that they form. This set is called the **solution set** of the inequality. For example, the solution set of the simple inequality $x \geq 5$ is the interval $[5, \infty)$, and the solution set of the inequality $x^2 < 0$ is the empty set $\varnothing$.

In this section you'll learn how to rearrange inequalities, and you'll see how you can use this technique to help you solve some types of inequality in one variable. You'll also see how the graphs of functions can help you visualise the solution sets of inequalities, and you'll learn some further techniques that you can use to extend the range of inequalities in one variable that you can solve.

5.2   Rearranging inequalities

You can rearrange inequalities using methods similar to those that you use for rearranging equations. However there are some important differences. Here are the three main ways to rearrange an inequality.

> **Rearranging inequalities**
>
> Carrying out any of the following operations on an inequality gives an equivalent inequality.
>
> - Rearrange the expressions on one or both sides.
> - Swap the sides, *provided you reverse the inequality sign.*
> - Do any of the following things to both sides:
>   - add or subtract something
>   - multiply or divide by something that's positive
>   - multiply or divide by something that's negative, *provided you reverse the inequality sign.*

To understand why these rules make sense, consider, for example, the simple, true inequality $1 < 2$.

- You can swap the sides of this inequality to obtain another true inequality, *provided you reverse the inequality sign.* This gives $2 > 1$.

- You can multiply both sides of the original inequality $1 < 2$ by the positive number 3, say, to obtain another true inequality. This gives $3 < 6$.

- You can multiply both sides of the original inequality $1 < 2$ by the negative number -3, say, to obtain another true inequality, *provided you reverse the inequality sign.* This gives $-3 > -6$.

When you're rearranging an inequality, you should not multiply or divide both sides by a variable, or by an expression containing a variable, unless you know that the variable or expression takes only positive values or takes only negative values. That's because in other cases you can't follow the rule about when to reverse the inequality sign, so usually the inequality that you obtain won't be equivalent to the original one.

5.3   Linear inequalities

As you'd expect, a **linear inequality in one unknown** is the same as a linear equation in one unknown, but with one of the four inequality signs in place of the equals sign. You can solve such an inequality by using the same methods that you use to solve a linear equation in one unknown (see Subsection 5.3 of Unit 1), except that you need to use the rules for rearranging inequalities instead of the rules for rearranging equations. Here's an example.

Example 12   *Solving a linear inequality*

Solve the inequality

$$\frac{5x}{2} - 1 > 4x + \frac{7}{2}.$$

Give your answer as a solution set in interval notation.

Solution

The inequality

$$\frac{5x}{2} - 1 > 4x + \frac{7}{2}$$

can be rearranged as follows.

🔍 Clear the fractions, by multiplying through by 2. This is a positive number, so leave the direction of the inequality sign unchanged. 💬

$$5x - 2 > 8x + 7$$

🔍 Get all the terms in the unknown on one side, and all the other terms on the other side. Collect like terms. 💬

$$5x - 8x > 7 + 2$$
$$-3x > 9$$

🔍 Obtain x by itself on one side, by dividing through by -3. This is a negative number, so reverse the inequality sign. 💬

$$x < -3$$

The solution set is the interval $(-\infty, -3)$.

Activity 54   *Solving linear inequalities*

(a) Solve the following linear inequalities. Give your answers as solution sets in interval notation.

(i) $5x + 2 < 3x - 1$ (ii) $6 - 3x \geq \frac{x}{2} - 1$

(b) An employee has achieved 54%, 69% and 72% in the first three of her four assignments in a workplace training course. She has to achieve an average of at least 60% over all four assignments (which are equally-weighted) to pass the course. Let $x\%$ be the score that she will achieve for her final assignment. Write down an inequality that x must satisfy if the employee is to pass the course, and solve it to find the acceptable values of x.

5.4 Quadratic inequalities

Sometimes you have to solve a **quadratic inequality**. As you'd expect, this is an inequality that's the same as a quadratic equation, but with one of the inequality signs in place of the equals sign.

The first step in solving a quadratic inequality is to simplify it, if possible, in the same ways that you'd simplify a quadratic equation (this was covered in Subsection 4.3 of Unit 2). In particular, you should get all the terms on one side of the inequality sign, leaving just the number zero on the other side. Of course, you have to simplify the inequality using the rules for rearranging inequalities.

Once you've simplified the inequality, you can solve it by considering the graph of the function whose rule is given by the quadratic expression on one side of the inequality, as illustrated in the next example.

Example 13   *Solving a quadratic inequality*

Solve the inequality

$$x^2 + 3 \geq 4x.$$

Solution

🔍 Get all the terms on one side. Simplify the inequality in other ways if possible – in this case there's no further simplification to be done. 💭

Rearranging the inequality $x^2 + 3 \geq 4x$ gives

$$x^2 - 4x + 3 \geq 0.$$

🔍 Roughly sketch the graph of $y = x^2 - 4x + 3$. The only features that you need to show are the x-intercepts and whether the parabola is u-shaped or n-shaped. In particular, there's no need to find the vertex. 💭

The x-intercepts of the graph of $f(x) = x^2 - 4x + 3$ are given by

$$x^2 - 4x + 3 = 0;$$

that is,

$$(x - 1)(x - 3) = 0,$$

so they are 1 and 3.

Also, the graph is u-shaped. So the graph is as follows.

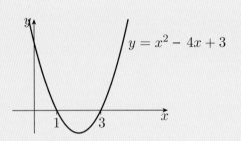

🔍 From the sketch you can see that the value of the expression $x^2 - 4x - 3$ is greater than or equal to zero precisely when $x \le 1$ or $x \ge 3$ (since the parabola lies above or on the x-axis for these values of x). 💬

The solution set is $(-\infty, 1] \cup [3, \infty)$.

As you become more familiar with the method in Example 13, you might find that you don't need to sketch the graph – instead you can just work out the intercepts, note whether the graph is u-shaped or n-shaped, and picture the sketch in your head. You might like to try this in the later parts of the next activity.

If you prefer, you can always make sure that the coefficient of x^2 is *positive* by, if necessary, multiplying the inequality through by -1 and reversing the inequality sign. Then you don't need to think about whether the parabola is u-shaped or n-shaped, as it will always be u-shaped.

Activity 55   *Solving quadratic inequalities*

Solve the following inequalities.

(a) $x^2 + x < 2$ (b) $-x^2 + 7x < 10$ (c) $-x^2 \ge 2x$

The next example illustrates an alternative method for solving a quadratic inequality. This method starts in the same way as the method that you've just seen – you rearrange the inequality to obtain a quadratic expression on one side. Then, instead of using a graph to determine the values of x that make the value of the quadratic expression greater than, less than or equal to zero, you obtain the same information by constructing a type of table known as a *table of signs*. You can use this alternative method whenever you can factorise the quadratic expression. It might seem a little more complicated than the method that you've just practised, but it's worth learning, as you can use it to solve more complicated inequalities. You'll see this in the next subsection.

Example 14   *Solving a quadratic inequality using a table of signs*

Solve the inequality

$$2x^2 + x - 6 \geq 0.$$

Solution

 Make sure that all the terms are on one side, and simplify the inequality in other ways if possible – here there's no simplification to be done. Next, factorise the quadratic expression on the left-hand side, and find the values of x for which the resulting factors are equal to zero.

Factorising gives

$$(x + 2)(2x - 3) \geq 0.$$

The factors $x + 2$ and $2x - 3$ are equal to zero when $x = -2$ and when $x = \frac{3}{2}$, respectively.

 Construct a table, as follows. In the top row, write, in increasing order, the values of x for which the factors are equal to zero, and also the largest open intervals to the left and right of, and between, these values. In the left-most column, write the factors $x + 2$ and $2x - 3$, and then their product $(x + 2)(2x - 3)$.

We have the following table.

x	$(-\infty, -2)$	-2	$(-2, \frac{3}{2})$	$\frac{3}{2}$	$(\frac{3}{2}, \infty)$
$x + 2$					
$2x - 3$					
$(x + 2)(2x - 3)$					

 The factor $x + 2$ is zero when $x = -2$, negative when $x < -2$ and positive when $x > -2$, so fill in its row appropriately. Use similar thinking to fill in the row for the factor $2x - 3$. Finally, use the signs of $x + 2$ and $2x - 3$ to find the signs of $(x + 2)(2x - 3)$ for the various values of x, and enter these in the bottom row. For example, if $x + 2$ and $2x - 3$ are both negative, then their product is positive.

x	$(-\infty, -2)$	-2	$(-2, \frac{3}{2})$	$\frac{3}{2}$	$(\frac{3}{2}, \infty)$
$x + 2$	$-$	0	$+$	$+$	$+$
$2x - 3$	$-$	$-$	$-$	0	$+$
$(x + 2)(2x - 3)$	$+$	0	$-$	0	$+$

 Use the entries in the bottom row to help you solve the inequality. Remember that you're looking for the values of x such that $(x + 2)(2x - 3)$ is positive or zero.

The solution set is $(-\infty, -2] \cup [\frac{3}{2}, \infty)$.

> **Activity 56**   *Solving quadratic inequalities using tables of signs*
>
> Solve the following inequalities using tables of signs.
> (a) $2x^2 - 5x - 3 < 0$ (b) $-2x^2 + 4x + 16 \leq 0$

5.5   More complicated inequalities

In this final subsection you'll see how to use tables of signs to solve more complicated inequalities. In particular, this method is useful for some inequalities that contain algebraic fractions, such as

$$\frac{3}{x-1} \leq 2x + 3.$$

When you're trying to solve an inequality that contains an algebraic fraction, remember that you're not allowed to multiply it through by a variable or expression, unless you know that the variable or expression takes only positive values or takes only negative values. That's because otherwise you can't follow the rule about when to reverse the inequality sign. So, for example, you can't simplify the inequality above by multiplying through by $x - 1$. (You could consider the two cases $x - 1 > 0$ and $x - 1 < 0$ separately, but it's more straightforward to use the method illustrated in the following example.)

Example 15   *Solving an inequality containing algebraic fractions*

Solve the inequality

$$\frac{3}{x-1} \leq 2x + 3.$$

Solution

🔍 Get all the terms on one side, leaving only 0 on the other side. 💬

$$\frac{3}{x-1} - (2x + 3) \leq 0$$

🔍 Combine the terms into a single algebraic fraction, and simplify it. 💬

$$\frac{3}{x-1} - \frac{(2x+3)(x-1)}{x-1} \leq 0$$

$$\frac{3 - (2x+3)(x-1)}{x-1} \leq 0$$

$$\frac{3 - (2x^2 + x - 3)}{x-1} \leq 0$$

$$\frac{-2x^2 - x + 6}{x-1} \leq 0$$

$$\frac{2x^2 + x - 6}{x-1} \geq 0$$

💬 Factorise the numerator and denominator, where possible. Find the values of x for which the factors are equal to 0. 💬

$$\frac{(2x-3)(x+2)}{x-1} \geq 0$$

A factor is equal to 0 when $x = -2$, $x = 1$ or $x = \frac{3}{2}$.

💬 Construct a table of signs to help you find the values of x for which the whole fraction is positive, negative or zero. You need a row for each of the three factors. 💬

x	$(-\infty, -2)$	-2	$(-2, 1)$	1	$(1, \frac{3}{2})$	$\frac{3}{2}$	$(\frac{3}{2}, \infty)$
$2x - 3$							
$x + 2$							
$x - 1$							
$\dfrac{(2x-3)(x+2)}{x-1}$							

💬 Fill in the row for each factor. Then use the signs of the factors to find the signs of the whole fraction, and enter these in the bottom row. Note that where a factor in the *denominator* takes the value 0, the fraction is undefined. Use the symbol $*$ to indicate this. 💬

x	$(-\infty, -2)$	-2	$(-2, 1)$	1	$(1, \frac{3}{2})$	$\frac{3}{2}$	$(\frac{3}{2}, \infty)$
$2x - 3$	$-$	$-$	$-$	$-$	$-$	0	$+$
$x + 2$	$-$	0	$+$	$+$	$+$	$+$	$+$
$x - 1$	$-$	$-$	$-$	0	$+$	$+$	$+$
$\dfrac{(2x-3)(x+2)}{x-1}$	$-$	0	$+$	$*$	$-$	0	$+$

💬 Use the entries in the bottom row to help you solve the inequality. Remember that you're looking for the values of x such that $(2x-3)(x+2)/(x-1)$ is positive or zero. 💬

The solution set is $[-2, 1) \cup [\frac{3}{2}, \infty)$.

Solve the following inequalities by using tables of signs.

(a) $\dfrac{3x - 4}{2x + 1} \leq 1$ (b) $\dfrac{2x^2 + 5x - 8}{x - 3} \geq 2$

You can check the solution set that you've found for an inequality by obtaining the graph of an appropriate function. For example, consider again the inequality in Example 15. It was rearranged into the form

$$\frac{(2x - 3)(x + 2)}{x - 1} \geq 0.$$

Figure 78 shows the graph of the equation

$$y = \frac{(2x - 3)(x + 2)}{x - 1},$$

as a computer would plot it. The expression in x here is the left-hand side of the inequality above. The graph shows that this expression takes values greater than or equal to zero roughly when x is in the set $[-2, 1) \cup [\frac{3}{2}, \infty)$. This accords with the solution set found in Example 15.

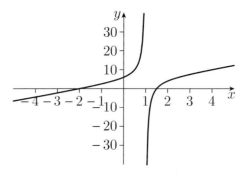

Figure 78 The graph of $y = (2x - 3)(x + 2)/(x - 1)$

You can also use graphs to check the solution set of an inequality directly from the original, un-rearranged version of the inequality. This provides a more thorough check on your working. To do this, you usually have to obtain *two* graphs on the same axes.

This method is illustrated in the next example, in which the solution set of the original version of the inequality in Example 15 is estimated from a graph.

Example 16   *Estimating solutions from a graph*

Use the graph below to estimate the solution set of the inequality

$$\frac{3}{x-1} \le 2x + 3.$$

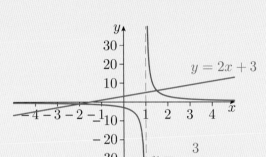

Solution

🔍 Estimate the values of x for which the graph of $y = 3/(x-1)$ lies below or on the graph of $y = 2x + 3$. 💭

The graph shows that $3/(x-1)$ is less than or equal to $2x + 3$ roughly when x is in the set $[-2, 1) \cup [\frac{3}{2}, \infty)$. So this set is the solution set of the inequality, at least approximately.

🔍 This agrees with the solution set found in Example 15. 💭

Estimating solution sets from graphs in the way illustrated in Example 16 can be useful not only as a check on algebraic working, but also when you need only an approximate solution set, or when you don't know a method for solving an inequality or equation algebraically.

Activity 58   *Estimating solutions from a graph*

Use the graph below to estimate the following.

(a) The solutions of the equation $x = \dfrac{15}{x-2}$.

(b) The solution set of the inequality $x \leq \dfrac{15}{x-2}$.

(c) The solution set of the inequality $x > \dfrac{15}{x-2}$.

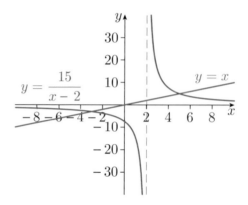

Learning outcomes

After studying this unit, you should be able to:

- understand and use the terminology and notation associated with functions

- work with graphs of functions

- work with a range of standard types of functions, and understand their properties and graphs

- understand the changes to the rules of functions that cause their graphs to be translated or scaled, horizontally or vertically

- form sums, differences, products, quotients and composites of functions

- understand what's meant by the inverse function of a one-to-one function, and find the inverse in some cases

- understand the properties and graphs of exponential and logarithmic functions

- work fluently and correctly with logarithms

- work with exponential models

- solve some types of inequalities in one variable

- construct tables of signs.

Solutions to activities

Solution to Activity 1

(a) True   (b) True   (c) False   (d) True

Solution to Activity 2

(a) $P \cap Q = \{2, 4, 6\}$

(b) $Q \cap R = \{6, 12\}$

(c) $P \cap Q \cap R = \{6\}$

(d) $P \cup Q = \{1, 2, 3, 4, 5, 6, 8, 10, 12\}$

Solution to Activity 3

(a) This set is an open interval.

(b) This set is not an interval.

(c) This set is a closed interval.

(d) This set is a half-open interval.

(e) This set is not an interval.

(f) This set is a closed interval. (It has only one endpoint, and it includes it.)

(g) This set is an open interval.

(h) This set is not an interval.

Solution to Activity 4

(a) (i)

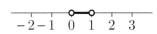

(ii)

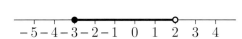

(iii)

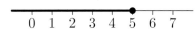

(iv)

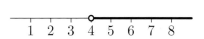

(b) (i) $-2 < x \leq 5$

(ii) $x \geq -4$

(iii) $x < 0$

(iv) $-3 \leq x < -1$

(v) $0 \leq x \leq 6$

(vi) $3 < x < 7$

Solution to Activity 5

(a) $(-2, 5]$

(b) $[-4, \infty)$

(c) $(-\infty, 0)$

(d) $[-3, -1)$

(e) $[0, 6]$

(f) $(3, 7)$

Solution to Activity 6

(a) $(-\infty, -5) \cup [-2, 1]$

(b) $[1, 2) \cup [3, 4) \cup [5, 6)$

(c) $(-\infty, 0) \cup (0, \infty)$

Solution to Activity 7

(a) $f(5) = 4 \times 5 = 20$ and $f(-3) = 4 \times (-3) = -12$

(b) $g(x) = 2x - 1$

Solution to Activity 8

(a) The image of 2 is 8, because $f(2) = 8$.

(b) The image of -1 is -4, because $f(-1) = -4$.

(c) The value of f at 0.5 is 2, because $f(0.5) = 2$.

(d) The value of f at -0.2 is -0.8, because $f(-0.2) = -0.8$.

(e) The number 11 has image 44 under f, because $f(11) = 44$.

(f) The number $\frac{1}{4}$ has image 1 under f, because $f(\frac{1}{4}) = 1$.

(g) The function f maps 4 to $f(4) = 16$.

(h) The function f maps -2 to -8 because $f(-2) = -8$.

Solution to Activity 9

(a) The domain of f is the set of all real numbers except 4, that is, the set $(-\infty, 4) \cup (4, \infty)$.

(b) The domain of g is the set of all real numbers except 2 and -3, that is, the set $(-\infty, -3) \cup (-3, 2) \cup (2, \infty)$.

(c) The domain of h is the set of all real numbers x such that $x - 1$ is non-negative. This set can be described more concisely as the set of all real numbers greater than or equal to 1. In interval notation this set is denoted by $[1, \infty)$.

Solution to Activity 10

(a)

x	-2	-1.5	-1	-0.5
x^3	-8	-3.375	-1	-0.125

x	0	0.5	1	1.5	2
x^3	0	0.125	1	3.375	8

(b) and (c)

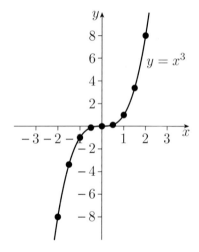

Solution to Activity 12

(a) The graph is part of the straight-line graph of $y = 3 - 2x$.

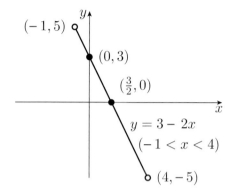

(b) The graph is part of an n-shaped parabola. Completing the square gives
$$f(x) = -\tfrac{1}{2}x^2 - 2x - 5$$
$$= -\tfrac{1}{2}(x^2 + 4x) - 5$$
$$= -\tfrac{1}{2}((x + 2)^2 - 4) - 5$$
$$= -\tfrac{1}{2}(x + 2)^2 + 2 - 5$$
$$= -\tfrac{1}{2}(x + 2)^2 - 3$$
So the vertex is $(-2, -3)$. Also
$$f(-5) = -\tfrac{1}{2}(-5)^2 - 2 \times (-5) - 5 = -\tfrac{15}{2}.$$
So the graph stops at the point $(-5, -\tfrac{15}{2})$ (which is included). These features give the following sketch.

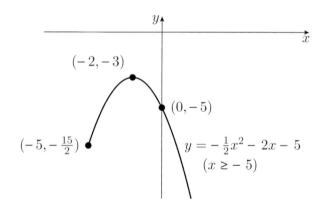

Solution to Activity 13

(a) The domain is $[1, 3]$.

(b) The domain is $(-\infty, -2] \cup [-1, \infty)$.

Solution to Activity 14

Diagrams (a), (c), (f), (h), (i) and (j) are the graphs of functions.

Solution to Activity 15

Graphs (a) and (b) show functions that are increasing on their whole domains.

(For the function in graph (c), if you take x_1 and x_2 to be values slightly less than 0 and slightly greater than 0, respectively, then the function takes a smaller value at x_2 than it does at x_1, so it is not increasing on its whole domain.

For the function in graph (d), you can find values x_1 and x_2 with $x_1 < x_2$ such that the function takes the same value at x_2 as it does at x_1, so it is not increasing on its whole domain.)

Solution to Activity 16

(a) The graph of f is part of an n-shaped parabola. Completing the square gives

$$\begin{aligned} f(x) &= -x^2 + 10x - 24 \\ &= -(x^2 - 10x) - 24 \\ &= -((x-5)^2 - 25) - 24 \\ &= -(x-5)^2 + 25 - 24 \\ &= -(x-5)^2 + 1. \end{aligned}$$

So the vertex is $(5, 1)$. Also

$$f(3) = -3^2 + 10 \times 3 - 24 = -3$$

and

$$f(6) = -6^2 + 10 \times 6 - 24 = 0.$$

So the graph stops at the points $(3, -3)$ (which is included) and $(6, 0)$ (which is excluded).

These features give the graph below. The image set is shown on the y-axis.

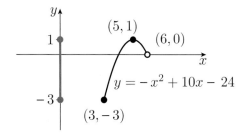

The graph shows that the image set of f is the interval $[-3, 1]$.

(b) The graph of f is below, with the image set shown on the y-axis.

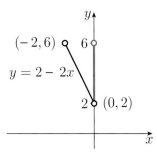

The graph shows that the image set is $(2, 6)$.

(c) The image set of f is the interval $[-1, \infty)$.

This is because the image set of the function $g(x) = x^2$ is $[0, \infty)$, since every non-negative number can be expressed as the square of a number. Hence the image set of the function $f(x) = x^2 - 1$ is $[-1, \infty)$.

(The graph of f is shown below, with the image set shown on the y-axis.)

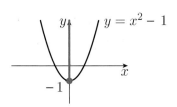

(d) The image set of f is the interval $(0, \infty)$.

This is because the image set of f doesn't contain any negative numbers, since the value of $1/x^2$ can't be negative. Similarly, the image set doesn't contain 0. However, the image set does contain every positive number, because every positive number can be expressed as $1/x^2$ for some number x.

(The graph of f is shown below, with the image set shown on the y-axis.)

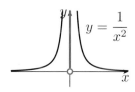

Solution to Activity 18

(The effects that you should have seen are described in the text after the activity.)

Solution to Activity 19

(The effects that you should have seen are described in the text after the activity.)

Solution to Activity 20

(a) $y = \dfrac{1}{x-2}$ is the equation of graph D.

(b) $y = \dfrac{1}{x} - 2$ is the equation of graph A.

(c) $y = \dfrac{1}{x} + 2$ is the equation of graph C.

(d) $y = \dfrac{1}{x+2}$ is the equation of graph B.

Solution to Activity 21

(a) $y = |x - 2| + 1$ is the equation of graph C.

(b) $y = |x + 2| + 1$ is the equation of graph D.

(c) $y = |x - 2| - 1$ is the equation of graph B.

(d) $y = |x + 2| - 1$ is the equation of graph A.

Solution to Activity 22

(The effects that you should have seen are described in the text after the activity.)

Solution to Activity 23

(a) $y = 2x^3$ is the equation of graph A.

(b) $y = \frac{1}{2}x^3$ is the equation of graph D.

(c) $y = -x^3$ is the equation of graph B.

(d) $y = -\frac{1}{2}x^3$ is the equation of graph C.

Solution to Activity 24

(a) The graph of $g(x) = 2|x| + 3$ can be obtained from the graph of $f(x) = |x|$ by first scaling it vertically by the factor 2 and then translating it up by 3 units.

(b) The graph of $h(x) = 2|x + 2| + 3$ can be obtained from the graph of $f(x) = |x|$ by first scaling it vertically by the factor 2, then translating it to the left by 2 units, and finally translating it up by 3 units.

(You can carry out the operations in any order, except that you have to do the vertical scaling before the vertical translation.)

(c) The graph of $j(x) = \frac{1}{2}|x - 3| - 4$ can be obtained from the graph of $f(x) = |x|$ by first scaling it vertically by the factor $\frac{1}{2}$, translating it to the right by 3 units, and finally translating it down by 4 units.

(You can carry out the operations in any order, except that you have to do the vertical scaling before the vertical translation.)

(d) The graph of $k(x) = -|x - 1| + 1$ can be obtained from the graph of $f(x) = |x|$ by first reflecting it in the x-axis (that is, scaling it vertically by the factor -1), then translating it to the right by 1 unit, and finally translating it up by 1 unit.

(You can carry out the operations in any order, except that you have to do the reflection before the vertical translation.)

Solution to Activity 25

(a) Completing the square gives
$$\begin{aligned} f(x) &= 2x^2 + 12x + 19 \\ &= 2(x^2 + 6x) + 19 \\ &= 2((x+3)^2 - 9) + 19 \\ &= 2(x+3)^2 - 18 + 19 \\ &= 2(x+3)^2 + 1. \end{aligned}$$

(b) This equation is obtained from the equation $y = x^2$ by first multiplying the right-hand side by 2, then replacing x by $x + 3$, and finally adding 1 to the right-hand side. So its graph is obtained from the graph of $y = x^2$ by first scaling vertically by a factor of 2, then translating to the left by 3 units, and finally translating up by 1 unit.

(You can carry out the operations in any order, except that you have to do the vertical scaling before the vertical translation. The resulting graph is shown below.)

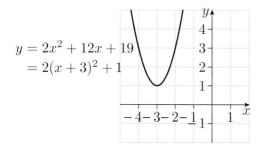

$$y = 2x^2 + 12x + 19$$
$$= 2(x + 3)^2 + 1$$

Solution to Activity 26

(The effects that you should have seen are described in the text after the activity.)

Solution to Activity 27

(a) $y = \sqrt{-x}$ is the equation of graph D.

(b) $y = -\sqrt{x}$ is the equation of graph H.

(c) $y = 2\sqrt{x} - 2$ is the equation of graph C.

(d) $y = \frac{1}{2}\sqrt{x} + 2$ is the equation of graph E.

(e) $y = -\frac{1}{2}\sqrt{x}$ is the equation of graph F.

(f) $y = -\sqrt{x} + 2$ is the equation of graph G.

(g) $y = -\sqrt{-x}$ is the equation of graph B.

(h) $y = \frac{1}{2}\sqrt{x} + 2$ is the equation of graph I.

(i) $y = -2\sqrt{x} + 2$ is the equation of graph A.

Solution to Activity 28

(a) The graph of the function $f(x) = 2|x| + 1$ can be obtained from the graph of $y = |x|$ by first scaling it vertically by a factor of 2 and then translating it up by 1 unit.

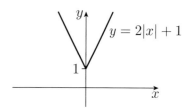

$$y = 2|x| + 1$$

(b) The graph of the function $h(x) = (x - 1)^3$ can be obtained from the graph of $y = x^3$ by translating it to the right by 1 unit.

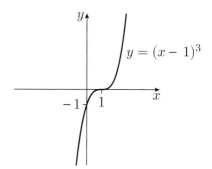

$$y = (x - 1)^3$$

(c) The graph of the function $g(x) = 1/(x + 3)$ can be obtained from the graph of $y = 1/x$ by translating it to the left by 3 units.

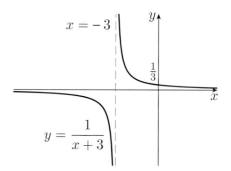

$$x = -3$$
$$y = \frac{1}{x + 3}$$

(You can find the y-intercept of this graph simply by substituting $x = 0$ into its equation.)

Solution to Activity 29

The sum of f and g has rule
$$h(x) = 2x - 1 + x + 3,$$
which can be simplified to
$$h(x) = 3x + 2.$$
One difference of f and g has rule
$$h(x) = 2x - 1 - (x + 3),$$
which can be simplified to
$$h(x) = x - 4.$$
The other difference of f and g has rule
$$h(x) = x + 3 - (2x - 1),$$
which can be simplified to
$$h(x) = -x + 4.$$
The product of f and g has rule
$$h(x) = (2x - 1)(x + 3),$$
which can also be expressed as
$$h(x) = 2x^2 + 5x - 3.$$
The two quotients of f and g have rules
$$h(x) = \frac{2x - 1}{x + 3}$$
and
$$h(x) = \frac{x + 3}{2x - 1}.$$

All of these functions have domain $\mathbb{R}$, except the final two functions, which have domains $(-\infty, -3) \cup (-3, \infty)$ and $(-\infty, \frac{1}{2}) \cup (\frac{1}{2}, \infty)$, respectively.

Solution to Activity 30

The function f maps 5 to 25, and the function g maps 25 to 26, so $(g \circ f)(5) = 26$.

Solution to Activity 31

(a) (i) $(g \circ f)(x) = g(f(x)) = g(x - 3) = \sqrt{x - 3}$
   (ii) $(f \circ g)(x) = f(g(x)) = f(\sqrt{x}) = \sqrt{x} - 3$
   (iii) $(f \circ f)(x) = f(f(x)) = f(x - 3)$
          $= (x - 3) - 3 = x - 6$
   (iv) $(g \circ g)(x) = g(g(x)) = g(\sqrt{x}) = \sqrt{\sqrt{x}}$
          $= (x^{1/2})^{1/2} = x^{1/4}$

(b) If x is in the domain of f, then $f(x) = x - 3$. For $x - 3$ to be in the domain of g, the value of $x - 3$ must be greater than or equal to zero, which means that the value of x must be greater than or equal to 3. That is, the domain of $g \circ f$ is $[3, \infty)$.

Solution to Activity 32

(a) $(f \circ g \circ h)(x) = f(g(h(x)))$
$$= f(g(\sqrt{x}))$$
$$= f\left(\frac{1}{\sqrt{x}}\right)$$
$$= \frac{1}{\sqrt{x}} + 2$$

(b) $(g \circ h \circ f)(x) = g(h(f(x)))$
$$= g(h(x + 2))$$
$$= g(\sqrt{x + 2})$$
$$= \frac{1}{\sqrt{x + 2}}$$

(c) $(f \circ h \circ g)(x) = f(h(g(x)))$
$$= f\left(h\left(\frac{1}{x}\right)\right)$$
$$= f\left(\sqrt{\frac{1}{x}}\right)$$
$$= f\left(\frac{1}{\sqrt{x}}\right)$$
$$= \frac{1}{\sqrt{x}} + 2$$

(d) $(f \circ g \circ f)(x) = f(g(f(x)))$
$$= f(g(x + 2))$$
$$= f\left(\frac{1}{x + 2}\right)$$
$$= \frac{1}{x + 2} + 2$$
$$= \frac{1 + 2(x + 2)}{x + 2}$$
$$= \frac{2x + 5}{x + 2}$$

Solution to Activity 33

(a) (i)   The rule of the inverse function of
$f(x) = x + 1$ is $f^{-1}(x) = x - 1$.

(ii)   The rule of the inverse function of
$f(x) = x - 3$ is $f^{-1}(x) = x + 3$.

(iii)   The rule of the inverse function of
$f(x) = \frac{1}{3}x$ is $f^{-1}(x) = 3x$.

(b) Some possible answers are $f(x) = x$, $f(x) = -x$
and $f(x) = 1/x$. There are many others, such
as $f(x) = 3 - x$ and $f(x) = 8/x$.

Solution to Activity 34

(a) The function $f(x) = |x|$ is not one-to-one. For
example, $f(1) = f(-1) = 1$.

(b) The function $f(x) = x + 1$ is one-to-one.

(c) The function $f(x) = x^4$ is not one-to-one. For
example, $f(1) = f(-1) = 1$.

(d) The function $f(x) = x^5$ is one-to-one.

(e) The function $f(x) = -x$ is one-to-one.

(f) The function $f(x) = 1$ is not one-to-one. For
example, $f(0) = f(1) = 1$.

Solution to Activity 35

Diagrams (a), (b), (e), (f), (h), (i) and (k) are the
graphs of one-to-one functions.

Diagrams (c), (d) and (j) are the graphs of
functions that aren't one-to-one.

Diagrams (g) and (l) are not the graphs of functions.

Solution to Activity 36

(a) The equation $f(x) = y$ gives
$$3x - 4 = y$$
$$3x = y + 4$$
$$x = \tfrac{1}{3}(y + 4).$$
Since the equation $f(x) = y$ can be rearranged
to express x as a function of y, the function f
has an inverse function f^{-1}, with rule
$$f^{-1}(y) = \tfrac{1}{3}(y + 4);$$
that is,
$$f^{-1}(x) = \tfrac{1}{3}(x + 4).$$
The domain of f^{-1} is the image set of f, which
is $\mathbb{R}$. So the inverse function f^{-1} is given by
$$f^{-1}(x) = \tfrac{1}{3}(x + 4).$$

(b) The equation $f(x) = y$ gives
$$2 - \tfrac{1}{2}x = y$$
$$2 - y = \tfrac{1}{2}x$$
$$x = 2(2 - y).$$
Since the equation $f(x) = y$ can be rearranged
to express x as a function of y, the function f
has an inverse function f^{-1}, with rule
$$f^{-1}(y) = 2(2 - y);$$
that is,
$$f^{-1}(x) = 2(2 - x).$$
The domain of f^{-1} is the image set of f, which
is $\mathbb{R}$. So the inverse function f^{-1} is given by
$$f^{-1}(x) = 2(2 - x).$$

(c) The equation $f(x) = y$ gives
$$5 + \frac{1}{x} = y$$
$$\frac{1}{x} = y - 5$$
$$x = \frac{1}{y - 5}.$$
Hence f has an inverse function f^{-1}, with rule
$$f^{-1}(y) = \frac{1}{y - 5};$$
that is,
$$f^{-1}(x) = \frac{1}{x - 5}.$$
The domain of f^{-1} is the image set of f, which
is $(-\infty, 5) \cup (5, \infty)$. This is the largest set of
real numbers for which the rule of f^{-1} is
applicable. So the inverse function f^{-1} is given
by
$$f^{-1}(x) = \frac{1}{x - 5}.$$

Solution to Activity 37

(a) The graph of f is shown below.

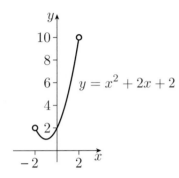

The graph shows that f isn't one-to-one. So it doesn't have an inverse function.

(b) The graph of f is shown below.

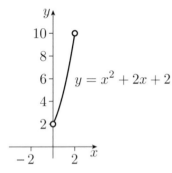

The graph shows that f is one-to-one and therefore has an inverse function. The equation $f(x) = y$ gives

$$x^2 + 2x + 2 = y$$
$$(x+1)^2 - 1 + 2 = y$$
$$(x+1)^2 + 1 = y$$
$$(x+1)^2 = y - 1$$
$$x + 1 = \pm\sqrt{y-1}$$
$$x = -1 \pm \sqrt{y-1}.$$

Since the domain of f is $(0,2)$, each input value x of f is greater than -1. So

$$x = -1 + \sqrt{y-1}.$$

Hence the rule of f^{-1} is

$$f^{-1}(y) = -1 + \sqrt{y-1};$$

that is,

$$f^{-1}(x) = -1 + \sqrt{x-1}.$$

The domain of f^{-1} is the image set of f. The graph shows that this is

$$(f(0), f(2)) = (2, 10).$$

So the inverse function of f is the function

$$f^{-1}(x) = -1 + \sqrt{x-1} \quad (x \in (2,10)).$$

(c) The equation $f(x) = y$ gives

$$1 - x = y$$
$$x = 1 - y.$$

Hence f has an inverse function f^{-1}, with rule

$$f^{-1}(y) = 1 - y;$$

that is,

$$f^{-1}(x) = 1 - x.$$

The domain of f^{-1} is the image set of f, which is

$$[f(1), f(-3)] = [0, 4].$$

Hence the inverse function of f is

$$f^{-1}(x) = 1 - x \quad (x \in [0, 4]).$$

(The graph of f, shown below, might help you find the image set of f.)

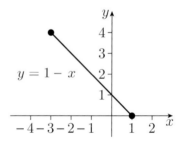

Solution to Activity 38

(a)

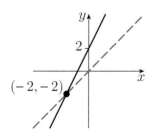

(b)

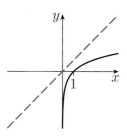

Hence the rule of g^{-1} is
$$g^{-1}(y) = 1 + \sqrt{y};$$
that is,
$$g^{-1}(x) = 1 + \sqrt{x}.$$
The domain of g^{-1} is the image set of g, which is $[0, \infty)$.

So the inverse function of g is the function
$$g^{-1}(x) = 1 + \sqrt{x} \quad (x \in [0, \infty)).$$

The graph of the function g is as shown below.

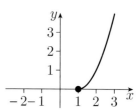

Hence the graph of g^{-1} is as shown below.

(c)

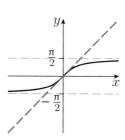

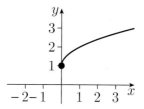

(Alternatively, you can take the domain of g to be $(-\infty, 1]$. Then g^{-1} is the function
$$g^{-1}(x) = 1 - \sqrt{x} \quad (x \in [0, \infty)).)$$

(d)

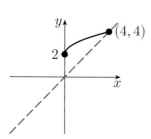

Solution to Activity 39

The image set of f is $[0, \infty)$.

A one-to-one function g that is a restriction of f and has the same image set as f is
$$g(x) = (x - 1)^2 \quad (x \in [1, \infty)).$$
The equation $g(x) = y$ gives
$$(x - 1)^2 = y$$
$$x - 1 = \pm\sqrt{y}$$
$$x = 1 \pm \sqrt{y}.$$
Since the domain of g is $[1, \infty)$, each input value x of f is greater than or equal to 1. So
$$x = 1 + \sqrt{y}.$$

Solution to Activity 40

(The effects that you should have seen are described in the text after the activity.)

Solution to Activity 41

(The answer is given in the text after the activity.)

Solution to Activity 42

(a) (i) $\log_{10} 10\,000 = 4$, since $10\,000 = 10^4$.

 (ii) $\log_{10} \frac{1}{100} = -2$, since $\frac{1}{100} = 10^{-2}$.

 (iii) $\log_{10} 10 = 1$, since $10 = 10^1$.

 (iv) $\log_{10} 1 = 0$, since $1 = 10^0$.

(b) If the number x is such that $\log_{10} x = \frac{1}{2}$, then $10^{1/2} = x$; that is, $x = \sqrt{10}$.

(c) (i) $\log_{10} 3700 = 3.568$ (to 3 d.p.)

 (ii) $\log_{10} 370 = 2.568$ (to 3 d.p.)

 (iii) $\log_{10} 37 = 1.568$ (to 3 d.p.)

 (iv) $\log_{10} 3.7 = 0.568$ (to 3 d.p.)

 (v) $\log_{10} 0.37 = -0.432$ (to 3 d.p.)

 (vi) $\log_{10} 0.037 = -1.432$ (to 3 d.p.)

(You'll be asked to explain the pattern in the answers to part (c) later in this section.)

Solution to Activity 43

(a) (i) $\log_3 9 = 2$, since $3^2 = 9$.

 (ii) $\log_2 8 = 3$, since $2^3 = 8$.

 (iii) $\log_4 64 = 3$, since $4^3 = 64$.

 (iv) $\log_5 25 = 2$, since $5^2 = 25$.

 (v) $\log_4 2 = \frac{1}{2}$, since $4^{1/2} = 2$.

 (vi) $\log_8 2 = \frac{1}{3}$, since $8^{1/3} = 2$.

 (vii) $\log_2 \frac{1}{2} = -1$, since $2^{-1} = \frac{1}{2}$.

 (viii) $\log_2 \frac{1}{8} = -3$, since $2^{-3} = \frac{1}{8}$.

 (ix) $\log_3 \frac{1}{27} = -3$, since $3^{-3} = \frac{1}{27}$.

 (x) $\log_8 \frac{1}{8} = -1$, since $8^{-1} = \frac{1}{8}$.

 (xi) $\log_3 3 = 1$, since $3^1 = 3$.

 (xii) $\log_4 \frac{1}{4} = -1$, since $4^{-1} = \frac{1}{4}$.

 (xiii) $\log_6 6 = 1$, since $6^1 = 6$.

 (xiv) $\log_5 \sqrt{5} = \frac{1}{2}$, since $5^{1/2} = \sqrt{5}$.

 (xv) $\log_7 \sqrt[3]{7} = \frac{1}{3}$, since $7^{1/3} = \sqrt[3]{7}$.

 (xvi) $\log_2 1 = 0$, since $2^0 = 1$.

 (xvii) $\log_{15} 1 = 0$, since $15^0 = 1$.

(b) (i) If $\log_2 x = 5$, then $x = 2^5 = 32$.

 (ii) If $\log_8 x = \frac{1}{3}$, then $x = 8^{1/3} = 2$.

 (iii) If $\log_7 x = 1$, then $x = 7^1 = 7$.

Solution to Activity 44

(a) (i) $\ln e^4 = 4$

 (ii) $\ln e^2 = 2$

 (iii) $\ln e^{3/5} = \frac{3}{5}$

 (iv) $\ln \sqrt{e} = \ln(e^{1/2}) = \frac{1}{2}$

 (v) $\ln \left(\dfrac{1}{e}\right) = \ln(e^{-1}) = -1$

 (vi) $\ln \left(\dfrac{1}{e^3}\right) = \ln(e^{-3}) = -3$

(b) If the number x is such that $\ln x = -\frac{1}{2}$, then $x = e^{-1/2} = 1/\sqrt{e}$.

(c) (i) $\ln 5100 = 8.537$ (to 3 d.p.)

 (ii) $\ln 510 = 6.234$ (to 3 d.p.)

 (iii) $\ln 51 = 3.932$ (to 3 d.p.)

 (iv) $\ln(51e) = 4.932$ (to 3 d.p.)

 (v) $\ln(51e^2) = 5.932$ (to 3 d.p.)

Solution to Activity 45

(a) $e^{\ln(7x)} = 7x$

(b) $\ln(e^{8x}) = 8x$

(c) $\ln(e^{2x}) + \ln(e^{3x}) = 2x + 3x = 5x$

(d) $\ln(e^2) - \ln e = 2 - 1 = 1$

(e) $\ln(e^{x/2}) + 3\ln 1 = \dfrac{x}{2} + 3 \times 0 = \dfrac{x}{2}$

(f) $e^{2\ln c} = e^{(\ln c) \times 2} = \left(e^{\ln c}\right)^2 = c^2$

(g) $e^{\ln(3a)} + 4e^0 = 3a + 4 \times 1 = 3a + 4$

(h) $\ln(e^{y+2}) + 2\ln(e^{y-1})$

 $= y + 2 + 2(y - 1)$

 $= y + 2 + 2y - 2$

 $= 3y$

(i) $e^{3\ln B} = e^{(\ln B) \times 3} = \left(e^{\ln B}\right)^3 = B^3$

(j) $e^{2+\ln x} = e^2 e^{\ln x} = e^2 x$

Solution to Activity 46

(a) (i) $\ln 5 + \ln 3 = \ln(5 \times 3) = \ln 15$

(ii) $\ln 2 - \ln 7 = \ln\left(\frac{2}{7}\right)$

(iii) $3 \ln 2 = \ln(2^3) = \ln 8$

(iv) $\ln 3 + \ln 4 - \ln 6 = \ln\left(\dfrac{3 \times 4}{6}\right) = \ln 2$

(v) $\quad \ln 24 - 2\ln 3 = \ln 24 - \ln 3^2$
$$= \ln\left(\frac{24}{3^2}\right)$$
$$= \ln\left(\tfrac{8}{3}\right)$$

(vi) $\frac{1}{3}\log_{10} 27 = \log_{10} 27^{1/3} = \log_{10} 3$

(vii) $\quad 3\log_2 5 - \log_2 3 + \log_2 6$
$$= \log_2 5^3 - \log_2 3 + \log_2 6$$
$$= \log_2\left(\frac{5^3 \times 6}{3}\right)$$
$$= \log_2 250$$

(viii) $\quad \frac{1}{2}\ln(9x) - \ln(x+1)$
$$= \ln(9x)^{1/2} - \ln(x+1)$$
$$= \ln\left(\frac{(9x)^{1/2}}{x+1}\right)$$
$$= \ln\left(\frac{3\sqrt{x}}{x+1}\right)$$

(b) (i) $\ln c^3 - \ln c = \ln\left(\dfrac{c^3}{c}\right) = \ln(c^2)$

(The final answer $2\ln c$ is just as acceptable.)

(ii) $3\ln(p^2) = \ln(p^6)$

(The answer $6\ln p$ is just as acceptable.)

(iii) $\quad \ln(y^2) + 2\ln y - \frac{1}{2}\ln(y^3)$
$$= \ln(y^2) + \ln(y^2) - \ln\left((y^3)^{1/2}\right)$$
$$= \ln(y^2) + \ln(y^2) - \ln(y^{3/2})$$
$$= \ln\left(\frac{y^2 \times y^2}{y^{3/2}}\right)$$
$$= \ln(y^{5/2})$$

(The final answer $\frac{5}{2}\ln y$ is just as acceptable.)

(iv) $\ln(3u) - \ln(2u) = \ln\left(\dfrac{3u}{2u}\right) = \ln(\tfrac{3}{2})$

(The final answer $\ln 3 - \ln 2$ is just as acceptable.)

(v) $\quad \ln(4x) + 3\ln x - \ln(e^6) = \ln(4x) + \ln x^3 - 6$
$$= \ln(4x \times x^3) - 6$$
$$= \ln(4x^4) - 6$$

(Other acceptable final answers include $\ln 4 + \ln(x^4) - 6$ and $\ln 4 + 4\ln x - 6$.)

(vi) $\frac{1}{2}\ln(u^8) = \ln(u^4)$

(The answer $4\ln u$ is just as acceptable.)

(c) The pattern can be explained as follows. It follows from the logarithm laws that, for any value of n,
$$\log_{10}(37 \times 10^n) = \log_{10} 37 + \log_{10}(10^n)$$
$$= \log_{10} 37 + n.$$
So if you multiply 37 by 10^n, then its common logarithm is increased by n.

(d) $\quad 1567 \times 2786 = e^{\ln(1567 \times 2786)}$
$$= e^{\ln 1567 + \ln 2786}$$
$$\approx e^{7.356\,918\,242 + 7.932\,362\,154}$$
$$\approx e^{15.289\,280\,4}$$
$$\approx 4\,365\,662$$

(This is the exact answer.)

Solution to Activity 47

(a) $\quad 5^x = 0.5$
$$\ln(5^x) = \ln 0.5$$
$$x\ln 5 = \ln 0.5$$
$$x = \frac{\ln 0.5}{\ln 5}$$
$$x = -0.430\,676\ldots$$
The solution is $x = -0.431$ (to 3 s.f.).

(Alternatively, you can proceed as follows:
$$5^x = 0.5$$
$$x = \log_5(0.5)$$
$$x = -0.430\,676\ldots.)$$

(b) $\quad 4e^{7t} = 64$
$$e^{7t} = 16$$
$$\ln(e^{7t}) = \ln 16$$
$$7t = \ln 16$$
$$t = \tfrac{1}{7}\ln 16$$
$$t = 0.396\,084\ldots$$
The solution is $t = 0.396$ (to 3 s.f.).

(c) $5 \times 2^{u/2} + 30 = 600$

$5 \times 2^{u/2} = 570$

$2^{u/2} = 114$

$\ln(2^{u/2}) = \ln 114$

$\frac{1}{2}u \ln 2 = \ln 114$

$u \ln 2 = 2 \ln 114$

$u = \dfrac{2 \ln 114}{\ln 2}$

$u = 13.665\,780\ldots$

The solution is $u = 13.7$ (to 3 s.f.).

(Alternatively, you can proceed as follows from the third equation above:

$2^{u/2} = 114$

$\dfrac{u}{2} = \log_2 114$

$u = 2 \log_2 114$

$u = 13.665\,780\ldots.)$

(d) $2^{3x-5} = 100$

$\ln(2^{3x-5}) = \ln 100$

$(3x - 5) \ln 2 = \ln 100$

$3x - 5 = \dfrac{\ln 100}{\ln 2}$

$3x = \dfrac{\ln 100}{\ln 2} + 5$

$x = \tfrac{1}{3}\left(\dfrac{\ln 100}{\ln 2} + 5\right)$

$x = 3.881\,285\,396\ldots$

The solution is $x = 3.88$ (to 3 s.f.).

(Alternatively, you can proceed as follows:

$2^{3x-5} = 100$

$3x - 5 = \log_2(100)$

$3x = \log_2(100) + 5$

$x = \tfrac{1}{3}(\log_2(100) + 5)$

$x = 3.881\,285\,396\ldots.)$

Solution to Activity 49

Since $\ln 3 = 1.098\,612$ (to 7 s.f.), the rule of f can be written, approximately, as

$f(x) = e^{1.098\,612x}.$

Using the original form of the rule gives

$f(1.5) = 3^{1.5} = 5.20$ (to 3 s.f.).

Using the alternative form gives

$f(1.5) = e^{1.098\,612 \times 1.5} = 5.20$ (to 3 s.f.).

Solution to Activity 50

(a) Let $f(t) = ae^{kt}$, where a and k are constants.

Then $f(9) = 300$ and $f(12) = 4200$, so

$$ae^{9k} = 300 \quad \text{and} \quad ae^{12k} = 4200. \qquad (5)$$

Hence

$\dfrac{ae^{12k}}{ae^{9k}} = \dfrac{4200}{300},$

which gives

$e^{12k-9k} = 14$

$e^{3k} = 14$

$3k = \ln 14$

$k = \tfrac{1}{3} \ln 14$

$k = 0.879\,685\ldots.$

The first of equations (5) can be written as $a(e^{3k})^3 = 300$ and substituting $e^{3k} = 14$ into this equation gives

$a \times 14^3 = 300,$

so

$a = \dfrac{300}{14^3} = \dfrac{75}{686}$

$= 0.109\,329\ldots.$

So $a = 0.109$ and $k = 0.880$, both to three significant figures.

Hence the required function f is given, approximately, by

$f(t) = 0.109e^{0.880t} \quad (8 \le t \le 24).$

(b) The predicted number of bacteria per millilitre after 24 hours is

$f(24) = (0.109\,329\ldots)e^{(0.879\,685\ldots) \times 24}$

$= 1.6 \times 10^8$ (to 2 s.f.).

Solution to Activity 51

(a) Every decade the size of the tree population is predicted to multiply by the factor

$e^{0.06 \times 1} = 1.06$ (to 3 s.f.).

(b) Every century (10 decades) the size of the tree population is predicted to multiply by the factor

$e^{0.06 \times 10} = 1.82$ (to 3 s.f.).

(c) Every five years (0.5 decades) the size of the tree population is predicted to multiply by the factor

$e^{0.06 \times 0.5} = 1.03$ (to 3 s.f.).

Solution to Activity 52

(a) Every year the level of radioactivity is predicted to multiply by the factor
$$e^{-0.035\times1} = 0.97 \text{ (to 2 s.f.)}.$$

(b) Every 25 years the level of radioactivity is predicted to multiply by the factor
$$e^{-0.035\times25} = 0.42 \text{ (to 2 s.f.)}.$$

(c) Every century (100 years) the level of radioactivity is predicted to multiply by the factor
$$e^{-0.035\times100} = 0.030 \text{ (to 2 s.f.)}.$$

Solution to Activity 53

(a) The exponential growth function in Activity 51 is
$$f(t) = 700e^{0.06t} \quad (10 \leq t \leq 50),$$
where $f(t)$ is the number of trees at time t (in decades) after the variety was introduced.

The doubling time p (in decades) for this exponential growth is given by
$$p = (\ln 2)/0.06 = 11.6 \text{ (to 3 s.f.)}.$$
So the number of trees doubles every 11.6 decades (116 years), approximately.

(b) The exponential decay function in Activity 52 is
$$r(t) = 2800e^{-0.035t} \quad (t \geq 0),$$
where $r(t)$ (in becquerels) is the level of radioactivity of the sample of radioactive material at time t (in years) after the level was first measured.

The half-life p (in years) for this exponential decay is given by
$$p = (\ln \tfrac{1}{2})/(-0.035) = 19.8 \text{ (to 3 s.f.)}.$$
So the level of radioactivity halves every 19.8 years, approximately.

Solution to Activity 54

(a) (i) Rearranging the inequality gives
$$5x + 2 < 3x - 1$$
$$2x < -3$$
$$x < -\tfrac{3}{2}.$$
The solution set is the interval $(-\infty, -\tfrac{3}{2})$.

(ii) Rearranging the inequality gives
$$6 - 3x \geq \frac{x}{2} - 1$$
$$12 - 6x \geq x - 2$$
$$-7x \geq -14$$
$$x \leq 2.$$
The solution set is the interval $(-\infty, 2]$.

(b) Each acceptable value of x satisfies the inequality
$$\frac{54 + 69 + 72 + x}{4} \geq 60.$$
Solving this inequality gives
$$\frac{195 + x}{4} \geq 60$$
$$195 + x \geq 240$$
$$x \geq 45.$$
So the employee must score at least 45% in her final assignment to pass the course.

Solution to Activity 55

(a) The inequality can be rearranged as follows:
$$x^2 + x < 2$$
$$x^2 + x - 2 < 0.$$
The graph of $f(x) = x^2 + x - 2$ is u-shaped. Its intercepts are given by
$$x^2 + x - 2 = 0;$$
that is,
$$(x + 2)(x - 1) = 0.$$
So they are $x = -2$ and $x = 1$.

Hence the graph is as shown below.

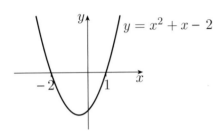

The solution set is $(-2, 1)$.

(b) The inequality can be rearranged as follows:
$$- x^2 + 7x < 10$$
$$- x^2 + 7x - 10 < 0.$$
The graph of $f(x) = -x^2 + 7x - 10$ is n-shaped. Its intercepts are given by
$$-x^2 + 7x - 10 = 0;$$
that is,
$$x^2 - 7x + 10 = 0,$$
or
$$(x - 5)(x - 2) = 0.$$
So they are $x = 5$ and $x = 2$. Hence the graph is as shown below.

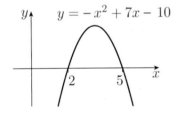

The solution set is $(-\infty, 2) \cup (5, \infty)$.

(c) The inequality can be rearranged as follows:
$$- x^2 \geq 2x,$$
$$- x^2 - 2x \geq 0$$
$$x^2 + 2x \leq 0.$$

The graph of $f(x) = x^2 + 2x$ is u-shaped. Its x-intercepts are given by
$$x^2 + 2x = 0;$$
that is,
$$x(x + 2) = 0$$
So they are $x = 0$ and $x = -2$. Hence the graph is as shown below.

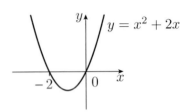

The solution set is $[-2, 0]$.

Solution to Activity 56

(a) The inequality is
$$2x^2 - 5x - 3 < 0,$$
which can be factorised as
$$(2x + 1)(x - 3) < 0.$$
A factor is equal to 0 when $x = -\frac{1}{2}$ or $x = 3$.

A table of signs for the expression on the left-hand side of the inequality is given below.

x	$\left(-\infty, -\frac{1}{2}\right)$	$-\frac{1}{2}$	$\left(-\frac{1}{2}, 3\right)$	3	$(3, \infty)$
$2x + 1$	$-$	0	$+$	$+$	$+$
$x - 3$	$-$	$-$	$-$	0	$+$
$(2x + 1)$ $\times (x - 3)$	$+$	0	$-$	0	$+$

The solution set is $\left(-\frac{1}{2}, 3\right)$.

(b) The inequality is
$$-2x^2 + 4x + 16 \leq 0;$$
that is,
$$x^2 - 2x - 8 \geq 0.$$
Factorising gives
$$(x + 2)(x - 4) \geq 0.$$
A factor is equal to 0 when $x = -2$ or $x = 4$.

A table of signs for the expression on the left-hand side of the inequality is given below.

x	$(-\infty,-2)$	-2	$(-2,4)$	4	$(4,\infty)$
$x+2$	$-$	0	$+$	$+$	$+$
$x-4$	$-$	$-$	$-$	0	$+$
$(x+2)$ $\times(x-4)$	$+$	0	$-$	0	$+$

The solution set is $(-\infty,-2]\cup[4,\infty)$.

(Here's a slightly different way to solve the inequality in part (b).

Unlike the working above, this alternative working doesn't involve multiplying through by a negative number to simplify the inequality, so the inequality sign stays the same way round as in the original inequality. You might find that this approach helps you to avoid errors.

The inequality is

$$-2x^2+4x+16\le 0.$$

Factorising gives

$$-2(x+2)(x-4)\le 0.$$

A factor is equal to 0 when $x=-2$ or $x=4$.

A table of signs for the expression on the left-hand side of the inequality is given below.

x	$(-\infty,-2)$	-2	$(-2,4)$	4	$(4,\infty)$
-2	$-$	$-$	$-$	$-$	$-$
$x+2$	$-$	0	$+$	$+$	$+$
$x-4$	$-$	$-$	$-$	0	$+$
$-2(x+2)$ $\times(x-4)$	$-$	0	$+$	0	$-$

The solution set is

$(-\infty,-2]\cup[4,\infty)$.)

Solution to Activity 57

(a) The inequality can be rearranged as follows:

$$\frac{3x-4}{2x+1}\le 1$$

$$\frac{3x-4}{2x+1}-1\le 0$$

$$\frac{3x-4}{2x+1}-\frac{2x+1}{2x+1}\le 0$$

$$\frac{3x-4-2x-1}{2x+1}\le 0$$

$$\frac{x-5}{2x+1}\le 0.$$

A factor of the numerator or denominator of the expression on the left-hand side is equal to 0 when $x=5$ or $x=-\frac{1}{2}$.

A table of signs for the expression follows.

x	$(-\infty,-\frac{1}{2})$	$-\frac{1}{2}$	$(-\frac{1}{2},5)$	5	$(5,\infty)$
$x-5$	$-$	$-$	$-$	0	$+$
$2x+1$	$-$	0	$+$	$+$	$+$
$\dfrac{x-5}{2x+1}$	$+$	$*$	$-$	0	$+$

The solution set is $(-\frac{1}{2},5]$.

(b) The inequality can be rearranged as follows:

$$\frac{2x^2+5x-8}{x-3}\ge 2$$

$$\frac{2x^2+5x-8}{x-3}-2\ge 0$$

$$\frac{2x^2+5x-8}{x-3}-\frac{2(x-3)}{x-3}\ge 0$$

$$\frac{2x^2+5x-8-2x+6}{x-3}\ge 0$$

$$\frac{2x^2+3x-2}{x-3}\ge 0$$

$$\frac{(2x-1)(x+2)}{x-3}\ge 0.$$

A factor of the numerator or denominator of the expression on the left-hand side is equal to 0 when $x=-2$, $x=\frac{1}{2}$ or $x=3$.

A table of signs for the expression follows.

To save space, the last row uses the notation

$$f(x) = \frac{(2x-1)(x+2)}{x-3}.$$

x	$(-\infty, -2)$	-2	$(-2, \frac{1}{2})$	$\frac{1}{2}$	$(\frac{1}{2}, 3)$	3	$(3, \infty)$
$2x-1$	$-$	$-$	$-$	0	$+$	$+$	$+$
$x+2$	$-$	0	$+$	$+$	$+$	$+$	$+$
$x-3$	$-$	$-$	$-$	$-$	$-$	0	$+$
$f(x)$	$-$	0	$+$	0	$-$	$*$	$+$

The solution set is $[-2, \frac{1}{2}] \cup (3, \infty)$.

Solution to Activity 58

(a) The solutions of the equation $x = \dfrac{15}{x-2}$ are roughly -3 and 5.

(b) The solution set of the inequality $x \leq \dfrac{15}{x-2}$ is roughly $(-\infty, -3] \cup (2, 5]$.

(c) The solution set of the inequality $x > \dfrac{15}{x-2}$ is roughly $(-3, 2) \cup (5, \infty)$.

(The answers given here are in fact exact.)

Acknowledgements

Grateful acknowledgement is made to the following sources:

Page 201: Erik De Graaf / Dreamstime.com

Page 210: Madhero88. This file is licensed under the Creative Commons Attribution-Share Alike Licence http://creativecommons.org/licenses/by-sa/3.0/

Page 285: Taken from: http://focustreatmentcenters.com/chronic-pain-addiction-to-prescription-drugs/

Page 287: Taken from: http://blogs.dallasobserver.com/unfairpark/2012/04/dallas-owned_west_texas_nuclea.php

Page 287: Taken from: http://www2.estrellamountain.edu/faculty/farabee/biobk/biobookmito.html

Page 291: Taken from: http://en.wikipedia.org/wiki/File:Willard_Libby.jpg

Page 291: Gareth Wiscombe. This file is licensed under the Creative Commons Attribution Licence http://creativecommons.org/licenses/by/3.0/

Every effort has been made to contact copyright holders. If any have been inadvertently overlooked the publishers will be pleased to make the necessary arrangements at the first opportunity.

Index

Index